MW00335132

11/10/2022
STP

Contemporary Perspectives on Crisis Intervention and Prevention

Albert R. Roberts, Editor

Rutgers—The State University of New Jersey

PRENTICE HALL, Englewood Cliffs, N.J. 07632

Library of Congress Cataloging-in-Publication Data

Contemporary perspectives on crisis intervention and prevention /
   Albert R. Roberts, editor.
       p.   cm.
      Includes bibliographical references and index.
      ISBN 0-13-173055-X
      1. Crisis intervention (Psychology)   2. Mental illness-
-Prevention.   I. Roberts, Albert R.
   RC480.6.C655   1991
   362.2'04251—dc20   90-14224
                                                           CIP

Editorial/production supervision and
   interior design: Barbara Reilly
Cover design: Patricia Kelly
Prepress buyer: Debra Kesar
Manufacturing buyer: Mary Ann Gloriande
Illustration sketches: Carole Roberts

> *I dedicate this book to the two most distinguished authors*
> *in the prevention field, Dr. George W. Albee and Dr. Martin Bloom.*
> *These two founding fathers of primary prevention are models of*
> *knowledge building, wisdom, and humanity.*

© 1991 by Prentice-Hall, Inc.
A Division of Simon & Schuster
Englewood Cliffs, New Jersey 07632

Printed in the United States of America
10 9 8 7 6 5 4 3 2 1

ISBN   0-13-173055-X

Prentice-Hall International (UK) Limited, *London*
Prentice-Hall of Australia Pty. Limited, *Sydney*
Prentice-Hall Canada Inc., *Toronto*
Prentice-Hall Hispanoamericana, S.A., *Mexico*
Prentice-Hall of India Private Limited, *New Delhi*
Prentice-Hall of Japan, Inc., *Tokyo*
Simon & Schuster Asia Pte. Ltd., *Singapore*
Editora Prentice-Hall do Brasil, Ltda., *Rio de Janeiro*

Contents

Preface

Since the early 1980s, several books have been published on crisis intervention strategies. But this is the first book to present both the application of the crisis intervention model and primary prevention programs and strategies. *Contemporary Perspectives on Crisis Intervention and Prevention* focuses on two important areas. The first pertains to programs designed to facilitate crisis resolution with persons in acute crisis. The second pertains to program models designed to prevent crisis episodes from occurring.

Books on this topic usually emphasize tertiary prevention, which refers to intervention and treatment after the person is already in crisis, in order to help the individual regain equilibrium and be better able to deal with highly stressful events in the future. The prevalence of acute crisis situations in our society necessitates the development of programs to help persons who are experiencing a crisis, and the enormous value of tertiary prevention programs should in no way be underrated. However, it is through primary and secondary prevention programs that we have the greatest opportunity to prevent some crisis events from occurring. Although the federal and most state governments are in a cost-cutting mode because of budget deficit difficulties, it is a far greater saving in the long run to allocate resources for primary prevention than to wait until people are experiencing a full-blown crisis.

The first major part of this volume (Sections I and II) focuses on crisis intervention programs. These types of programs are generally developed to reduce trauma and facilitate the individual's return to his or her precrisis level of functioning. Although clinicians view crisis treatment as tertiary prevention, these programs are more commonly known as crisis intervention. Crisis intervention programs, no matter whom they are intended to serve, have the objective of minimizing the impact and negative consequences of intense stressors and resolving crisis episodes quickly.

The second major part of this volume (Section III) focuses on primary and secondary prevention strategies. Dr. Martin Bloom (in Chapter 9) describes primary prevention as "systematic and planned activities undertaken simultaneously to prevent the occurrence of some predicted untoward event" and to protect a person's present level of healthy functioning. For example, primary prevention efforts aimed at eliminating the conditions that breed abuse of women would include the following elements:

> Eliminating sex-role stereotyping
> Improving the quality of life for all families
> Providing family life education for children and adults
> Changing society's attitude toward family violence through community education programs

Secondary prevention (as adapted from the public health model) includes any activities that are related to *early* casefinding, diagnosis, and therapeutic intervention. To continue with the family violence example used for primary prevention, secondary prevention would involve identifying and helping women in the earliest stages of an abusive relationship. Research has shown that the course of a violent relationship starts with an initial slap or punch on rare occasions; the lover or husband usually apologizes profusely and says that it will never happen again. But as time goes on, the violent incidents usually become progressively more frequent and severe until the woman finds herself in a deadly, life-threatening situation. Thus secondary prevention is geared to providing education and counseling (for both the man and the woman, if possible) after the initial manifestation of violence, before it escalates into an acute crisis situation.

This book contains original, specially written chapters from some of the leading clinical social workers and community and clinical psychologists. The 20 nationally prominent contributors have extensive experience providing crisis assessment and treatment or conducting research on crisis intervention. *Contemporary Perspectives on Crisis Intervention and Prevention* will be of special interest to clinicians and graduate students in social work, clinical psychology, and community psychology. It is intended as a resource to aid professionals in resolving crises and in reducing the number of individuals who require crisis intervention. This volume brings together a wealth of information on a wide range of prevention and crisis intervention strategies.

Contributors

ARLENE BOWERS ANDREWS, Ph.D., Associate Professor, College of Social Work, University of South Carolina, Columbia, South Carolina

ALAN L. BERMAN, Ph.D., Professor, Department of Psychology, The American University, Washington, D.C. (and former President, American Association of Suicidology)

MARTIN BLOOM, Ph.D., Professor, School of Social Work, Rutgers—The State University of New Jersey, New Brunswick, New Jersey

GRACE H. CHRIST, A.C.S.W., Director, Department of Social Work, Memorial Sloan-Kettering Cancer Center, New York, New York (and Editor in Chief, *Journal of Psychosocial Oncology*)

DEBORAH DARO, D.S.W., Director, National Center on Child Abuse Prevention and Director of Research, National Committee for the Prevention of Child Abuse, Chicago, Illinois

IRENE C. GAFFNEY, M.S., Family Therapist and Coordinator, Pilot Stress Research Project, Family and Child Development Department, Northern Virginia Graduate Center of Virginia Polytechnic Institute, Falls Church, Virginia

LES GALLO-SILVER, A.C.S.W., Medical Social Worker, Memorial Sloan-Kettering Cancer Center, New York, New York

JUDITH GRISSMER, M.S., Counseling Coordinator, Pilot Stress Research Project, Family and Child Development Department, Northern Virginia Graduate Center of Virginia Polytechnic Institute, Falls Church, Virginia

DAVID A. JOBES, Ph.D., Assistant Professor, Department of Psychology, The Catholic University of America, Washington, D.C.

JOHN KALAFAT, Ph.D., Director, Department of Education, St. Clares–Riverside Medical Center, Denville, New Jersey (and Visiting Professor, Graduate School of Applied and Professional Psychology, Rutgers—The State University of New Jersey)

JUDITH MANNING KENDRICK, A.C.S.W., Clinical Director of Family Programs, Visiting Nurse Service, Indianapolis, Indiana

LINDA F. LITTLE, Ph.D., Associate Professor and Director, Pilot Stress Research Project, Family and Child Development Department, Northern Virginia Graduate Center of Virginia Polytechnic Institute, Falls Church, Virginia

JOANNE E. MANTELL, Ph.D., Senior Research Scientist and Principal Investigator, Perinatal HIV Prevention Demonstration Project, New York City Department of Health, New York, New York

SISTER ROSEMARY MOYNIHAN, A.C.S.W., Assistant Director, Department of Social Work, Memorial Sloan-Kettering Cancer Center, New York, New York

ALBERT R. ROBERTS, D.S.W., Associate Professor and Director, Administration of Justice Program, School of Social Work, Rutgers—The State University of New Jersey, New Brunswick, New Jersey

STEVEN P. SCHINKE, Ph.D., Professor, School of Social Work, Columbia University, New York, New York

ROSALIE STREETT, A.C.S.W., Director, Friends of the Family, Inc., Baltimore, Maryland

THOMAS STRENTZ, Ph.D., Special Agent and Training Instructor (Retired), Federal Bureau of Investigation and F.B.I. Training Academy, Quantico, Virginia

MARLENE A. YOUNG, J.D., Ph.D., Executive Director, National Organization for Victim Assistance (NOVA), Washington, D.C.

LAURIE SCHWAB ZABIN, Ph.D., Associate Professor of Population Dynamics, Johns Hopkins School of Hygiene and Public Health, with a joint appointment in the Department of Obstetrics and Gynecology in the School of Medicine, Baltimore, Maryland (and former Chair, Board of Directors, Alan Guttmacher Institute)

Introduction
and
Overview

What is an acute crisis? What types of events are most likely to precipitate a crisis state? What is meant by crisis intervention? What are the major steps in the crisis intervention process? Answers to these and related questions are provided in Chapter 1, written by Dr. Albert R. Roberts. The application of crisis theory and the crisis intervention model to high-risk groups is a crucial step in helping persons in acute crisis. This chapter provides an overview of crisis intervention: the emergence of the field, the crisis concepts and definition of a crisis reaction, and the seven stages in the crisis intervention model.

The chapter begins with case illustrations of acute crisis situations and ends with the seven-stage model:

1. Assess lethality and safety needs
2. Establish rapport and communication
3. Identify the major problem
4. Deal with feelings and provide support
5. Explore possible alternatives
6. Assist in formulating an action plan
7. Follow up

Although crisis theory and practices have been extensively developed since the early 1970s, there remains a need for published material on the functions and organizational patterns of crisis centers nationwide. Chapter 2 reports on Dr. Albert Roberts's recent national survey on the organizational structure and functions of 107 crisis centers and units. The chapter includes an examination of the objectives, activities, most frequent presenting problems of clients, sources of funding, and staffing patterns of crisis centers. The survey found that the most frequently mentioned objectives of crisis units were, in descending order, suicide prevention, crisis intervention, referral, and community education (prevention), with most respondents citing at least three objectives. It was found that the most frequently cited presenting problems were depression, substance abuse, and suicide ideation.

Conceptualizing Crisis Theory and the Crisis Intervention Model

Albert R. Roberts

1

INTRODUCTION

Some crisis situations are personal family matters; others are triggered by a tragic occurrence such as an airplane crash, a hostage situation, or a mass murder that can cause widespread crisis for dozens, hundreds, or even thousands of people.

Case Study

Shortly after 9:00 A.M. on October 20, 1987, the pilot of a malfunctioning Air Force attack jet tried unsuccessfully to make an emergency landing at the Indianapolis International Airport. The out-of-control jet clipped the top of a nearby bank building, then rammed into the lobby of the Ramada Inn and exploded, killing ten people and injuring several others.

This tragic accident resulted in hundreds of persons in crisis: the persons injured in the explosion, the family members of the dead and injured, the guests and surviving employees at the hotel who witnessed the horror, and the employees and customers at the bank building that was struck by the plane, even though no one at the bank was physically hurt.

A look at two more cases will provide more insight on the dimensions of the problems that crisis counselors work with.

Case Study

Joe begins to barbecue the hamburgers for tonight's dinner. His wife and their two daughters are expected home in about 20 minutes. His older daughter had a track meet, and his wife and younger daughter went to watch her. The phone rings and Joe is informed by a police officer that his wife and both children have been killed by a drunken driver who sped through a red light and smashed into their car two blocks from their house. His life will never be the same.

Case Study

Liz, a 21-year-old college senior majoring in English, is very depressed. She and her fiancé have just broken up, and she feels unable to cope. She cries most of the day, feels agitated, and isn't sleeping or eating normally. Since the beginning of the relationship a year ago, Liz has become socially isolated. Her family strongly dislikes her fiancé, and her fiancé discouraged her from spending time with her friends. Liz now doubts that she will find a job upon graduation in three months and is considering moving home. She is from a large family, with parents who are very much involved with the other children. Thoughts of moving back home and losing her independence as well as the broken romance and the lack of a support system have immobilized Liz. Liz has cut all her classes for the past week. She has not talked with friends or family about the breakup, and she is "holed up" in her room in the dormitory, drinking herself into a stupor and refusing to eat or leave the dormitory even for a walk.

Both Joe and Liz are experiencing crises: highly stressful events that provoke overwhelming feelings of anxiety, depression and guilt, helplessness, fear, and exhaustion.

CRISIS AND INTERVENTION

A crisis can be defined as a period of psychological disequilibrium, experienced as a result of a hazardous event or situation that constitutes a significant problem that cannot be remedied by using familiar coping strategies.

A crisis occurs when a person faces an obstacle to important life goals that generally seem insurmountable through the use of customary habits and coping patterns. The goal of crisis intervention is to resolve the most pressing problem within a 1- to 12-week period through focused and directed intervention aimed at helping the client develop new adaptive coping methods.

Crisis reaction refers to the acute stage, which usually occurs soon after the hazardous event (sexual assault, battering, suicide attempt). During this phase, the person's acute reaction may take various forms including helplessness, confusion, anxiety, shock, disbelief, and anger. Low self-esteem and serious depression are often produced by the crisis state. The person in crisis may appear to be incoherent, disorganized, agitated, and volatile or calm, subdued, withdrawn, and apathetic. It is during this crisis reaction period that the individual is often most willing to seek help, and crisis intervention is usually more effective at this time (Golan, 1978).

THEORETICAL DEVELOPMENT

As far back as 400 B.C., physicians have stressed the significance of crisis as a hazardous life event. Hippocrates himself defined a crisis as a sudden state that gravely endangers life. But the development of a cohesive theory of crisis and approaches to crisis management had to await the twentieth century.

The movement to help people in crisis began in 1906 with the establishment of the first suicide prevention center, the National Save-A-Life League in New York City. However, contemporary crisis intervention theory and practice were not formally elaborated until the 1940s, primarily by Erich Lindemann and Gerald Caplan.

Lindemann and his associates at Massachusetts General Hospital introduced the concepts of crisis intervention and time-limited treatment in 1943 in the aftermath of Boston's worst nightclub fire, at the Cocoanut Grove, in which 493 people perished. Lindemann (1944) and colleagues based the crisis theory they developed on their observations of the acute and delayed reactions of survivors and grief-stricken relatives of victims. Their clinical work focused on the psychological symptoms of the survivors and on preventing unresolved grief among relatives of the persons who had died. They found that many individuals experiencing acute grief often had five related reactions:

1. Somatic distress
2. Preoccupation with the image of the deceased
3. Guilt
4. Hostile reactions
5. Loss of patterns of conduct

Furthermore, Lindemann and colleagues concluded that the duration of a grief reaction appears to be dependent on the success with which the bereaved person does his or her mourning and "grief work." In general, this grief work refers to achieving emancipation from the deceased, readjusting to the changes in the environment from which the loved one is missing, and developing new relationships. We learned from Lindemann that people need to be encouraged to permit themselves to have a period of mourning and eventual acceptance of the loss and adjustment to life without the parent, child, spouse, or sibling. By delaying the normal process of grieving, negative outcomes of crises will develop.

Lindemann's work was soon adapted to interventions with World War II veterans suffering from "combat neurosis" and bereaved family members.

Gerald Caplan, who was affiliated with Massachusetts General Hospital and the Harvard School of Public Health, expanded Lindemann's pioneering work in the 1940s and 1950s. Caplan studied various developmental crisis reactions, as in premature births, infancy, childhood, and adolescence, and accidental crises such as illness and death. Caplan was the first psychiatrist to relate the concept of homeostasis to crisis intervention and to describe the stages of a crisis. According to Caplan (1961), a crisis is an upset of a steady state in which the individual encounters an obstacle (usually an obstacle to significant life goals) that cannot be overcome through traditional problem-solving activities. For each individual, a reasonably constant balance or steady state exists between affective and cognitive experience. When this homeostatic balance or stability in psychological functioning is threatened by physiological, psychological, or social forces, the individual engages in problem-solving methods designed to restore the balance. However, in a crisis situation, the person in distress faces a problem that seems to have no solution. Thus homeostatic balance is disrupted, or an upset of a steady state ensues.

Caplan (1964) explains this concept further by stating that the problem is one in which the individual faces "stimuli which signal danger to a fundamental need satisfaction . . . and the circumstances are such that habitual problem-solving methods are unsuccessful within the time span of past expectations of success" (p. 39).

Caplan also described four stages of a crisis reaction. The first stage is the initial rise of tension that comes from the emotionally hazardous crisis-precipitating event. The second stage is characterized by an increased level of tension and disruption to daily living because the individual is unable to resolve the crisis quickly. As the individual attempts and fails to resolve the crisis by emergency problem-solving mechanisms, tension increases to such an intense level that the individual may go into a depression. The person going through the final stage of Caplan's model may experience either a mental collapse or breakdown or may partly resolve the crisis by using new coping methods. J. S. Tyhurst (1957) studied transition states—migration, retirement, civilian disaster, and so on—in the lives of persons experiencing sudden changes. Based on his field studies on individual patterns of responses to community disaster, Tyhurst identified three overlapping phases, each with its own manifestations of stress and attempts at reducing it:

1. A period of impact
2. A period of recoil
3. A posttraumatic period of recovery

Tyhurst recommended stage-specific intervention. He concluded that persons in transitional crisis states should not be removed from their life situation, and intervention should focus on bolstering the network of relationships.

Lydia Rapoport built on the pioneering work of Lindemann and Caplan. In addition, she was one of the first practitioners to write about the linkage of modalities such as ego psychology, learning theory, and traditional social casework (Rapoport, 1970). In Rapoport's first article on crisis theory (1962), she defined a crisis as "an upset of a steady state" that places the individual in a hazardous condition. Rapoport pointed out that a crisis situation results in a problem that can be perceived as a threat, a loss, or a challenge. She then stated that there are usually three interrelated factors that create a state of crisis:

1. A hazardous event
2. A threat to life goals
3. An inability to respond with adequate coping mechanisms

In their early works, Lindemann and Caplan briefly mentioned that a hazardous event produces a crisis, but it was Rapoport (1967, 1970) who most thoroughly described the nature of this crisis-precipitating event. Rapoport clearly conceptualized the content of crisis intervention practice, particularly the initial or study phase (assessment). She began by pointing out that in order to help persons in crisis, it is necessary that the client have rapid access to the crisis worker. She stated: "A little help, rationally directed and purposefully focused at a strategic time, is more effective than more extensive help given at a period of less emotional accessibility" (Rapoport, 1967, p. 38).

This was echoed by Naomi Golan (1978), who concluded that during the state of active crisis, when usual coping methods have proved inadequate and the individual and his or her family are suffering from pain and discomfort, a person is frequently more amenable to suggestions and change. Clearly, intensive, brief, appropriately focused treatment during a period when the client is motivated can produce more effective change than long-term treatment during periods when motivation and emotional accessibility are lacking.

Rapoport (1967) asserted that during the initial interview, the first task of the practitioner is to develop a preliminary diagnosis of the presenting problem. It is most critical during this first interview that the crisis therapist convey a sense of hope and optimism to the client concerning successful crisis resolution. Rapoport suggested that this sense of hope and enthusiasm can be properly conveyed to the client when the interview focuses on mutual exploration and problem solving, along with clearly delineated goals and tasks. The underlying message is that client and therapist will be working together to resolve the crisis.

Seeking Help

In the late 1960s the suicide prevention movement took hold, and suicide prevention centers were developed across the United States. From the outset, the initial request for help was generally made via a telephone hotline, and this practice continues to the present day. Aided by funding from the National Institute of Mental Health's Center for Studies of Suicide Prevention, these centers grew from 28 in 1966 to almost 200 by 1972. These centers built on Caplan's crisis theory and the work of Edwin Schneidman and Norman Farberow at the Los Angeles Suicide Prevention Center (Roberts, 1975, 1979). An enormous boost to the development of crisis intervention programs and units came about as a result of the community mental health movement. The availability of 24-hour crisis intervention and emergency services was considered to be a major component of any comprehensive community mental health center (CMHC). As a prerequisite to receiving federal funding under the Community Mental Health Centers Act of 1963, CMHCs were required to include an emergency services component in their system plan. During the 1970s the number of CMHCs that contained crisis intervention units grew rapidly, more than doubling from 376 in 1969 to 796 as of 1980 (Foley & Sharfstein, 1983).

What motivates people in crisis to seek help? Ripple, Alexander, and Polemis (1964) suggest a balance of discomfort and hope is necessary to motivate a distressed person to seek help. *Hope* as defined by Stotland (1969) is the perceived possibility of attaining a goal. The pressure to act comes from a sufficient amount of both discomfort and hope for the individual in crisis to make a concerted effort to seek help.

The crisis clinician knows that coping patterns differ for each of us. The crisis clinician also knows that for an individual to suffer and survive a crisis (such as losing a loved one, living through an earthquake or a tornado, attempting suicide, or being sexually assaulted), that person must have a conscious purpose to live and grow. Each individual in crisis must define his or her own purpose. Persons in crisis need to ventilate, to be accepted, and to receive support, assistance, and encouragement to discover the paths to crisis resolution.

It is useful for the client to understand the specific personal meaning of the event and how it conflicts with his or her expectations, life goals, and belief system. Thoughts, feelings, and beliefs usually flow out freely when a client in crisis talks. The crisis clinician should listen carefully and note any cognitive errors or distortions (overgeneralizing, catastrophizing) or irrational beliefs. The clinician should avoid prematurely stating rational beliefs or reality-based cognitions for the client. Instead, the clinician should help the client to recognize discrepancies, distortions, and irrational beliefs. This is best accomplished through carefully worded questions such as "How do you view yourself now that you realize that everyone with less than five years' seniority got laid off?" or "Have you ever asked your doctor whether he thinks you will die from cancer at a young age or what your actual risk of getting cancer is?"

An unwanted pregnancy, a divorce, a broken engagement, being the victim of a domestic assault, and being the close relative of a person killed in an automobile accident or a plane crash are all highly stressful events. The persons involved may use denial and express anger and fear, grief and loss, but they can all survive. Crisis intervention can reduce immediate danger and fear, as well as provide support, hope, and alternative ways of coping and growing.

CRISIS INTERVENTION MODELS

Several models have been developed to guide clinicians who work with clients in crisis. The most widely known models are Caplan's (1964) four-stage model, Rapoport's (1967) three-stage model, Baldwin's (1978 and 1980) four-stage model, and Golan's (1978) three-phase model. Roberts, expanding on the previously developed systems, has devised a seven-step model that offers an integrated problem-solving approach to crisis resolution. Before exploring this new model, let us examine the most useful of the earlier ones.

Golan's Model

Naomi Golan's (1978) model is very useful to clinicians because it provides the crisis worker with examples of selective empathetic statements and questions to ask the client during each phase of treatment—the beginning (first interview), the middle (from first to fourth interview), and the ending phase of termination (last one or two interviews). More specifically, during the first interview, Golan directs the crisis worker to begin with the here and now by focusing on the precipitating event, including "scope, persons involved, outcome, severity of effect, and the time the event occurred" (p. 84). The triggering factor is the event or incident that prompted the individual to contact the crisis center. After allowing the client to verbalize what happened, he or she should be encouraged to ventilate by expressing such feelings as frustration, anger, or guilt. The crisis worker is encouraged to elicit subjective reactions about the event from the client while also trying to obtain his or her affective responses to the recent past and to the part the client played in it. These are Golan's prompting statements for crisis workers:

> "You must have felt terrible about it!"
> "No wonder you sound so upset."
> "Can you put your finger on what started this off?"
> "Things really began to change after you came to college."
> "I suppose in the beginning you were in a state of shock."
> "How were you able to handle all this with your husband in the hospital?"
> "You're in a real dilemma; I guess the most important thing is to come to a decision as to whether or not to leave your husband."

Roberts's Model

Roberts's seven-stage model, outlined in Figure 1–1, is presented here for the first time. It can be applied to specific clients in crisis and can promote effective early crisis resolution.

Note that the order of stages 1 and 2 can be reversed, depending on the type of crisis that triggers the phone call. If the caller is a battered woman, there is a real possibility that she may be making a call—while the batterer searches for her whereabouts—to get information on a safe place to stay. In such cases, establishing rapport can wait until the woman is safe; it is essential that the crisis worker immediately assess the lethality of the situation. By contrast, if the caller is not a battered woman and is timid about divulging the reason for the call, establishing rapport so that the caller will feel comfortable about sharing personal problems becomes the first order of business.

1. Assess Lethality and Safety Needs

Determine the person's degree of risk for serious injury or death from self-destructive acts or from the violent acts of another person. It is necessary to assess the level and seriousness of threats to the caller's safety. Roberts and Roberts (1990) studied the crisis intervention techniques used by telephone hotlines and emergency shelters for battered women. The shelters indicated that their number one action is to ensure the safety of the women and their children. Here are some examples of the questions crisis workers ask:

"Are you or your children in danger now?"
"Is the abuser there now?"
"Do you want me to call the police?"
"Do you want to leave and can you do so safely?"
"Do you or your children need medical attention?"

If the crisis caller is a battered woman, she should be encouraged to call the police, go to the emergency room of the nearest hospital if medical care is needed, or take refuge at the local battered women's shelter if emergency housing is needed.

To detect and assess battery systematically, adult abuse protocols have been developed at large city hospitals in some cities, including Boston, Chicago, Indianapolis, Philadelphia, and Seattle. The first and most comprehensive such protocol was developed by Karil Klingbeil and Vicky Boyd at Harborview Medical Center in Seattle (Roberts, 1984). Although the adult abuse protocols were formulated for use by social workers on call in the hospital emergency room, they can easily be adapted for use by crisis units of community mental health centers, physicians in private practice, and prenatal clinics.

2. Establish Rapport and Communication

Initial rapport can be established when the crisis worker lets the caller know that he or she has done the right thing by contacting the crisis unit. The

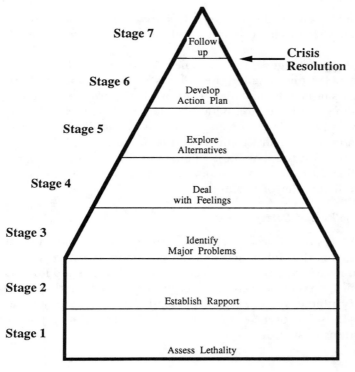

Figure 1-1 Roberts's Seven-stage Crisis Intervention Model

crisis worker should also convey a willingness and an ability to help. This is accomplished by active listening in an accepting, concerned, patient, and helpful manner.

In Chapter 4, David Jobes and Alan Berman point out the importance of making rapid interpersonal contact and establishing a clinical relationship with the client as early as possible because of the clear and imminent risk of death among suicidal adolescents.

> The importance of the clinical relationship (and the techniques used to enhance it) in the suicidal crisis cannot be overestimated. . . . Particularly in a crisis, the ability to make interpersonal contact is critical, and a supportive working relationship must be rapidly established. . . . Suicidal clients must know (and feel) that they are talking with a person who is actively interested in their well-being. Any technique or approach that potentially strengthens the relationship and connectedness should therefore be employed. . . . Empathic listening, mirroring of feelings, emotional availability, honesty, warmth, and caring can help foster a sense of trust and a willingness to examine possibilities other than self-destruction. Though empathy and support are crucial, it is important to remember that suicidal adolescents often feel out of control. Accordingly, a more active and directive role than would normally be seen in ongoing individual psychotherapy can provide valuable reassurance and structure in a time of crisis.

3. Identify the Major Problem

It is useful to explore with the client the immediate past and the present. The immediate past refers to the "last straw," the precipitating factor (a violent assault, rejection, an extremely humiliating event) that led the client to seek help at this time. Clinicians also find it useful to determine how the client was functioning just prior to the crisis. Many clients present themselves with multiple problems, including those of other people such as a spouse or a sibling. The clinician should help the client to focus on his or her own problems, not on a third party. Efforts should center on helping the client to rank order and prioritize the problems, with the goal of attending to the immediate and major problem. In general, it is usually much more productive to isolate the precipitating event or problem that led the client to seek help and to focus on that central area of concern first.

After identifying the triggering or precipitating event and the person's level of functioning prior to the crisis, the crisis worker should focus on the person's current feelings (affect). Also important is the impact of the crisis on relationships with family members and friends, the impact of daily living and routines (work, exercise, entertainment), the impact on the person's physical health (somatic symptoms), and the cognitive impact, including fantasies and daydreams, intrusive thoughts, fears and phobic reactions, and dreams and nightmares.

4. Deal with Feelings and Provide Support

This stage involves active listening and communicating through empathic statements. The worker should encourage the client to express the intense feelings around the crisis. With clients who are used to expressing their feelings, empathic statements may be all that is necessary. Other clients will need to be educated about feelings and given permission to express themselves verbally. Fear, anxiety, sadness, and guilt are normal reactions to crisis, and clients often need to be reassured that they are not "crazy." Catharsis of feelings is often very productive. Finally, crisis workers should listen for and note cognitive distortions (overgeneralizations, catastrophizing), misconceptions, and irrational belief statements. The crisis worker should be careful not to confront the client with the cognitive errors prematurely; instead, the worker should use questions and clarifying statements, such as "What do you think of yourself now that he has walked out?" "Do you really have that view of yourself?" "Should we trust Anthony's insulting judgments? Anthony has insulted you again and again for years! Can you trust his opinion of you?" "You feel very sad and angry that a person like that doesn't love you? Why should Lisa's problem be reflected in your self-image?" Most experienced clinicians concur that cognitive crisis treatment has a better chance of success when the client discovers cognitive errors and distortions independently.

5. Explore Possible Alternatives

This exploration includes an examination of past adaptive and maladaptive coping methods. One of the key components of crisis intervention involves identifying and modifying the client's coping patterns at both the preconscious and conscious levels. It is useful for the crisis worker to attempt to bring the client's coping behavior that is operating just below the surface (at the preconscious level) to the conscious level and then to inform the client about methods of modifying maladaptive coping responses.

A whole range of alternative coping methods are available to clients. In an effort to counteract the person's feelings of helplessness and despair, crisis workers should encourage clients to think of alternative ideas, coping methods, and solutions. The crisis worker can suggest other related solutions. The proposed solutions, including potential obstacles, must be thoroughly discussed to help the individual recognize possible pitfalls.

6. Assist in Formulating an Action Plan

The sixth component involves helping the person in crisis to come up with a short-term approach for resolving the crisis. This active step may involve the client agreeing to search for an apartment in a low-crime area, for example, or it may involve the client finding and making an appointment with a divorce attorney.

The final part of an action plan involves cognitive mastery: restructuring, rebuilding, or replacing irrational beliefs and erroneous cognitions with rational beliefs and new cognitions. This may involve providing new information through cognitive restructuring, homework assignments, or referral to others who have lived through and mastered a similar crisis (a support group for widows, for persons with AIDS, or for depressed adolescents, for example).

Encouraging and mobilizing the clients to be committed to positive action is of paramount importance. Once the worker and client agree on an action plan, the client needs to be bolstered so that he or she will follow through. Persons in acute crisis are often highly distressed and lethargic because prior attempts to cope have failed. They need to be told about other clients who were able to overcome obstacles and resolve their crisis.

7. Follow Up

The final stage in crisis intervention entails an agreement between the worker and client to have another meeting at a designated time and place or to talk by telephone in order to gauge the client's progress toward crisis resolution. The follow-up stage gives the crisis worker the opportunity, if necessary, to refer the client to an agency for further treatment.

Personal Assessment, Self-care, and Preventing Burnout among Crisis Interveners

Crisis interveners are exposed to an enormous amount of intense stress and personal demands from the crisis callers. Whether responding to individuals in a family crisis (such as a suicide attempt) or a sudden disaster (such as an airplane crash), the clinician runs the risk of devoting extensive amounts of time and considerable psychological energy to the clients. An unfortunate outcome of overextending oneself emotionally may be burnout. The burnout syndrome can be characterized as a state of fatigue, irritability, and exhaustion that occurs rather suddenly.

Burnout involves physical, emotional, and mental exhaustion among workers who have highly stressful caseloads. Individuals with a large caseload and an all-encompassing passion to solve clients' serious conditions and dysfunctions in a relatively brief time period are most susceptible to burnout. It is important for clinicians to know their limitations and the fact that some problems such as terminal cancer and AIDS cannot be solved by short-term treatment. However, clients with life-threatening illnesses can be made more comfortable, and the quality of their lives can certainly be improved through crisis intervention.

It is important for agency administrators and crisis intervention unit (CIU) supervisors to recognize the physical and emotional demands that crisis intervention work places on the crisis clinician. This recognition must result in frequent opportunities for the worker to express concerns and to ventilate stressful feelings in small group and staff development meetings as well as staff support groups. There are two major causes of burnout in the human services:

1. Unrealistic and excessively high goals and expectations and overextending oneself to meet these unattainable goals in view of limited resources
2. The workaholic syndrome—devoting 60 to 80 hours a week to work, while skipping meals and neglecting exercise or recreation

Carlton Munson, in his classic volume *An Introduction to Clinical Social Work Supervision* (1983), underscores the importance of striving for balance in one's life in order to overcome stress reactions and prevent burnout among clinicians:

A BICYCLE RIDE THREE TIMES A WEEK REDUCES STRESS

The worker needs to develop boundaries on work time and use his or her own time to develop outside interests. Work diversions such as drug use, heavy drinking, and gambling merely add to the worker's problem. Hobbies, recreation, physical exercise, and various other activities can serve as healthy outlets. Such activities do not have to be limited to nights and weekends. A lunch period can be used to pursue some interests. Vacations can be planned in advance, and the activities of planning a vacation can be a wholesome diversion from work. (p. 208)

CONCLUSION

This chapter has focused on the development of crisis theory and the crisis intervention model. In order to function effectively and harmoniously in daily living, each person must find a way to regain equilibrium in the aftermath of a crisis reaction. Since crisis situations have been found to have a peak or a sudden turning point, it is imperative that crisis workers maximize the clients' opportunities for crisis resolution. This can be done by following the seven-stage process model described in this chapter. The crisis intervention model takes into account the characteristics of persons in crisis and the need to apply a planned yet flexible strategy so that the client can regain equilibrium in a timely manner.

REFERENCES

BALDWIN, BRUCE A. (1978). "A Paradigm for the Classification of Emotional Crises: Implications for Crisis Intervention," *American Journal of Orthopsychiatry, 48,* 538–551.

BALDWIN, BRUCE A. (1980). "Styles of Crisis Intervention: Toward a Convergent Model," *Journal of Professional Psychology, 11,* 113–120.

CAPLAN, GERALD. (1961). *An Approach to Community Mental Health.* New York: Grune & Stratton.

CAPLAN, GERALD. (1964). *Principles of Preventive Psychiatry.* New York: Basic Books.

FOLEY, HENRY A. and SHARFSTEIN, STEVEN S. (1983). *Madness and Government: Who Cares for the Mentally Ill?* Washington, D.C.: American Psychiatric Press.

GOLAN, NAOMI. (1978). *Treatment in Crisis Situations.* New York: Free Press.

HALPERN, HOWARD A. (1973). "Crisis Theory: A Definitional Study," *Community Mental Health Journal, 9,* 342–349.

LINDEMANN, ERICH. (1944). "Symptomatology and Management of Acute Grief," *American Journal of Psychiatry, 101,* 141–148.

MUNSON, CARLTON E. (1983). *An Introduction to Clinical Social Work Supervision.* New York: the Haworth Press.

RAPOPORT, LYDIA. (1962). "The State of Crisis: Some Theoretical Considerations," *Social Service Review, 36,* 211–217.

RAPOPORT, LYDIA. (1967). "Crisis-oriented Short-Term Casework," *Social Service Review, 41,* 31–43.

RAPOPORT, LYDIA. (1970). "Crisis Intervention as a Mode of Brief Treatment." In R. W. Roberts and

R. H. Nee (Eds.), *Theories of Social Casework,* pp. 265–312. Chicago: University of Chicago Press.

RIPPLE, LILLIAN, ERNESTINA ALEXANDER, and BERNICE POLEMIS. (1964). *Motivation, Capacity, and Opportunity.* Chicago: University of Chicago Press.

ROBERTS, ALBERT R. (1975). *Self-Destructive Behavior.* Springfield, IL.: Charles C. Thomas.

ROBERTS, ALBERT R. (1979). "Organization of Suicide Prevention Agencies." In Leon D. Hankoff and Bernice Einsidler (Eds.), *Suicide: Theory and Clinical Aspects,* pp. 391–399. Acton, Mass.: Publishing Sciences Group.

ROBERTS, ALBERT R. (1984). *Battered Women and Their Families.* New York: Springer.

ROBERTS, ALBERT R., and BEVERLY SCHENKMAN ROBERTS. (1990). "A Comprehensive Model for Crisis Intervention with Battered Women and Their Children." In Albert R. Roberts (Ed.), *Helping Crime Victims and Witnesses: Policy, Practice, and Research,* pp. 186–205. Newbury Park, Calif.: Sage.

SLABY, ANDREW E. (1985). "Crisis-oriented Therapy." In Frank R. Lipton and Stephen M. Goldfinger (Eds.), *Emergency Psychiatry at the Crossroads,* pp. 21–34. San Francisco: Jossey-Bass.

STOTLAND, EZRA. (1969). *The Psychology of Hope.* San Francisco: Jossey-Bass.

TYHURST, J. S. (1957). "The Role of Transition States—Including Disasters—in Mental Illness." In *Symposium on Social and Preventive Psychiatry.* Washington, D.C.: Walter Reed Army Institute of Research.

Crisis Intervention Units and Centers in the United States
A National Survey

Albert R. Roberts

2

INTRODUCTION

Each year, millions of people experience crisis-inducing stressful events. Unable to afford the high cost of psychotherapy, many individuals in crisis never see a social worker, clinical psychologist, or psychiatrist in private practice. They must find some other method of obtaining immediate professional help. Consequently, over 1.5 million persons in acute crisis annually seek help from a crisis center or hotline in their community. Whether the person in crisis is suffering from depression, a suicide attempt, substance abuse, marital problems, or homelessness, trained volunteers and professional staff are available 24 hours a day to respond to callers in crisis.

Throughout the nation, a growing number of such crisis intervention programs have been developed to respond to callers in crisis quickly and effectively. This national survey was conducted to determine the objectives, priorities, funding sources, staffing patterns, and types of services provided by crisis intervention programs.

Over the years, the number and types of crisis intervention programs have varied. As the number and types of federal and state grants and contracts have changed, so have the objectives and the number of crisis intervention programs. In the late 1960s, when suicide prevention hotlines were rapidly expanding, crisis intervention activities were limited for the most part to persons contemplating suicide. By the mid-1970s, as a result of federal funding through the Community Mental Health Centers Act, over 700 local community mental health centers had been opened, each with a crisis intervention unit.

As public pressure mounts to provide adequate and accessible crisis services to all citizens, it is important to know about the extent of crisis intervention programs within health and hospital settings, mental health centers, and suicide prevention agencies. Crisis intervention practices and programs have come a long way in the past 25 years. In 1966, there were only 28 suicide prevention centers in the United States (Roberts, 1970). Two years later, there were 63 (Haughton, 1968). By 1989, there were more than 225 suicide prevention centers listed in the directory of the American Association of Suicidology.

This chapter is about the work of crisis centers. It focuses on the organizational structure and functions of crisis intervention units, centers, and hotlines nationwide and presents the major findings of a national survey of crisis units and centers. This survey provides data on the major priorities, components, and problems of crisis centers. Data were gathered on the following topics:

Objectives of the crisis centers and programs
Types of services provided
The callers' most frequent presenting problem
Agencies or programs to which clients are frequently referred
Organizational issues (e.g., total number of persons served annually, annual budgets, funding sources, staffing patterns)

Program development in crisis intervention and preventive risk reduction strategies have increased considerably since the start of the 1970s.

HISTORICAL BACKGROUND

The origin of crisis intervention services in the United States can be traced to the opening of a suicide prevention program in New York City in 1906, known as the National Save-A-Life League. The league was started by Reverend Harry M. Warren, Jr., an ordained minister and pastoral counselor keenly interested in helping individuals who were contemplating suicide. The New York City program continued its suicide prevention activities throughout the major nationwide expansion of such programs between 1965 and 1972, but it remained a very small program with two to four full-time staff members and a strong reliance on trained volunteers and student interns from local social work education and psychology programs.

A second early influence on the history of the suicide prevention movement was Louis I. Dublin, a life insurance actuary and statistician, public health reformer, and demographer. In 1933, Dublin published his seminal book, *To Be or Not to Be,* in which he attempted to awaken and stimulate society's awareness to the problem of suicide. Three decades later, Dublin (1963) took county and state health department officials to task for neglect and apathy toward the problem of suicide—a preventable cause of death. (After his retirement in 1970, Dublin was hailed as the "pioneer of suicidology.")

During the 1950s, clinical psychologists Norman Farberow and Edwin S. Shneidman came upon several hundred authentic suicide notes in the files of the Los Angeles County medical examiner. They used these in the first of what became many retrospective analyses of the psychological processes of individuals about to take their own life. The researchers revealed states of ambivalence and clues to eventual self-destruction. As a result of these early "psychological autopsies," these two suicidologists became convinced that suicide could be prevented and many lives could be saved (Farberow and Shneidman, 1965).

Farberow and Shneidman received two multiyear demonstration grants from the National Institute of Mental Health (NIMH). The first award, in 1958, was a five-year grant that enabled the Los Angeles Suicide Prevention Center (LASPC) to become fully operational. The second grant was for a period of seven years (1963–1969). Between 1958 and 1965, the LASPC staff developed the concepts, procedures, training manuals, and empirical data that constituted the foundation and technology of the suicide prevention movement. New programs throughout the United States were developed based on the following contributions by the LASPC:

1. The 24-hour telephone intervention service
2. Telephone method of determining lethality, establishing rapport and communication, and formulating an action plan
3. Training of volunteer housewives for telephone crisis duty
4. Semiannual training institutes for new staff members at suicide prevention and crisis intervention services from all over the United States (including social work interns, clinical psychology interns, medical students, and psychiatric residents)
5. A one-year residence program for research fellows of the Center for the Scientific Study of Suicide

By the last half of the 1960s, the suicide prevention movement had made significant strides. In December 1966, NIMH set up the now defunct Center for Studies of Suicide Prevention. The center was the first large-scale effort by the federal government to plan and fund research and demonstration projects on suicide prevention.

The goals of suicide prevention agencies have not changed much in the ensuing decades. The primary goal of these agencies has been the immediate and long-term deterrence of suicide. The selection, evaluation, referral, and crisis intervention activities of suicide prevention agencies are conducted with this goal in mind (Roberts, 1975).

Another important parallel development to the emergence and growth of suicide prevention and 24-hour crisis services was the Community Mental Health Centers (CMHC) Act of 1963, which mandated five essential services for all of these centers that were federally funded. Among the most important developments as a result of this legislation were 24-hour crisis intervention and emergency services. The primary emphasis of the community mental health movement was to return mental health services to community settings rather than restricting care to large state mental institutions.

Additional emphasis was placed on early intervention in order to prevent problems and crisis events from developing into serious psychopathology. Thus 24-hour crisis intervention and emergency services were viewed as a major component by a number of the newly built CMHCs. Currently, several hundred 24-hour crisis intervention units are in operation. Over 700 of them serve as a major component of CMHCs, providing early intervention and crisis stabilization not only for suicidal callers but also for substance abusers, crime victims, and people suffering from psychiatric emergencies (Roberts, 1990).

THE SURVEY

Purpose

The purpose of the national survey of crisis intervention units and centers was to systematically collect and analyze data on the structure, functions, and services provided by these centers. The author wanted to learn more about the specific services provided by these centers, their objectives, availability, initial procedures with crisis callers, referral policy, funding sources, and staffing patterns. The survey provides a national perspective on 107 crisis intervention centers located in the ten major geographic regions of the United States.

Methodology

A membership list of 225 crisis centers and programs was obtained from the American Association of Suicidology (AAS). A detailed five-page questionnaire was developed, pretested, revised, and mailed to each of the centers in November 1987. The questionnaire was sent with two cover letters: one letter introduced the survey and the other one, written by Julie Pearlman, executive director of the AAS, cited the importance of the survey. A follow-up letter and another copy of the questionnaire were sent to all nonrespondents in early February 1988. By May of that year, completed questionnaires had been received from 107, or 47.5 percent, of the centers.

The respondents were from 37 states, representing the ten major geographic regions of the nation. Some states were adequately represented by the responding programs; others were underrepresented. The states with the largest number of responding crisis centers were California (10), Florida (7), New Hampshire (6), Ohio (6), Illinois (5), and Michigan (5). The following 12 states and the District of Columbia had no respondents: Hawaii, Idaho, Indiana, Mississippi, Montana, Nebraska, New Jersey, New Mexico, South Dakota, Vermont, West Virginia, and Wyoming.

The two regions of the United States with the largest number of responding crisis centers were the Great Lakes states (21 respondents) and the southern states (17 respondents). The Great Lakes states consist of Illinois (5), Indiana (0), Michigan (1), Minnesota (1), Ohio (6), and Wisconsin (4). The southern states consist of Alabama (1), Florida (7), Georgia (1), Kentucky (3), Mississippi (0), North Carolina (1), South Carolina (2), and Tennessee (2).

Results

Objectives and Purposes of Crisis Centers

The overwhelming majority of the 107 respondents indicated that they have four or more objectives. The most frequently mentioned objectives were these:

> Suicide prevention (99 responses)
> Crisis intervention (96)
> Referral (93)
> Community education (87)

Additional objectives, identified by one-fifth to almost one-third of the programs, were these:

> Acute psychiatric emergencies (33)
> Family violence intervention (27)
> Rape crisis work (24)

The listed objective with the smallest number of responses was forensic services to the local jail (14 responses).

The data indicate that crisis centers and units provide not only crisis intervention services (tertiary prevention) in order to facilitate resolution of acute crisis episodes but also primary and secondary prevention activities.

Availability of Crisis Services

All of the respondents indicated that they provide telephone crisis intervention services, and 9 out of 10 indicated that their services were available on a 24-hour-a-day basis. Thus most of the crisis services are able to provide help quickly to persons at risk of suicide or experiencing acute crisis episodes. In addition to the crisis hotline, 59 programs offer direct, face-to-face services, and 35 programs provide outreach services.

The Year Crisis Services Were Established

One-half of the programs were established between 1968 and 1972. The peak year was 1970, when 15 of the crisis services became operational. Prior to 1968, only 12 respondents were in operation. Over one-third (37 programs) were established between 1974 and 1987. Although human service programs were buffeted by budget woes throughout the 1980s (which has been referred to as the decade of scarcity because of federal, state, and local budget cuts), close to one-fourth (25) of the crisis services were established between 1980 and 1987. How-

ever, 10 of the 25 programs were established in 1980 and 1981, before the most severe budget slashing took place.

Physical Setting

The sponsorship and autonomy of a crisis service plays a significant role in determining its location. Being located in or near a hospital or a community mental health center increases the accessibility of a crisis service and the likelihood of drop-ins and face-to-face contact with callers. In other cases, suicide prevention crisis services, with only limited staff and telephone services, keep their location unknown to the general public in order to protect the anonymity of callers and to discourage drop-ins.

Slightly over one-third (37, or 34.9 percent) of the 106 programs that responded to this question indicated that they are autonomous and housed in a building separate from the hospital or community mental health center. Of this group, 12 are housed in a building located near a hospital, while 23 are located more than ten blocks from a hospital. One-quarter of the respondents (27, or 25.4 percent) indicated that they are housed in a building with other social services, and another quarter (26, or 24.5 percent) indicated that their services are located in a free-standing community mental health center.

Only 12 services (11 percent) indicated that they are located in a hospital. Of those, five stated that they deliver only part of their services there; they also have facilities outside the hospital. For example, one program provides prehospital screening at the hospital, operates a sexual abuse program and a crisis shelter at a second location, and offers other services at a third location. Another operates from a community mental health center during business hours but provides services after hours and on weekends from a hospital setting. There were ten responses in the "other" category, including being housed in an office building, a county jail, a church, or a mobile unit. Two respondents stated that their location is kept confidential.

Informing the Community

The agencies were asked to identify the three most frequently used methods of informing the community of their services. Some identified more than three, resulting in 352 responses. The seven most frequently cited methods were public information talks, often mentioned in conjunction with a speaker's bureau (52 respondents); newspaper ads and articles (47); public service announcements (42); radio announcements (30); television appearances (29); brochures and fliers (40); and telephone directory listings and ads (23). The least frequently mentioned methods were billboards (2), annual reports (1), and bumper stickers (1).

Presenting Problems

Sixty-four of the respondents provided estimates of the percentage of their clients (totaling 578,793 served during 1986–1987) who had specific presenting problems. The five most frequently cited presenting problems were these (see Table 2-1):

Depression (19.3 percent)
Substance abuse (14.6 percent)
Suicide attempt (12.4 percent)
Marital maladjustment (8.6 percent)
Behavioral crisis (7.9 percent)

Nearly one-fifth of the persons contacting crisis services during the 1986–1987 fiscal year did so because of depression. Persons suffering from clinical depression are often unable to function in everyday life. This mood disturbance can interfere with a person's ability to think, concentrate, and function adaptively. Some depressed people are at a high distress and discomfort level and as a result are willing to call a hotline or crisis line in the hope that they can be helped.

Table 2-1   Most Frequent Presenting Problems

PROBLEM	FREQUENCY	PERCENTAGE OF CLIENTS
Depression	111,709	19.3
Substance abuse	84,946	14.6
Suicide attempt	72,250	12.4
Marital maladjustment	49,504	8.6
Behavioral crisis	45,716	7.9
Homelessness	35,656	6.2
Problems of sexuality	25,530	4.4
Psychiatric emergency	23,633	4.0
Woman abuse	19,948	3.4
Child abuse	15,694	2.7
Rape trauma victims	4,738	0.8
Victims of violent crime	3,102	0.5
Vehicular accident victims	958	0.2
Other	85,409	14.7

Based on a total of 578,793 clients.

Staff Training

A distressed person experiencing an acute crisis episode is in no position to assess the qualifications of the crisis interveners answering their calls to hotlines and crisis lines. However, in the life-threatening situations often encountered by volunteer hotline workers, it matters greatly whether the volunteer staffers have been adequately trained and whether the crisis center's director has the appropriate professional credentials.

Nearly all of the responding crisis services indicated that they provide both orientation and in-service training for their staff. Only one program administrator indicated that training is not provided. However, there was enormous variation to the type and length of the training. The number of training hours for new staffers and volunteers ranged from a low of two hours to a high of 112 hours, with an average of 38. The type and frequency of in-service training also varied greatly, with almost half (47 percent) of the programs stating that they provide in-service training once a month. The length of the training sessions ranged from a low of one hour to a high of ten hours.

Two-thirds (67 percent) of the crisis center directors had a master's degree in social work, psychology, guidance and counseling, or education. A bachelor's was the highest degree for one-quarter of the directors. Only 6 percent had a Ph.D. in psychology.

Agencies to Which Clients Are Most Frequently Referred

Respondents were asked to identify, in rank order, the types of agencies to which they most frequently refer their clients (see Table 2-2). The overwhelming majority of respondents to this question (73, or 84.8 percent) stated that the most frequent referral is to outpatient mental health services. The referral agencies with the second and third highest frequency are substance abuse treatment facilities (66, or 76.7 percent) and family service agencies (38, or 44.2 percent).

Table 2-2   Agencies to Which Callers Are Most Frequently Referred

| | RANKING | | | TOTAL RANKED |
AGENCY	1	2	3	RESPONSES
Outpatient mental health	59	12	2	73
Substance abuse treatment	4	27	35	66
Family service agency	11	16	11	38
Inpatient mental health	4	12	6	22
Private practice	1	7	10	18
Women's shelter	6	4	7	17
Salvation Army	0	1	6	7
Child guidance clinic	0	2	4	6
Women's center	0	1	4	5
Child sexual abuse program	0	1	1	2
Community support program	1	0	0	1

Based on a total of 86 services.

Organizational Issues

The survey results provided information on a number of organizational issues, including staffing patterns, the use of volunteers, and the range and size of crisis center budgets and the variety of sources used to fund them.

Budget   The annual budgets for the 1987–1988 fiscal year ranged from a low of $5,800 to a high of $5 million. Table 2-3 shows a sampling of program locations for the lowest and highest annual budgets. Note that some programs, such as those housed in community mental health centers, were unable to report

Table 2-3 Comparison of Services in High and Low Budgetary Ranges

Four services in the over $1 million range

GEOGRAPHIC LOCATION	POPULATION	TYPE OF CLIENT CONTACT	1988 BUDGET	NUMBER OF PAID STAFFERS		NUMBER OF VOLUNTEER STAFFERS	
				Full Time	Part Time	Full Time	Part Time
Minneapolis, Minn.	370,951	T, D, O	$1,000,000	13	30	0	0
Lakewood, Calif.	74,654	T, D	5,002,000	7	8	0	0
Port Huran, Mich.	33,981	*	1,200,000	26	3	3	0
Pinellas Park, Fla.	32,811	T, D, O	4,677,400	72	5	0	0

Six services in the under $50,000 range

GEOGRAPHIC LOCATION	POPULATION	TYPE OF CLIENT CONTACT	1988 BUDGET	NUMBER OF PAID STAFFERS		NUMBER OF VOLUNTEER STAFFERS	
				Full Time	Part Time	Full Time	Part Time
Milwaukee, Wis.	636,212	T, D	$11,000	*	*	*	*
Colorado Springs, Colo.	215,000	T, D	43,000	1	0	0	4
San Bernardino, Calif.	118,000	T	40,600	1	0	0	40
Tuscaloosa, Ala.	73,267	T, D	16,000	*	*	*	*
Keene, N.H.	21,449	T, D	30,900	0	4	0	45
Capitola, Calif.	9,095	T	5,800	0	0	0	50

T = Telephone service; D = Direct contact; O = Outreach
*Service did not provide these data.

budget information for the crisis intervention unit separate from that for the overall agency. The great variation in budget and staff size among the respondents was not surprising since some are part of an established community mental health center, others are suicide prevention hotlines providing telephone crisis services, and still others are small voluntary crisis support services (such as the Samaritans).

Funding Sources   Table 2-4 shows the number and percentage of responses in each funding category. The two most frequently mentioned sources of funding were the United Way (47, or 46 percent) and county or state deficit funding (46, or 45 percent). Private donations reported by close to one-third of the centers accounted for the third-largest funding category (32, or 31.4 percent), followed by private foundation grants (27, or 26.5 percent). Direct client payments were cited by only 15 centers (14.7 percent).

Administrative Coordinator   Ninety-eight programs provided information regarding the professional degree held by the administrative coordinator of their center (see Table 2-5). One program indicated that this position was shared by two staff members, resulting in a total of 99 professionals. Nearly two-thirds of

Table 2-4 Funding Sources

SOURCE	FREQUENCY	PERCENTAGE
Title XX	9	9
Third-party payments	18	18
County or state deficit funding	46	45
Municipal court contracts	3	3
Direct client payments	15	15
Private foundation grants	27	27
Other:		
United Way	47	46
Private donations	32	31
Fund-raising	11	11
Contracts	10	10
Department of Mental Health	16	16
Grants	7	7
City	4	4
Provincial government	4	4
Fees for training	2	2
Title XIX	1	1
F.E.M.A.	1	1
S.O.A.	1	1
Local liquor tax	1	1
O.A.D.A.P.	1	1
Interest	1	1
Self-generated	1	1

Based on 257 responses from 102 respondents.

Table 2-5 Professional Degree of the Administrative Coordinator

DEGREE	FREQUENCY	PERCENTAGE
Bachelor's level	25	25.2
B.A. or B.S. (19)		
B.S.W. (4)		
B.S.N. (2)		
Master's level	65	66.3
M.A. or M.S. (29)		
M.S.W. (22)		
M.B.A. (3)		
M.Ed. (6)		
M.Div. (4)		
M.S.N. (1)		
Ph.D. level	6	6.1
No degree	3	3.0

Based on 99 responses from 98 services.

the crisis services (65) indicated that they were coordinated by a person holding a master's degree, with 29 (44.6 percent) having either an M.A. or an M.S. degree and 22 (33.8 percent) an M.S.W. degree. Twenty-five of the coordinators had a bachelor's-level degree. Of these, the vast majority (19, or 76 percent) had a B.A. or a B.S. degree, and 4 (16 percent) had a B.S.W. degree. Six coordinators held a Ph.D.

Volunteer Staff Slightly over three-quarters of the 99 centers that provided staffing information indicated that they rely on volunteer workers, with a total of 5,667 volunteers reported. Although volunteer staff outnumbered professional staff by more than six to one, it should be recognized that volunteers may work as little as a half day per week. Program administrators indicated that volunteer staffers are an asset to centers when the funding enables paid staff members to do careful screening and to provide adequate training and support. However, because of the rapid turnover rate and attrition of volunteer staffers, caution should be used in relying heavily on volunteers.

Case Examples

A brief description of four crisis programs is provided here, including the sources and amounts of funding, staffing patterns, the number and types of services they provide, and areas of self-identified strengths.

Gryphon Place Crisis Intervention Center

This private, nonprofit center is located in Kalamazoo, Michigan. It has been in operation since 1970 and provides telephone and direct contact as well as professional outreach services. The program employs 11 full-time, 5 part-time, and 10 contractual staff members and has 65 part-time volunteers. During the 1987 fiscal year, this center provided services to approximately 7,000 clients. Its strongest self-reported program features are having a "strong volunteer force backed by a highly professional emergency staff" and a "strong relationship with other providers." It listed the following funding sources for the 1987 fiscal year:

Funding Source	Amount	Percentage of Budget
County and state contracts	$350,000	70
United Way	85,000	17
Private foundation grants	25,000	5
Unspecified other	20,000	4
Donations	10,000	2
Training grant	6,000	1
Title XX	6,000	1
Total	$502,000	100

The Samaritans of Keene, Inc.

Located in Keene, New Hampshire, this center has been in operation since 1981, providing a 24-hour-a-day, seven-day-a-week telephone suicide prevention service as well as limited direct contact with clients. In 1986, the staff—consisting of 3 part-time codirectors and 45 volunteers—answered approximately 11,000 calls.

The program is located in a building with other social services. The Samaritans of Keene identified its major strength as "dedicated, well-trained volunteers." It listed the following funding sources for 1988:

Funding Source	Amount	Percentage of Budget
United Way	$17,598	57
Donations	12,500	40
Unspecified other	800	3
Total	$30,898	100

Emergency Service—Mental Health Center

Located in southern Wisconsin, this organization began providing emergency crisis-oriented services in 1968 and is housed at the local community mental health center. The program provides telephone, direct contact, and professional outreach services to its clients, which numbered 2,950 in 1986. The center employs seven full-time and 17 part-time staffers and has three volunteers. It considers its strongest features to be the "easy availability and outpatient orientation" of the center and the fact that "clients are followed until resolution of the crisis situation." The funding sources for 1987–1988 were as follows:

Funding Source	Amount	Percentage of Budget
County and state funding	$700,000	95
Third party payments	20,000	3
Title XX	10,000	1
Direct client payments	5,000	1
Total	$735,000	100

Crisis Intervention Unit (Triage Program) of the Englewood Community Mental Health Center

This unit, located in the western section of Chicago, was established in 1984 and now provides 24-hour, seven-day-a-week telephone crisis intervention as well as direct contact with clients. Most callers indicate that their primary problem is an acute psychiatric emergency, depression, or a behavioral crisis. During the 1987 fiscal year, the staff of six full-time social workers, nurses, and behavioral clinicians served 1,205 clients. The director of this unit indicated that in the past they were not able to provide adequate service to victims of violent crimes, rape, child physical and sexual abuse, vehicular accidents, woman abuse, or the homeless. But in 1988, as a result of a special grant, this unit was able to expand services to rape/trauma victims and also recently initiated a case management interagency program for the homeless.

SUMMARY

Survey results indicate that crisis centers continue to provide valuable services in their communities. All of the respondents provide telephone hotline services.

Many also provide such services as face-to-face counseling and outreach. Though staffing patterns vary greatly among the programs, many use volunteers to supplement the paid professional staff. Respondents reported that volunteers are a valuable asset as long as they are carefully selected, trained, and supervised.

While most of these critically needed crisis intervention programs seem to respond effectively to the crisis-oriented needs of depressed and suicidal callers, there are three vulnerable groups of persons in crisis that were not adequately served by crisis centers during 1986 and 1987. Forty-two of the respondents indicated that they were not able to provide crisis services to homeless persons, 18 respondents indicated that they were not able to serve victims of violent crimes, and 15 respondents reported that they were not able to serve vehicular accident victims. The respondents stated that they needed additional resources in order to meet the crisis needs of these groups.

The centers' most significant challenge is to maintain adequate service levels for increasing numbers of clients with limited full-time staff and less than adequate funds. Inadequate funding was identified as one of the top three problems by 87 respondents; 53 of them ranked funding as the number one problem.

REFERENCES

DUBLIN, L. I. (1933). *To Be or Not to Be: A Study of Suicide.* New York: Random House.

DUBLIN, L. I. (1963). *Suicide: A Sociological and Statistical Study.* New York: Ronald Press.

FARBEROW, N. L., and E.S. SHNEIDMAN (Eds.). (1965). *The Cry for Help.* New York: McGraw-Hill.

HAUGHTON, A. (July, 1968). "Suicide Prevention Programs in the United States: An Overview." *Bulletin of Suicidology,* pp. 25–29.

ROBERTS, A. R. (1970). "An Organizational Study of Suicide Prevention Agencies in the U.S." *Police 14,* 64–72.

ROBERTS, A. R. (Ed.) (1975). *Self-destructive Behavior.* Springfield, Ill.: Thomas.

ROBERTS, A. R. (1990). "An Overview of Crisis Theory and Crisis Intervention," in A. R. Roberts, *Crisis Intervention Handbook: Assessment, Treatment, and Research.* Belmont, Cal.: Wadsworth Publishing Co.

Crisis Intervention Strategies with High-risk Groups

SECTION

II

The six chapters that comprise Section II focus on crisis intervention with high-risk groups, such as abused children, suicidal youth, victims of violent crime and disaster, and persons diagnosed as positive for the human immunodeficiency virus (HIV).

In Chapter 3, Judith Kendrick discusses intensive, home-based crisis treatment with abused children and their families. The program described is the Family Life Education Program (FLEP) of Indianapolis. It is modeled after the Homebuilders crisis intervention program first established in Tacoma, Washington. Kendrick explains the ways in which timely crisis intervention can reduce current stressors, help families to function, protect children, and prevent further abuse. Intensive, short-term intervention, applied to abusive and neglectful families who are in crisis, can provide a valuable opportunity for effecting change. Several practical case illustrations are provided.

Chapter 4, by David Jobes and Alan Berman, systematically examines the complexities of youthful suicidal behaviors, a phenomenon that has exhibited alarming increases in the past two decades. Although reliable clinical prediction of suicide is virtually impossible, practitioners can nevertheless optimize their capacity to respond effectively to the suicidal crises of youths by developing skills in suicide risk assessment and intervention. The comprehensive crisis intervention model presented in this chapter incorporates three clinical services that are needed to respond effectively to the range of suicidal crises. The first is emergency medical treatment (first aid), which may be required after a suicide attempt. The second is crisis intervention in response to a suicide crisis in which an attempt has not yet been made but could occur in the near future. After resolution of the crisis, the third service, follow-up counseling or psychotherapy, can help to prevent future suicidal crises.

In Chapter 5, Grace Christ, Sister Rosemary Moynihan, and Les Gallo-Silver vividly illustrate the crisis points and cognitive crisis intervention strategies that they have found to be effective in helping persons diagnosed with AIDS (at Memorial Sloan-Kettering Cancer Center in New York City) to cope with their crisis. The authors discuss the social conditions related to the transmission of the human immunodeficiency virus (HIV) among various groups, including homosexual and bisexual men, intravenous (IV) drug users, and persons infected through blood transfusions. Emphasis is placed on the psychosocial tasks and short-term intervention associated with the five major crises in the progression of AIDS.

In Chapter 6, Marlene Young, the founder and executive director of the National Organization for Victim Assistance (NOVA), describes the work of the National Crisis Response Teams following a communitywide disaster. These disasters are often precipitated by criminal acts (e.g., a mass murder) or accidents (e.g., a plane crash). The relatives, friends, neighbors, and coworkers of deceased or seriously injured victims are often in crisis. This chapter reviews the types of crisis and stress reactions among individuals in the aftermath of community disasters. The author also provides NOVA's guidelines for working with injured victims and the loved ones of deceased victims. NOVA also educates caregivers, mental health professionals, victim advocates, and members of the clergy regarding grief reactions, stress reactions, and posttraumatic stress disorder.

Chapter 7, by Thomas Strentz, focuses on the crisis of being taken hostage by a terrorist group. It features a discussion of the crisis management practices used by the FBI's special hostage negotiators. Strentz includes a review of the specific guidelines for crisis negotations, crisis counseling strategies, and the four phases of a hostage situation: alarm, crisis, accommodation, and resolution. Since this program was initiated, hundreds of hostage situations have been successfully resolved through the use of crisis management and intervention techniques.

Chapter 8, by Arlene Bowers Andrews, examines a variety of crisis-oriented interventions developed to facilitate an individual's recovery from family violence and to reduce the risk of further abuse and long-term psychosocial damage. The chapter leads with a presentation of the conceptual framework that integrates stress theory and family violence. The author provides two case illustrations of the crisis reactions of children and adolescents to the multiple and extraordinary stressors of family violence. Andrews describes three levels of crisis intervention. The first is psychological first aid. The second level is survivor needs assessment, empathetic support, information, and advocacy. The third level (which requires greater skill in psychoeducation and psychotherapy than the first two levels) consists of several steps, including helping the survivor of family violence to maximize social supports; identifying, examining, and accepting one or more possible solutions; providing assistance in taking concrete action; and preparing for follow-up.

Crisis Intervention in Child Abuse
A Family Treatment Approach

Judith Manning Kendrick | 3

INTRODUCTION

Case examples are used in this chapter to illustrate clinical thinking and strategies for intervention with families in crisis as a result of child abuse and neglect. A description of the Family Life Education Program (FLEP) is included to explain the philosophy, staffing, funding and application of family-based services in a traditional home-care agency. A family systems approach to treatment is used with a variety of family therapy modalities. Efficacy is explored as the problems of child abuse and neglect and out-of-home placement of children continue to grow and the need for appropriate services increases.

The difficulties of providing timely, effective and appropriate services to children and families who are experiencing problems of child abuse and neglect are challenging to treatment providers. As the incidence of abuse is increasingly recognized and reported, the demand for treatment escalates. Clinicians in traditional settings are often frustrated in their attempts to engage and retrain abusive families in treatment, as well as working with a child welfare system that is overloaded and in crisis.

The treatment program presented in this chapter is an example of a nontraditional approach to working with abusive families while they are in crisis. Case examples are presented to illustrate the complex nature of the problems leading to abuse and some strategies that FLEP employs to reduce the risk of further abuse. Program philosophy, structure, and efficacy are examined in an attempt to identify the components of success.

Mandy

Case Study

Mandy was a 14-year-old who had recently begun living with her mother, Mrs. Rogers, and her stepfather, Mr. Rogers. This was the first time she had lived with her mother since she was 2 years old and was abandoned by her mother into the care of her father, who raised her but began molesting her when she was 8. She was removed from his care when she was 13 and disclosed the sexual assaults. Mandy then lived with a maternal aunt for a time and was eventually sent to a foster home, then, two months previously, to live with her mother. At the time of the referral, Mrs. Rogers was requesting that Mandy be placed outside her home because of problems with fighting at school and a "bad attitude" at home.

I first met with Mr. and Mrs. Rogers and the caseworker from the Welfare Department to assess the problems from the parents' perspective and see if there was any commitment to work on staying together. Mrs. Rogers talked initially about her problems in dealing with Mandy and thought that Mandy ought to be more responsible, thoughtful, and cooperative. When I suggested that those attributes are mostly absent during normal adolescence and that perhaps their lack might be expected in Mandy because of her life experience, Mrs. Rogers let me know that expected or not, such an attitude would not be tolerated, and if she couldn't follow their rules, Mandy was gone! Mrs. Rogers also let me know that her history of emotional problems and her life experiences were not relevant to the issue, which was whether Mandy could "shape up" enough to live with them. She did acknowledge that Mr. Rogers's health problems, which left him unable to work at the present time, and the stress of being the sole financial provider for the family made her situation difficult. She was also able to join with Mandy in being angry at Mandy's father for his assaults on her and talked about going after him with a gun because the process of prosecuting him was taking too long. Mr. Rogers assured me that he had stopped her from doing this and would continue to do so. Mrs. Rogers also stated that her mother and other family members were non-supportive and in fact interfered with her efforts to care for Mandy. This lengthy first session gave me clear guidelines as to what issues could be addressed and which ones I ought to steer clear of. I accepted the case with guarded optimism, as I had not yet met Mandy.

At the second session I met with Mandy and the Rogerses. The mood was much more relaxed and comfortable, and I immediately acknowledged how difficult it is to constantly be working with helpers and wondering if they're really going to be useful as they pry into the intimate details of one's life. This session was focused on explaining the rules for Mandy's behavior and appropriate consequences for violation of the rules. Mandy participated by talking about the demands that were difficult for her and about compromises. Mandy said that she wanted things to work out with her mother, and it was obvious that they were having some fun working together on makeup and clothes. But it was also evident that Mandy knew that few options were open to her. At least when it came to her frustrations about the delay in the prosecution of her father, Mandy and her mother could connect on a feeling level, and Mandy felt supported by her mother's anger. However, because that issue was so volatile (I could imagine them plotting to kill him), I searched to find another common ground. Mrs. Rogers's conflicted relationship with her own mother and her feelings that her ex-husband was robbing her of the opportunity to be a mother to Mandy were issues that I thought might incite Mrs. Rogers to be more tolerant and caring of Mandy, and this did work for a time.

After two more sessions, the family decided that they were on an even course and didn't need to see me on a regular basis. They agreed to contact me if things got out of balance. Mrs. Rogers did contact me about one month later when she and Mandy had an argument that ended in a physical fight. By the time I saw them, they felt that it had been resolved and weren't prepared to deal with the problems that led to the explosion. We went back to our agreement that I would be available as needed.

Four months passed, during which time I would contact them by phone to see how things were going. Everyone reported good progress. At about the six-month point, however, I received several urgent phone messages from Mrs. Rogers. I soon discovered that over the past three weeks, the situation had changed drastically. Mr. Rogers's health problems had necessitated an operation, and he had just returned from the hospital. Mandy had a boy in the home while Mrs. Rogers was at the hospital and had spent the past week at the home of family friends. Mrs. Rogers wanted Mandy out of the home immediately and said that she was afraid that she'd kill her if she came home. I arranged to see them immediately and asked her to get Mandy home for my visit. Mrs. Rogers was hysterical but agreed to do this.

Mandy had not yet arrived when I got to the family home, and, in fact, the family who was caring for her called after my arrival to make sure that it would be safe to bring her. I listened to the frustrations of the recent family events and agreed that the stresses in the home were intense. Mrs. Rogers wanted Mandy out of the home immediately and wanted her placed in a correctional facility. When Mandy arrived, Mrs. Rogers again said that she wanted her gone and never wanted to see her again. Mandy was tearful and sad, in great contrast to her mother's hysterical anger. In the midst of this, Mr. Rogers began to hemorrhage from his tracheotomy incision, and Mrs. Rogers was preparing to take him to the emergency room. All agreed that Mandy should continue to stay with the family friends, and I arranged to meet with them the following day. On that occasion they said that they wanted to adopt Mandy, and after calming down, Mrs. Rogers agreed to let them do that. I remained involved for a while to help Mandy sort out this next big change in her life. She agreed to the adoption, as she liked the family and sadly realized that her options were limited. This family also supported her through the prosecution of her father and followed through with counseling to deal with the sexual abuse and other issues. Mrs. Rogers was also counseled to help her deal with the feelings of guilt at having failed Mandy again, essentially by making her realize that her situation did not allow her to meet the demands that caring for Mandy required. There were tense moments during the lengthy process that led to Mandy's adoption, but it was eventually finalized, and Mandy and her mother were able to have a relationship that enabled both of them to grow.

This case presented some very real threats and opportunities for violence and abuse and warranted ongoing therapy from the beginning. But the family was only willing to work when in extreme crisis, when the pain was unbearable. By safeguarding the forbidden issues and assisting in concrete ways to work on the problems initially presented during the original crisis, the pain of the subsequent crisis allowed for hope that I might be able to help. **This mixture of pain and hope, so necessary to an effective crisis resolution, allowed for a much more positive outcome for Mandy** than might have been possible in other circumstances.

Some people might contend that the reuniting of Mandy with her mother was doomed from the start. I expressed guarded optimism after my first encounter, fully aware of the "pathology" of the system we were attempting to blend. Satir (1986) says that all parents do the best they can, this being dependent on what they have learned and how they feel about themselves. And looking at current behavior as a specific response to a specific behavior at an earlier point in time helps the therapist to understand and key in to how that event and the manner in which it was coped with leads to greater understanding of subsequent behaviors. Looking at family problems in this light allows us to be optimistic and focus on family strength rather than pathology, realizing that positive changes will originate from the health of the family, not the sickness.

We could look at the conclusion of the Rogers case and consider it a failure because Mandy was not able to continue to live with her mother. However, that would negate the many positive aspects of their having had this time together, to know each other. Mandy understood her mother's inability to be her parent and knew that it had nothing to do with her. She wasn't defective or bad because her mother couldn't care for her. The final blowup had more to do with stress overload than failures of the people involved. Mrs. Rogers, subconsciously or otherwise, selected loving alternative caregivers for Mandy, who were able to provide her with a permanent home. The final resolution left everyone able to go on with their lives with a sense that they had coped with a very difficult problem successfully.

The Rogers family was unique, as are all families, because the members' individual and collective experiences are unique. Yet they were not atypical in their response to the offer of help. Child abuse and neglect present significant challenges to people attempting to intervene. Kendrick (1988) addresses the issues related to a family's attitudes toward treatment being dependent on who has already been involved and whether treatment is viewed as help or punishment. Helfer (1987) states that the frequency data reflecting both incidence and prevalence are high. Treatment is largely reactive, although preventive programs dealing with parent education are more accessible than in the past. Counseling is seen as a way to interrupt the cycle of abuse but is usually not offered or mandated until there has been an incidence of abuse or neglect. Unfortunately most parents do not feel free to ask for help, as there is an unspoken assumption that everyone should be able to be parents, not because they've been trained but because they themselves had parents. The point at which most parents feel justified in seeking help is after a child has begun to act in a way that attracts negative attention and pressure to the family. It is much more acceptable to have a "bad kid" than to seek counsel in regard to the difficult, demanding responsibility of raising children. Volumes are being published in the field of parent education (see Chapter 10 for a detailed discussion), but a proactive approach to the task of being a parent is not the norm. We, as professionals, can do much toward acknowledging the awesome responsibility of caring for a dependent human being from birth through emancipation. It is the most important work most of us will ever do, and yet we are all so ill prepared. This understanding is necessary and important when dealing with those identified as having failed their children by hurting or not providing adequate care for them.

Crisis theory (see Chapter 1), when applied to child abuse and neglect cases, affords a rich opportunity to effect change in a limited amount of time. The timing is critical, as is the attitude of the crisis intervener. (The attitudinal component is discussed later in the chapter.) If too much time has elapsed between the event that led to the family's involvement with the child protection system and therapeutic intervention, the defense mechanisms that allow families to live with their dysfunction have been reassembled, and they are far less likely to feel the pain that the crisis produced. Crisis intervention is also not to be mistaken for treatment of the myriad of problems that the family may have been experiencing prior to the event that led to identification by the authorities. It does offer help for the current stressor, with the added benefit that if the crisis intervention produced results that the family identifies as helpful, seeking help in the future to work on other problems may not seem as threatening and may encourage a hopeful attitude toward the benefits of therapy when weighed against the cost of doing nothing.

The following cases illustrate the utility of crisis intervention at the point of involvement with the system and how two families responded to the intervention.

Tammy and Teresa

Case Study

The school reported that Tammy (age 9) and her sister, Teresa (age 7), were both bruised on the legs and buttocks as a result of a beating administered by their stepfather. The police placed the children in protective custody. I spoke with the parents that evening and arranged to meet with them the following morning. The Child Protective Services worker told me that if I felt that the abuse was not ongoing and if the parents agreed to work with me, we could return the children. The family consisted of Mr. Freeman, the stepfather; Mrs. Freeman, the mother of the two girls; a 16-year-old brother; and an infant, the child of Mr. and Mrs. Freeman. Both parents were employed, and they had been married for five years. There had been no previous involvement with protective services.

The parents were frantic when I arrived, and I asked them to tell me what had happened. They related that Mr. Freeman had beaten both girls with a belt after being frustrated by their continual fighting with each other. They shared much about their family and were anxious to see their children. Mr. Freeman was somewhat defensive about his actions, and Mrs. Freeman was able to verbalize the frustration they both felt in trying to elicit better behavior from their children. They readily agreed to cooperate with me as well as to refrain from further physical discipline. I assured them that I would teach them new ways to discipline, as I was not advocating that they let their children run wild. I asked them to fill out the Child Abuse Prevention Inventory (Form VI, 1986) to measure their overall abuse potential and also get a better idea of where the stresses were coming from. We then went to the school to meet with the girls.

Tammy, the elder, was very fearful at first meeting, not sure of how her parents would react to what had happened. Teresa was obviously glad to see her mom and dad and baby brother. I explained to the children that they had done nothing wrong and that they had a right not to be abused and hurt by their parents. I had asked Mr. Freeman to apologize for hurting them and causing this upset in their lives. This he did. I explained to the children, for the parents' benefit too, that parents are supposed to protect their children from harm and that their father had been wrong to hurt them. I further assured them that they had been right to tell, and I encouraged the parents to let the girls know that they also approved because it would lead their family to finding new ways to get along. We made arrangements for the girls to come home after school. I did brief therapy with the Freemans, at first around their controlling the children's behavior by using timeouts and restricting privileges, with the girls and the 16-year-old boy. We also addressed issues around the blended family and how little time and attention were devoted to the parents' relationship, as they had never been without children. As they became more comfortable with me, the issues they wanted to address moved to things not directly involved in child care. When I last saw them, they were taking some time for themselves, thus having more collective energy to deal with the challenges of the children. Their own care of themselves as a couple had been set aside to be parents, when in reality the fact that they were ignoring their own needs made child care more difficult and unrewarding. They basically got in trouble for putting their perceived duty first.

Billy

Case Study

Billy Storm, age 10, was removed from his home when the school noticed that he had a black eye, which he attributed to his father's pushing him into a table. Billy said that his father had "gone off" on him because he had accidentally hurt his 2-year-old stepsister, Polly. I met with Mr. and Mrs. Storm and found them to be open in discussing the incident that led to Billy's injury. They were also open in discussing their problems related to Mr. Storm's alcoholism and the events that led to Billy's living with them. I mention this openness at my first meeting with them because after the immediate crisis of Billy's removal had passed, they recovered their defenses and were not nearly as cooperative. I elicited the usual agreement not to use physical punishment as a condition for Billy's return home, gave them the Child Abuse Potential Inventory (which they later gave to their 2-year-old to cut up), and suggested withdrawal of privileges as a way to moderate Billy's behavior.

During the initial session, the Storms talked about how difficult Billy's life had been with his mother, who had custody of him and lived a chaotic life. Moving from state to state, Billy had been responsible for himself from a young age, as well as for caring for his younger siblings. Mr. Storm had pursued Billy to regain custody of him for several years and had finally succeeded about 18 months previously. Mr. Storm had expected that because of the increased stability of life with his father and his stepmother, Billy, now 10 years old, would be grateful. In fact, their efforts to provide Billy with a more carefree, childlike existence were what Billy was rebelling against. When I suggested this to the Storms, they were perplexed, but as we examined it further, they were willing to concede that it made sense. It made even more sense to me when Mr. Storm revealed that he was an alcoholic. He had recently gone through a treatment program but was not following up with the Alcoholics Anonymous meetings he knew were vital to his recovery. When I asked Mrs. Storm if she attended Al-Anon, she said that she went once but wasn't comfortable in the group environment. She preferred to deal with her issues independently.

When I next met with the Storms, Billy and his 2-year-old sister were present. I found both children to be bright and verbal. The Storms assured Billy that he could talk freely with me, and when I asked him what bothered him about his family, he said that he worried about dad's drinking. My view of Billy was that he was already assuming the role of adult parent as a result of the chaotic life he had led with his mother; then he went to his father's home, only to be confronted with the alcoholism, which only served to reinforce Billy's need to be in charge. The work of this session was to explore Billy's rights (basic needs, medical care, love) and privileges (computer, activities). The family discussed what behaviors were important and what they would do if there was a violation of the accepted behavior. At the next session, they were much less open with me, but Billy felt that things were better. Mrs. Storm sheepishly told me that the nonphysical disciplines were working.

My work with the family concluded after two more sessions. They were optimally ready to work during the crisis period, when Billy was removed, but as they stabilized, they became much less willing to allow me into their intimate life. I felt comfortable that the issues around Mr. Storm's alcoholism were more open and that both parents had learned more effective ways to discipline Billy and encourage his being a child. It was my hope that by sticking to the child-related agenda and not assuming that they wanted help with the effects of Mr. Storm's alcoholism, it might be easier for them to seek help when they were ready to deal with that.

Analysis

Both of the foregoing cases were short-term and responded well because of the crisis. The people involved were willing to try new behaviors where old ones caused pain; also, both families were in shock at their children's being removed from their care, and that made them more willing to try new behaviors to keep that from happening again. In both cases, long-term treatment could have been beneficial, but in both cases, one parent began to shut down after the immediate crisis had passed. The risk to the children in both cases was minimized, and that was the purpose for intervention. Neither family has slipped back into abuse.

These families and all case examples used here are families who were involved with the Family Life Education Program.

THE AGENCY

The Family Life Education Program (FLEP), Visiting Nurse Service, Indianapolis, Indiana, began in response to the demand for services for families as a result of the Adoption Assistance Act of 1980, with the intent to prevent placement of children in out-of-home care or to shorten the length of stay in out-of-home care if children are placed. The program began in 1984 as a small, time-limited, home-based, family-centered service for the major metropolitan county and the seven surrounding counties. Increasing demands for such family-based services had led to the development of the program into a comprehensive array of services including family therapy, provided by five masters level social workers with advanced training in family therapy; monitoring and supervision, provided by two bachelor level social workers; parenting classes; family support services, provided by four paraprofessionals; and parent aides, volunteers trained by another community agency. All referrals come from the Children's Services Division of the county departments of public welfare, and funding is under Title 4-B. In addition, the agency provides field placements for the Indiana University School of Social Work, so there are usually senior B.S.W. or M.S.W. students involved in the program.

All families have had at least one report to the Child Protective Services regarding abuse or neglect. They may be referred to FLEP at the beginning of their involvement with CPS or at any point thereafter. The program is sometimes used in hopes of avoiding prolonged involvement in the child welfare system and at other times after lack of progress or completion of other services. Intervention at the point of crisis, early in a family's involvement with the child welfare system, presents the best opportunity to engage a family to work for change. However, crisis referrals represent only about 25 percent of the families referred for FLEP services. The others represent more chronic, multiproblem families who tend to be involved in treatment much longer. Prevention Report (1988), in discussing the factors related to success and failure in family-based services, found, not surprisingly, that family-based services are more effective when families can be reached at earlier stages. They further reported:

Programs offering more comprehensive, in-home services to families with more risk factors—that is those working with the most troubled, multi-problem families—had higher placement rates. Yet even the program with the highest placement rate, placement was prevented in 75% of the cases served. For the most part, these preventive family-based services were successful at what they set out to do—averting the placement of children from families in crisis.

FLEP services have followed the national trend of preventing placement in 85 to 90 percent of the families served.

Philosophy

Homebuilders (Kinney et al., 1977; Roberts, 1989) and the St. Paul Family-centered Project (Horejsi, 1981) were major influences in the development of the Family Life Education Program. FLEP subscribes to the basic assumptions, principles, and values of the Child Welfare League of America (1984) in regard to services for children and families in their own homes. The National Resource Center on Family Based Services (University of Iowa School of Social Work) outlined the principles of family-centered service, as follows:

1. The first and greatest investment must be made to the care and treatment of children in their own homes before more radical measures are considered.
2. Services are as complete, comprehensive, and intense as is necessary to resolve problems and to strengthen and maintain the family. Staff is available 24 hours a day, seven days a week, often serving as an extended family.
3. The service setting is primarily the home but includes problem-solving efforts in the family's "ecosystem" (where family interacts with community systems).
4. The parents remain in charge, and the family is the service unit. The family is recognized as the primary care provider, health center, source of nurture, and educator.
5. The focus may be developmental or remedial (or both), and the services extended may be under social, health, or educational auspices; in any case, the needed service components are made available. (Programs devoted to developmental or primary prevention rather than correction may be less intensive.)
6. Maximum use is made of family resources, the extended family, and the community.
7. Many of the programs provide help with any problem presented by the family or observed by the service team. If the home-based family-centered team does not have the expertise or resources needed, it arranges for or creates them.
8. The "family in community" is the hub around which services are provided, problems are solved, and coping techniques are taught.

The St. Paul Family-centered Project of the early 1950s was developed to work with families commonly referred to as multiproblem or chronic. Horejsi (1981) looked again at this model project and found much of value to inform service delivery 30 years later. Four factors related to the successful use of outreach were these:

1. The approach must be purposeful, related to a definite problem in the situation. It may be delinquency or truancy or other evidence of child neglect.

2. The approach should be open-minded, ready to hear and truly understand the family's point of view.
3. It should be made with genuine confidence in the ultimate potential of each human being and respect for human dignity.
4. It should be persistent. Interveners must go often enough and stay long enough, despite rebuffs, discourtesy, hostility, or denial of need or wish to use the service.

Bryce (1979) cites the importance and the soundness of giving greater attention to persons in their natural context and the opportunities that that presents for the worker in regard to modeling, teaching, nurturing, and directing. He states, "Working with families in their own homes conveys far more regard for the family's integrity, honor and rights than placement of one of its members." In my own work in an office setting, I relied on my own experiences and values to try to arrive at a picture of what a family's life was like outside the artificial setting of the office. I took the client's words and constructed what I took to be the reality of their lives in their home and community. Seeing families in their homes was a shocking affront to my version of reality and opened the door to finally understanding the complex nature of the family influences inside and outside the home. All the senses are activated and directed toward greater understanding and appreciation of the total experience of the family, thus offering increased options for intervention.

According to the most recent statistics from the National Resource Center on Family-based Services (Prevention Report, 1988), 269 programs were listed in its 1987 directory. The first National Family-based Conference, held in Minneapolis in 1987, included family-based workers from across the United States. More is being published about family-based services than ever before, in books and journals.

Approach to Treatment

FLEP uses a family systems approach in the treatment of child abuse and neglect. The family is targeted to receive services, and masters level social workers working in the program go through a two-year training program in family therapy with Ernest Andrews at the Family Therapy Institute of Cincinnati. This training helps to equip the workers to deal with very difficult situations without being overwhelmed. Structural and strategic approaches are often used in treatment. Haley (1976), Napier and Whitaker (1978), Minuchin and Fishman (1981), Madanes (1981), and other heroes in the field of family therapy inform and energize our work. The "brief therapy" thinking of Bergman (1985), de Shazer (1985, 1988), and Gustafson (1986) help us to work in the time frame we realistically have with most families. The work of Pittman (1987) in the area of transition and crisis helps us to use these points in time as powerful tools in motivating change. The exciting new work of Visher and Visher (1988) helps us to understand further the dynamics of working with stepfamilies.

The strategies for crisis counseling outlined in Chapter 1 provide a useful framework for crisis work with child abuse.

Early assessment of risk is the vital first step in intervention. A child has been hurt; that fact led to the family's involvement with FLEP. They did not ask for help but are informed that FLEP's efforts will be geared toward keeping their family together or getting them back together if children are placed outside the home. Joining with the family is imperative, and they are usually relieved to have someone working with them in the process of encountering a system that is often perceived as threatening and powerful. Most people see the help coming to them, in their own home, as positive, and it offers a good opportunity to evaluate the risk factors more fully. The initial visit agenda, beyond risk assessment and establishing rapport with the family, includes defining the problem as the family sees it and exploring the stressors that precipitated the abusive event. Questions are asked about family composition, dynamics, substance abuse, stability, sexual and physical abuse history, suicide, physical and mental limitations, employment and financial history, psychiatric history, problems in the community, relationships among family members, discipline, supervision, knowledge of child development, and problems with violence or other criminal activity to help in understanding the dimensions of the problem. Past coping events are explored to understand what has already been tried, successfully or otherwise. Open expression of feelings and emotions is encouraged throughout this process, and feelings are not challenged. Reframing is often used as a way to keep negative emotions toward children from resulting in further maltreatment. For instance, a tirade about the terrible behavior a child is exhibiting might be reframed as a parent being very concerned about the child.

In the initial session, a prescription to address the immediate concern of the parent will be offered. This is usually behavior-specific and intended as a tool for the parents as well as an indicator for the child that the parent is willing to make changes. Because of the risks, an action plan is necessary from the beginning. During the initial session, a verbal contract for a specific number of sessions, usually eight, is agreed on. This time limit lets the family know that there is a limited time to work and avoids confusion about the purpose of involvement. Goals are formulated at that time but are also expanded as treatment continues. The FLEP staff involves the family in working with other community agencies and programs that can be resources for them. All persons involved in the family system are involved in the treatment so that they can be useful to the family through the change process and also once FLEP services are no longer involved. Figure 3-1 illustrates the flow of service.

Working with abusive and neglectful families requires not only a well-informed practice but also constant monitoring of risk. The health and safety of children is at stake, and within the context of therapy, there must be a continued assessment of the factors that present risk. This makes work with families around abuse and neglect stressful and challenging but also rewarding as we see children and parents being kinder to each other and hope for amelioration of the same problems in the next generation. The Abel case illustrates ongoing risk assessment during the course of therapy.

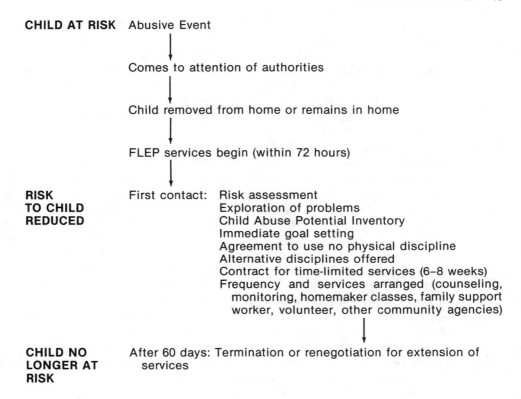

CHILD AT RISK   Abusive Event

Comes to attention of authorities

Child removed from home or remains in home

FLEP services begin (within 72 hours)

RISK   First contact: Risk assessment
TO CHILD   Exploration of problems
REDUCED   Child Abuse Potential Inventory
                                  Immediate goal setting
                                    Agreement to use no physical discipline
                                    Alternative disciplines offered
                                    Contract for time-limited services (6–8 weeks)
                                    Frequency and services arranged (counseling,
                                        monitoring, homemaker classes, family support
                                        worker, volunteer, other community agencies)

CHILD NO   After 60 days: Termination or renegotiation for extension of
LONGER AT   services
RISK

Figure 3-1   Course of FLEP Intervention

Case Study

The Abel family was referred for family-based services following harsh discipline of 17-year-old Rachel by her stepmother. The family had no phone at this time, so I stopped by to see when I could meet with them. I was met on the front porch by 4-year-old Ashley, and I asked if her parents were home. She told me that her mother was at work and her father was inside, drunk. She was, in fact, carrying some empty beer cans to the trash container. Another child, 13-year-old Peter, then came out the door. I introduced myself and explained that his parents had been told that I would be coming to see them, gave him my card, and asked him to have his parents call me to schedule an appointment. Mrs. Abel called that evening, and I arranged to meet with them the following day.

    Present for the first session were Mr. and Mrs. Abel, 17-year-old Rachel and 14-year-old Amy (Mr. Abel's daughters from a previous marriage), 13-year-old Peter and 10-year-old Patty (Mrs. Abel's children from a previous marriage), and 4-year-old Ashley (Mr. and Mrs. Abel's child). I began by asking the family to tell me about the problems that had caused them to come to the attention of

Child Protective Services and led to the temporary removal of Rachel from the home. Mrs. Abel explained that she had become totally frustrated with Rachel's attitude and behavior and had slapped her face, leaving marks. When I asked for Rachel's view of the problems, she told me that talking about things just made them worse, so she wasn't going to talk. She attempted to leave the living room, and I asked her to please stay, assuring her that she didn't have to talk because I didn't want things to be worse for her, realizing that she had been through a lot in the past few days.

I asked the rest of the family to tell me what they saw as the problem, and their responses all indicated that Rachel was the problem, which helped me to understand that scapegoating her was distracting from issues that they weren't ready to discuss. During this first session, Mrs. Abel acted as the spokesperson, with all the children except Rachel offering information. The family was experiencing financial problems, especially since Mr. Abel lost his job as a truck driver, due to his loss of driving privileges for driving while intoxicated. However, he assured me that he was not an alcoholic. His explanation of the problem was that Rachel was acting out due to her mother's abandoning her and her three siblings eight years ago. He was afraid that she was going to be like her mother, whom he described as a whore. Mrs. Abel was ready to throw in the towel. She was working at a low-paying, unrewarding job and coming home to conflict. She felt that she was pulling the whole load and not getting anything back. I was struck by her bond with all the children, except Rachel, and how loving and spontaneous they were with each other. The child who was most distressed by this crisis in the family was 14-year-old Amy, who worried what would happen to her if the family split up. This initial session ended with everyone, except Rachel, of course, agreeing to do specific tasks to make Mrs. Abel's job easier. I also asked Mr. Abel to take total control of his daughter, Rachel, referring to his earlier comments about being committed to caring for his children after their mother's abandonment. He agreed to do this. The family also agreed to meet with me for eight sessions.

Everstine and Everstine (1983) note that a family perceives a therapist who is asked to intervene by the authorities as a threat. Even though approaching the family in a nonthreatening personal manner, the therapist is an uninvited stranger intruding into the family's most intimate space. That is why the first visit to a family who has come to the attention of the authorities because of abuse or neglect must begin by trying to understand the family's perception of the presenting difficulty while at the same time evaluating the risks to the children in the home. The first visit is also an opportunity to demonstrate that the therapist can be helpful to the family by meeting an immediate need. That may be as basic as helping the family to obtain food or as complex as beginning to restructure family operations. The family also has the right to know the professional qualifications and beliefs of the person who is trying to be helpful. If the therapist is young, the family may wonder if the person has had enough experience to understand or can relate to the experience of being a parent. All such spoken and unspoken questions need to be addressed forthrightly; this is not a time to apply psychoanalytic reflection. The family needs to know, "Can this person truly help me?" The therapist's response must convey a sincere willingness to understand; it must communicate that even if the therapist has not experienced the difficulties the family faces, he or she has been able to help other families in similar circumstances. Sincerity from the professional is imperative and helps to relieve the threatening nature of the intrusion into the family's lives and homes.

The second session with the Abel family found Mrs. Abel and all the children present, although Rachel left the room after my arrival. Mr. Abel was unable to be present because he was doing an odd job for money (a very good way to avoid the session). In this session, I got a much more profound sense of the family's pain and fear that they might not endure as a family. I asked the family to focus on their own issues and not to involve Mr. Abel or Rachel, as they were not present. I also suggested that if they wanted Mr. Abel and Rachel at the family sessions, they must not share with them what we did but must instead invite them to come and see for themselves. The family members present all reported that they had been more cooperative in doing the household chores, which had a very positive effect on Mrs. Abel. She was also letting Mr. Abel deal with Rachel, although the children still experienced her as a problem for them, seeing her as mean, nasty, and threatening to the stability of the family. I expressed amazement that one family member had so much control over them and that she possessed so many negative qualities, since she had lived with this group for so long and they were so obviously caring and loving with each other. During this session, these family members discussed some fun activities that they could enjoy together, and I encouraged them not to expect Mr. Abel and Rachel to want to accompany them, since they weren't in on the planning. Their energy and enthusiasm and obvious hope that they could work together enabled them to work together. However, the next two sessions included Mr. Abel only once and Rachel not at all. At the end of the fourth session, I gave Mrs. Abel a note for Rachel that read:

> Dear Rachel,
>
> Thank you so much for not participating in our family sessions, as it gives us such a good opportunity to plot against you.
>
> Judy

Her reply, which was written on my original note and which mom was embarrassed for me to read, said:

> Dear Judy,
>
> Fuck you! Like I don't give a shit what you think.
>
> Rachel

My reason for the note was to try to discover whether or not she was involved in the family and our work. Her reply let me know that she was, or else it would have been ignored. She spent the last several sessions more in evidence, although she never actually entered the living room while we met. For one session where we discussed giving her what she wanted, to live with her mother or grandmother, she actually stood right outside the door for the entire session. She was also in evidence during a session when I was attempting to get the family to stop blaming her for its problems by making a list of her good qualities. The list was quite extensive, and everyone felt that she was nicer to them following that session. It was in this same session that we were making a list of the good things about the family and got stuck. To encourage them to come up with strengths, I started the sentence, "This family really . . . ," and hung onto the *really,* waiting for a response. Ten-year-old Patty jumped out of her chair and enthusiastically shouted, "Needs help!" It disarmed all of us, and we laughed until we cried together. If this had been staged, it couldn't have been more perfect to get the family moving and keeping Mr. Abel involved in the work. I concluded my work with the family at the point where Mrs. Abel was attending Al-Anon. Mr. Abel was still denying that he was an alcoholic but was still taking control of Rachel and planned to let her live with her grandmother as a way to transit into emancipation. When Rachel discovered that she was getting what she had asked for, she began to back down on the request, but I encouraged her father to carry out his plans. A parent aide was assigned to the family and kept in touch with me for a couple of years. I was encouraged to know that Rachel's relationship with her family improved. Mr. Abel began to attend AA and started working again. As might have been expected, Amy began to act out following Rachel's departure from the home, but it was short-lived, and the Abels worked together to handle the problem.

The Baker case is cited as an example of a family who would not acknowledge or deal with their problems of alcohol and violence as the Abel family did, but did refrain from further abuse of the child.

Case Study

The Baker family was referred for services following an abusive incident by Mr. Baker that resulted in a bruising to his 13-year-old daughter from his first marriage. Mrs. Baker, his second wife, and their 1- and 2-year-old sons left the home with Marilyn, the daughter, at the time of the incident and went to a crisis shelter because of her fear of Mr. Baker. Other services had been offered to the family and been rebuffed. At the time I received the referral, the family was back together and was now aligned against the Child Protective System.

This alignment of the family against the system is not unusual. Although the family members may bring the abuse or conflict to the attention of the authorities, once the initial crisis has passed, the family returns to its precrisis state and can come to resent the intrusion of outsiders into their closed system. Further, if they perceive that the perpetrator of the abuse is being treated unfairly, they quickly rally around that person. Solin (1986) discusses the displacement of affect in families following disclosure of incest. This displacement is also evident in families brought into the child welfare system because of physical abuse and neglect.

The family mirrors traditional family norms despite the existence of often violent conflict within the home. And despite the family pain, the intrusion of outsiders into the family system sends the family into disequilibrium, preventing them from returning to the precrisis state. Displacement of affect allows the family to syphon off the negative feelings toward the perpetrator of abuse while still allowing those angry feelings to be ventilated. The Baker family seemed to evidence this displacement phenomenon.

Mr. Baker was described to me as an alcoholic, angry bully who had been totally uncooperative with others who had attempted to work with him. My initial telephone contact with Mr. Baker to set up a meeting time was tense, and he made it clear that he did not want further intrusion into his family life; he only wanted to get out of the system. I assured him that that was the purpose of my involvement, and he agreed to a family meeting but insisted that it could occur only on a Saturday evening at 6:00 P.M. I accepted this unorthodox time, realizing that he obviously needed to challenge me and to be in control.

The Baker family spent much of the first session verbalizing their anger at the system and its intrusion into their lives. The immediate crisis of the abusive event had passed, and they had regrouped. They did talk openly about present pressures but denied serious problems of alcoholism and family violence. Mr. Baker had worked for the same company for 17 years, his evidence that he didn't have problems with drinking. Mrs. Baker denied serious violence and offered as evidence her healthy state and that of her children. Both of these denials were in the face of the original problem that led to Mrs. Baker's seeking shelter, numerous police calls to the family residence because of fighting, and Mr. Baker's history of alcohol-related driving offenses. The family had refused to attend the batterers' group recommended to them and had rejected an alcohol evaluation.

I realized that Mr. Baker was clearly in charge of the family and listened intently to his description of the problem. Then I told him that I thought the reason they had asked for our help with his family was to discover just how dangerous it was for children to live there as well as to come to some agreements as to how to get them out of the system. I agreed that the toddlers looked very healthy, happy, and spontaneous, certainly not abused or fearful. I also accepted Marilyn's statements that she wanted to live with her father and stepmother. She was also able to say that sometimes her father got mad and that this was frightening to her. The recent incident was because of a failing grade in school, and Mr. Baker was able to articulate that because of his lack of education, it was very important that his children succeed in school, thus having more opportunities than he enjoyed.

To make myself believable to them, I worked with them on a plan to help Marilyn with her school performance. I also asked for a verbal agreement that there would be no physical punishment. We explored alternatives to hitting and also ways that Mr. Baker could diffuse his anger, like leaving the house and walking until he cooled down. I told them that I thought that I could help to get them out of the system but that I needed to know that they were willing to try new behaviors. At the end of this lengthy session, Mr. Baker apologized for his anger earlier in the evening and explained that it was not me he was angry with but the system, which left him feeling helpless to control his own life. Mrs. Baker said that they felt that they weren't free to make decisions about anything, that if, for instance, she and Mr. Baker wanted to divorce, they wouldn't be able to because it might jeopardize their children's custody. This "doorknob" comment was very revealing, but I did not address it then.

I saw the family three more times. They began to cooperate with the system during that time, seeing it as the way to regain control of their own lives. I, of course, identified many problems but concentrated on the goals that the family identified as important. I supported Mrs. Baker's desire to go to work, ostensibly to relieve the financial burdens the litigation had imposed. When my work with the family ended, she was working and feeling good about herself. Mr. Baker was taking much more responsibility for the care of the children and was actually feeling proud that he was involved. The intervention by no means resolved the serious problems this family faced, but it did enable them to move beyond the crisis, which had immobilized them. However, I noted with some dismay that Mr. and Mrs. Baker filed for divorce about two months after our work concluded.

This case is cited not because of the brilliance of any intervention technique but for the lack of such technique. I knew in the beginning that two very competent professionals had been thwarted in their efforts to help the family, so in my initial encounter with the family, I decided not to go against the resistance but somehow to flow with it. Frank Pittman (1987) says that people come into therapy in order not to change and the therapist needs to discover what change is more feared, join with the family in protecting against that change, and once that change is secured, all other changes are less threatening. He further states that change precedes insight and exists as behavior independent of the psychodynamics or the conflicts in the family, and once change has taken place, it becomes part of the family repertoire. It was my feeling that the Baker family was very threatened by what they perceived as a direct assault on their most vulnerable points of conflict and that when the pressure was taken off the obvious, they were able to move on to activities that gave them the distance needed to make major decisions about their family life. In this case, it was to dissolve the marriage, but that could not happen while they were so involved in protecting the family unit against the system.

EFFICACY OF INTENSIVE HOME-BASED SERVICES

The proliferation of home-based, family-centered services in the treatment of child abuse indicates that it is a successful way to prevent the placement of children and at the same time prevent further maltreatment. Homebuilders, a division of the Behavioral Science Institute in Washington, D.C. (the model for intensive in-home crisis intervention programs), cites success rates in preventing placement of children in families experiencing child abuse or neglect at 95 percent from 1974 to 1986. This translates to a dollar saving to the State Department of Social and Health Services of nearly $8.5 million. This success rate is consistent with other similar programs employing comprehensive social work services. In reviewing 17 preventative services programs, Jones (1985) found that the failure rate (defined as children placed) of the counseling and therapy programs was from 12 to 30 percent, whereas the failure rate for the social work programs was from 4 to 17 percent. The social work programs tended to be of longer duration than the counseling and therapy programs, which tended to last six months or less. Jones also observed that the lack of a theory of home-based services impedes research. Wald and colleagues (1988) examined whether it is best for children to remain in their homes with special services provided or to place them in foster care. Their findings were that neither alternative significantly improved the well-being of the children studied. They did state that if the only goal of the present public policy is to prevent severe physical harm to children, the current policy is justifiable. However, if the developmental problems that are associated with abuse and neglect are to be overcome, the children and their caretakers must be provided with extensive services, which are neither short-term nor inexpensive. The variables associated with the success of home-based services are currently being examined, and this is certainly warranted in light of the necessity of providing these services to those who are most likely to succeed with the family-centered approach. Bribitzer and Verdieck (1988) attempted to identify variables associated with success in evaluating a program in Virginia. They identified single-parent and single-child families as the least likely to be helped. All of these findings point to the need for further research about the efficacy and the appropriate target population for home-based, family-centered services.

SUMMARY

Crisis intervention with families who have entered the Child Protection System because of child abuse or neglect is a viable way to resolve the immediate crisis that led to the abusive incident while providing protection for children. The Family Life Education Program (FLEP), Indianapolis, Indiana, serves as the treatment model presented. This program is modeled after Homebuilders (Kinney et al., 1977) and FAMILIES (Ryan, 1979), both of which have demonstrated successful intervention using home-based, family-centered treatment. Family therapy and brief therapy theory are also employed in FLEP's approach to treatment of abusive and neglectful families. Quick response and intensity of comprehensive social work services, ranging from sophisticated therapy to basic needs, are the best predictors of successful intervention. These services not only prevent further abuse but also keep children in the home while families learn new and better ways to function in meeting the needs of their members.

REFERENCES

BERGMAN, J. S.   (1985). *Fishing for Barracuda.* New York: Norton.

BRIBITZER, M. P., and M. J. VERDIECK.   (1988). "Home-based, Family-centered Intervention: Evaluation of a Foster Care Prevention Program." *Child Welfare, 67,* 255–266.

BRYCE, M.   (1979). "Home-based Care: Development and Rationale." In S. Mayhanks and M. Bryce (Eds.), *Home-based Services.* Springfield, Ill.: Thomas.

Child Welfare League of America.   (1984). *Standards for Children and Families in Their Own Homes.* New York.

DE SHAZER, S. (1985). *Keys to Solution in Brief Therapy.* New York: Norton.

DE SHAZER, S. (1988). *Clues: Investigating Solutions in Brief Therapy.* New York: Norton.

EVERSTINE, D. S., and L. EVERSTINE. (1983). *People in Crisis: Strategic Therapeutic Interventions.* New York: Brunner/Mazel.

GUSTAFSON, J. P. (1986). *The Complex Secret of Brief Psychotherapy.* New York: Norton.

HALEY, J. (1976). *Problem-solving Therapy.* San Francisco: Jossey-Bass.

HELFER, R. E. (1987). "The Developmental Basis of Child Abuse and Neglect: An Epidemiological Approach." In R. E. Helfer and R. S. Kempe (Eds.), *The Battered Child* (4th ed.). Chicago: University of Chicago Press.

HOREJSI, C. R. (1981). "The St. Paul Family-centered Project Revisited: Exploring an Old Gold Mine." In M. Bryce and J. Lloyd (Eds.), *Treating Families in the Home: An Alternative to Placement.* Springfield, Ill.: Thomas.

JONES, M. A. (1985). *A Second Chance for Families, Five Years Later: Follow-up of a Program to Prevent Foster Care.* New York: Child Welfare League of America.

KENDRICK, J. M. (1988). "Individual, Group, and Family Treatment." In O. C. S. Tzeng and J. J. Jacobson (Eds.), *Sourcebook for Child Abuse and Neglect.* Springfield, Ill.: Thomas.

KINNEY, J., B. MADSEN, T. FLEMING, and D. A. HAAPALA. (1977). "Homebuilders: Keeping Families Together." *Journal of Consulting and Clinical Psychology, 45,* 667–673.

MADANES, C. (1981). *Strategic Family Therapy.* San Francisco: Jossey-Bass.

MINUCHIN, S., and H. C. FISHMAN. (1981). *Family Therapy Techniques.* Cambridge, Mass.: Harvard University Press.

NAPIER, A., and C. A. WHITAKER. (1978). *The Family Crucible.* New York: Harper & Row.

PITTMAN, F. S., III. (1987). *Turning Points: Treating Families in Transition and Crisis.* New York: Norton.

Prevention Report. (1988). *Annual Survey of Family-based Service Programs.* Iowa City, Iowa: National Resource Center on Family-based Services.

ROBERTS, A. R. (1989). *Juvenile Justice: Policies, Programs, and Services.* Belmont, Cal.: Wadsworth Publishing Co.

RYAN, M. (1979). "FAMILIES Program Design: Giving Families Relevance in Treatment." In S. Maybanks and M. Bryce (Eds.), *Home-based Services.* Springfield, Ill.: Thomas.

SATIR, V. (1986). "A Partial Portrait of a Family Therapist in Process." In H. C. Fishman and B. L. Rossman (Eds.), *Evolving Models for Family Change.* New York: Guilford Press.

SOLIN, C. A. (1986). "Displacement of Affect in Families Following Incest Disclosure." *American Journal of Orthopsychiatry, 56,* 570–576.

VISHER, E. B., and J. S. VISHER (1988). *Old Loyalties, New Ties: Therapeutic Strategies with Families.* New York: Brunner/Mazel.

WALD, M. S., J. M. CARLSMITH, and P. H. LEIDERMAN. (1988). *Protecting Abused and Neglected Children.* Stanford, Calif.: Stanford University Press.

Crisis Intervention and Brief Treatment for Suicidal Youth

David A. Jobes and Alan L. Berman

4

INTRODUCTION

Case Studies

A 16-year-old high school sophomore was brought to the school counselor's office after superficially cutting his wrists in an angry outburst in front of several other students. He was known as a sullen, rebellious, and often explosively hostile young man, with a chronic history of substance abuse. He was generally avoided by his peers as he frequently misperceived others' intentions and behaved suspiciously and threateningly in response to anticipated harm. Recently he had become obsessed with the martial arts and with guns.

A 13-year-old female was brought to the emergency room by her mother after threatening to "slice up" her baby sister with a kitchen knife. Her mother described a long history of behavior problems and temper outbursts leading to numerous school suspensions and runaway behavior. Her mother complained that she could no longer discipline her daughter, as two recent attempts to control her had precipitated suicidal threats and gestures. Two weeks prior to this visit, the girl was admitted to this hospital after ingesting a handful of her mother's antidepressant medication.

A 12-year-old learning-disabled male with a history of hyperactivity, low frustration tolerance, and aggressive behavior was brought to the attention of the school counselor after a playground fight with a classmate. Angry and tearful, he reported being teased by his peers; this day he had been excluded from eating with some classmates and at recess had had mud thrown on a new jacket that he had asked his mother to buy him. He described himself as a "loser" and talked openly of wanting to be dead.

The acute suicidal crisis is produced by a unique confluence of individual, environmental, social, situational, and temporal variables. As a response to life crises, suicide and self-destructive behaviors are used by people of every age, sex, race, religion, and economic and social class. As clients may respond to life crises with suicidal behavior, clinicians are faced with the immediate tasks of assessing possible self-harm behavior while concurrently protecting against that possibility. These tasks must be accomplished often under conditions of discongruent expectations and goals. Suicidal people tend to defy the health professional's expectation that fostering and maintaining life is a shared goal of patient and doctor (Hoff, 1984). Suicidal individuals are typically brought to treatment by others under conditions of acute and volitional threat to life. These are not characteristics of the "good patient"; instead, these characteristics bring tension and instability to the necessary working alliance with the caregiver and can potentially impede it (Vlasak, 1975). Thus working with depressed and suicidal people can be a terrifying and difficult undertaking. Indeed, the assessment, treatment, and general management of an acute suicidal crisis is perhaps one of the most difficult challenges faced by any mental health professional, despite its being the most frequently encountered of all mental health emergencies (Schein, 1976).

Suicide is a complex and rare event. Ideally, clinicians would like to be able to predict future occurrences of suicidal behavior and thereby make appropriate interventions. Attempts to construct inventories and use psychological tests to predict suicide (in a statistically valid and reliable manner) have so far failed. Since suicide and self-destructive behaviors occur so infrequently, most instruments tend to identify a prohibitive number of false positives (the identification of individuals as suicidal who do not kill themselves). Clinicians are therefore forced to make interventions in accordance with an inexact and subjective assessment and calculation of potential suicide risk.

Nevertheless, clinicians can strengthen their ability to effectively assess and intervene by increasing their understanding of suicidal behaviors. The tragic finality of suicide demands that clinicians develop a knowledge base and a level of competence in suicide risk assessment and intervention. As suicidologists point out, suicidal impulses and behaviors are largely temporal, transient, and situation-specific. Suicide intent is state-dependent and tends to wax and wane, disappear and return (Berman & Jobes, in press). Empirical research indicates that most people who kill themselves give some form of prior warning (see Shafii et al., 1985) and often desire an outcome other than the termination of their biological existence (Shneidman, 1985). The crisis clinician is therefore in a pivotal position. Accurate risk assessment and appropriate and timely interventions can literally make a life-or-death difference.

Making a life-saving difference is perhaps all the more poignant when the object of assessment and intervention is a young person. Society has long and fondly held the view that youthful years are a carefree time, a time of innocence, play, and exciting exploration. As members of society, clinicians must struggle with the incongruity between this view and evidence that for some youngsters these may be days of intense turmoil, abject despair, and loss of hope. In recent years, the prevalence of these youth at risk has become ever more evident, making increasingly imperative the development and application of effective strategies of clinical evaluation and treatment.

SCOPE OF THE PROBLEM

In 1985 there were 29,453 certified suicides in the United States (National Center for Health Statistics, 1987). A total of 5,399 of these deaths, approximately 18 percent, were of young people between the ages of 5 and 24; 2,124 were between the ages of 10 and 19. The age-specific rate of youthful suicide (12.9 per 100,000 for 15- to 24-year-olds) was about equal to that for all other ages combined (12.3). However, over the past three decades, the suicide rate for youth between 15 and 24 has tripled, making suicide now the third leading cause of death (preceded by accident and homicide) for young people in that age bracket. For example, young white males aged 15 to 19 appear to constitute a subgroup particularly at risk, with a 305 percent increase in their suicide rate from 1950 to 1980 (Rosenberg et al., 1987). The 1985 rate for 15- to 19-year-olds (10.0 per 100,000) was the highest annual rate ever reported for this age group.

Nearly five times more adolescent males than females complete suicide in the United States. In contrast, females are three times as likely to make nonfatal attempts as males. Whereas approximately 2,000 American youths under the age of 19 complete suicide annually, as many as 2 million teenagers may make nonfatal attempts at some point in their teenage lives (Smith & Crawford, 1984). One plausible explanation for these observed sex differences lies in the choice of methods employed. While the majority of both sexes use guns to complete suicide (in 1985, 62 percent of males and 50 percent of females), the overwhelming majority of suicidal behaviors is comprised of ingestion overdoses, better than 80 percent of which are effected by females. The ingestion of poisons, the lethality of which depends on a number of factors including the greater chance of rescue and intervention given the time necessary for toxic action, accounted for only 293 suicide deaths in 1985.

Suicidal death among adolescents is more common among whites than blacks, with white males comprising the majority of all youth suicides. However, black youth under 25 account for a greater proportion of all black suicides (25 percent) than white youth do (18 percent). For all youth, the highest rates are recorded for residents of the West, primarily the intermountain states.

OVERVIEW OF THE CRISIS INTERVENTION MODEL

Effective intervention and treatment of depressed and suicidal people always begins with a thorough assessment. Through all phases of working with depressed and suicidal individuals, ongoing risk assessment is an imperative. Clinicians must be prepared to face a range of potential suicidal crisis situations. Suicidal crises may range from a telephone call from a desperate client who has just ingested a potentially lethal overdose to a borderline personality in an unstable, intense, and dramatically shifting mood state to a client in session simply expressing vague suicidal ideation and hopelessness in a context of a history of impulsive acting out.

As described by Hoff (1984), people in suicidal crisis should have access to three specific kinds of clinical services: emergency medical treatment, crisis intervention, and follow-up counseling or psychotherapy. It is the role of the crisis clinician to assess the appropriateness of each respective service and to facilitate and oversee the implementation of clinical interventions and services to the client.

Working with Youth

Young people inherently bring to the suicidal crisis a unique set of developmental and emotional issues that complicate effective assessment and intervention. Adolescence and young adulthood is a time of tremendous change and turmoil. As Berman (1984) has discussed, adolescents are developmentally caught between childhood and adulthood, which engenders the conflictual task of separating from the world of parents and family. Paradoxically, the young person simultaneously seeks protection from and inclusion within the family system. Accordingly, developmental distrust of adults further complicates the assessment of the young person's emotional status. An example of youthful distrust can be seen when a young person tells a friend of suicidal thoughts with the clear understanding that the peer is not to betray this confidence to an adult. Youthful distrust of adults has been substantiated in the empirical literature. One recent study of a youthful sample of completed suicides revealed that 83.3 percent had made suicidal threats in the week prior to their deaths, and of these, half made their suicidal intention known *only* to a peer or sibling (Brent et al., 1988).

Other developmental forces also increase the assessment challenge. With limited life experience, youth tend to be more focused on the present than the future. A young person under stress may have a limited view of future possibilities, making momentary and immediate solutions seem appealing (Berman, 1984). Adolescents characteristically have a limited capacity to delay gratification. Plainly stated, if something is wrong, it has to be fixed immediately. As Cantor (1976) has pointed out, the situation is further complicated by suicidal fantasies, which may be common among adolescents. This combination of adolescent impulsivity, poor problem-solving skills, and suicidal fantasies (of escape and relief from pain) can become a recipe for lethal action. Furthermore, adolescents are highly vulnerable to peer influence and are often eager to imitate role models as they seek to develop their own sense of identity. It is therefore important to assess and intervene in youthful crises with a keen awareness of the unique developmental issues of the population.

THE PRACTICE OF CRISIS INTERVENTION

Emergency Medical Treatment

As illustrated in Figure 4-1, the practice of suicide crisis intervention involves multiple decision points and actions. In its perhaps most anxiety-provoking

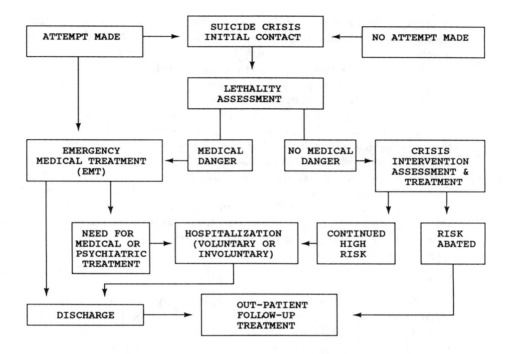

Figure 4-1 Suicide Crisis Intervention Paradigm

presentation, crisis intervention with the suicidal client begins with an attempt already initiated. The clinician must be prepared to respond to such an individual, whose suicide attempt may require immediate first aid or medical treatment.

The client's level of consciousness and orientation, rationality, rage, and anxiety all affect the level of cooperation he or she may give to the immediate assessment of the need for emergency intervention. With appropriate cooperation, questions need to be raised and answered regarding the location of the client, exactly what the client has done, and the availability of significant others. The clinician's immediate task, to assess the lethality of the attempt, is greatly aided by the availability of published lethality scales (Smith et al., 1984). Where medico-biological danger has been determined to exist or where sufficient data for that determination are not available, emergency medical intervention is required. As discussed by Hoff (1984), immediately dangerous situations should be handled by police and rescue squads, who can assure rapid transportation to a hospital emergency room. Rapid medical evaluation is an essential first step to resolving a current and future suicidal crisis.

In addition to lethality scales, many hospitals have poison control centers that can be called for specific overdose information. The exact amount of drug needed to effect a fatal overdose is difficult to ascertain as the effects vary according to the size of the person, the amount and kind of drug taken, and the person's tolerance for a drug. In general, major tranquilizers, sleeping pills, anti-

depressants, and common analgesics (aspirin, acetaminophen) are dangerous overdose drugs (especially in combination with alcohol). One rule of thumb is that
a lethal dose is ten times the normal dose; in combination with alcohol, as little
as half the normal dose may result in death (Hoff, 1984; Cocores & Gold, 1990).

It is useful for the clinician to have ready access to emergency phone numbers for the police, emergency rescue squad, hospital emergency rooms, and poison
control centers. Needless to say, it is essential to maintain active contact and communication with the client while these procedures are being effected. As part of
this communication, the clinician should begin to structure the client's expectations through clear directives about what will happen, thus increasing the chances
that a therapeutic alliance with both Emergency Medical Technician (EMT) and
emergency room personnel will be established. Future treatment may be facili-
tated by the presence of the clinician during the medical crisis. Close contact and
follow-up after the immediate medical danger is resolved ensures that the client
is not simply treated and discharged without an appropriate crisis prevention
strategy in place.

Crisis Intervention

The clinician must also be prepared to intervene in suicide crises in which an
attempt has not yet been made but could occur in the near or immediate future.
Also, a decision that an attempt in progress does not require immediate medical
intervention should not be construed to mean that the crisis situation no longer
exists. There are two critical components to the effective resolution of a clear and
imminent suicide crisis: thorough assessment of suicide risk and appropriate clinical interventions based on the assessment of risk and of conditions that predispose
the individual to be at risk.

Relationship

The importance of the clinical relationship (and the techniques used to
enhance it) in the suicidal crisis cannot be overestimated. A number of authors
have discussed the difficulties inherent in working with a suicidal individual (Farberow, 1970; Shneidman, 1980; Hendin, 1981). As Shneidman (1980) has observed,
working with a highly suicidal person demands a different kind of involvement.
Particularly in a crisis, the ability to make interpersonal contact is critical, and
a supportive working relationship must be rapidly established. Hipple and Cimbolic (1979) have noted that suicidal clients must know (and feel) that they are
talking with a person who is actively interested in their well-being. Any technique
or approach that potentially strengthens the relationship and connectedness
should therefore be employed. Eye contact, posture, and other nonverbal cues
may be used to express a level of interest, concern, and involvement. Empathic
listening, mirroring of feelings, emotional availability, honesty, warmth, and caring can help foster a sense of trust and a willingness to examine possibilities other
than self-destruction. Though empathy and support are crucial, it is important
to remember that suicidal adolescents often feel out of control. Accordingly, a

more active and directive role than would normally be seen in ongoing individual psychotherapy can provide valuable reassurance and structure in a time of crisis.

Assessment Interview

Ideally, an assessment interview should draw on theory, the strength of the therapeutic relationship, and empirical and clinical knowledge specific to suicidal individuals. Theoretical knowledge provides a conceptual frame and foundation, while the therapeutic relationship (alliance) becomes the vehicle of assessment and treatment. Empirical and clinical knowledge is used to assess key variables that bear on the assessment of suicide risk. In the course of the suicide assessment interview, it is essential for the clinician to listen closely, make direct inquiries, and assess and evaluate key variables and issues.

Cues to Suicide   The clinician must listen carefully for indicators or "cues" that may tip off suicidal intent. Often the clinician is alerted by a direct or indirect comment made by a client or some nonverbal behavior. The vast majority of suicidal people provide clues to their self-destructive feelings. Close scrutiny of the client is essential as the clinician must determine whether the youth shares some commonality with others who have acted out their suicidal fantasies (Berman & Jobes, in press). As Hipple and Cimbolic (1979) have discussed, the suicidal individual may make only veiled or disguised verbal references to suicidal feelings. The clinician must be alert for veiled threats such as "Sometimes it's just not worth it; I feel like giving up," "I'm just so tired, I just want to sleep," and "People would be a lot happier if I weren't around." Often other communications (diaries, journals, school essays, drawings, poems, etc.) contain valuable nonverbal clues to the adolescent's ideational focus.

Asking about Suicide   The assessment of suicide risk fundamentally requires direct inquiries about suicidal thoughts and feelings. Simply stated, vague suicidal comments should *always* elicit a direct question from the clinician as to whether the client is thinking about suicide (e.g., "Are you thinking about killing yourself?").

Even for the experienced clinician, asking directly about suicide can be unsettling. Accordingly, there may be a tendency to underestimate the seriousness of the situation and a strong temptation to avoid asking about suicide directly. Frequently, potential helpers fear that a direct inquiry might introduce a dangerous and new option that the client had not previously contemplated (i.e., planting the idea of suicide in the client's mind).

While avoidance and fear are understandable reactions to suspicions of suicide, clinical and empirical evidence strongly support the value of direct inquiry (Hipple & Cimbolic, 1979; Beck et al., 1979; Pope, 1986; Curran, 1987; Alberts, 1988). Critically, direct inquiry gives the potentially suicidal individual permission to discuss feelings that may have seemed virtually undiscussable. Direct inquiry can bring great relief to the client—at last the inner battle of life or death can be openly discussed and explored in a safe, supportive, and accepting climate.

Moreover, a direct inquiry opens the doors for further assessment, potentially bringing out otherwise veiled resistances. The expression of resistances in the therapeutic context may alert the clinician to the distinct possibility of suicidal urges in the client signaling an interpersonal alienation common to the suicidal character. It is our experience that when clinicians are sensitive and attentive to their suspicions of suicide, they are more often correct than incorrect (i.e., suicide will probably have been at least a consideration for the client).

If suicide is genuinely not being considered by the client, the clinician can easily move on to other areas of inquiry. But if suicide is being considered by the client and the clinician avoids direct inquiry, the client may interpret the therapist's behavior as clear evidence of a lack of caring, confirming his or her sense of both unlovability and the impossibility of help. Hopelessness is therefore reinforced iatrogenically, and suicide risk increases.

Imminent Risk?

Assuming that the clinician has attended to suicidal cues and that the client has affirmed some degree of suicidal thoughts or feelings upon direct inquiry, the clinician must determine whether there is imminent danger of suicidal behavior which endangers the life of the client. The degree and immediacy of suicide risk must be evaluated for clinical, legal, and ethical purposes. When voluntary hospitalization is refused in extreme cases, the law often requires involuntary hospitalization (commitment) when there is evidence of clear and imminent danger to self or others. Therefore, the clinician must establish whether the risk of suicide is acute and immediate or chronic and long-term. Is this indeed a crisis situation with a risk of a suicide attempt in the immediate or near future? Is there sufficient upsetness, agitation, and emotional energy to create an immediately dangerous situation?

More than 80 percent of all suicides occur in a state of acute impulsive crisis. Only a small percentage of suicides are methodical or planned (especially among youthful populations). It can be reassuring to both the client and the clinician to know that most cases are *transient* crises. Getting through the crisis phase provides the young person with the opportunity to consider more constructive and reversible options for coping. Therefore, one of the most important aspects of suicide assessment, the temporal evaluation of imminent versus long-term risk of self-harm, is essential to further assessment, intervention, and treatment.

The final determination of imminent danger depends on the assessment of key variables or risk factors that reflect the degree of suicide risk. It is important to assess the following (not necessarily in this order): psychological intent, the suicide plan, the history of previous suicidal behavior, the degree of psychological pain, clinical risk variables, and strengths and weaknesses.

Assessing Psychological Intent   Many have attempted to operationally define the concept of suicide (see Jobes et al., 1987; Jobes et al., in press; Rosenberg et al., 1988; Shneidman, 1985). Most such definitions assert that suicide is a death which is both self-inflicted and psychologically intended. Clearly, an individual who dies a self-inflicted accidental death does not psychologically seek an end to life, whereas one who dies by suicide does.

Thus the motive of ending one's existence versus the motive of receiving more attention from a loved one reflects very different kinds of suicidal intent. It is therefore critical to assess the intention, purpose, motive, or goal of the suicidal individual—what does the option of suicide mean to the youth? As Berman and Jobes (in press) have discussed, the stated intent of a suicidal motive in young people is often interpersonal and instrumental. In general, the intended goals of youthful suicidal behavior involve an effort to escape the experience of pain, helplessness, hopelessness, and the emotions and cognitions associated with the suicidal state. For some, this means seeking relief through death; for others, relief may be sought through changes in others' behavior, changes effected by gambling with their own life.

Assessing the Suicide Plan   The presence or absence of a plan to attempt suicide is critical to ascertain. The plan reflects both the desired and expected consequences of suicidal behavior and therefore provides one of the best indicators of what may actually come to pass (Berman & Jobes, in press). Again, direct inquiry about a potential suicidal plan is necessary. If a plan is acknowledged, it is important to assess the lethality (or dangerousness) of the plan. Suicidal plans generally reveal whether the risk is acute or chronic in that the degree of intent can often be inferred from certain features of the plan (particularly the identified method for the attempt).

Empirical research indicates that there tends to be a relationship between level of intent and the lethality of a method identified in the suicidal plan. In one study, Brent (1987) found that a robust relationship appeared to exist between medical lethality and suicidal intent in a study of youthful attempters. The planned use of more lethal methods (firearms, hanging, jumping) reflects a greater degree of suicidal intent and imminent risk, in contrast to less lethal methods (overdose, superficial cutting). In general, lethal plans tend to be concrete and specific and involve dangerous methods. Risk increases when there is evidence of a carefully thought-through and articulated self-harm strategy. Similarly, the availability of lethal means (such as guns or lethal quantities of medications) about which the youngster is knowledgeable also increases the suicide risk.

A plan that minimizes the chance of intervention and rescue reflects a greater suicide risk. Conceptually and empirically, the potential for rescue has been found to be central to two well-respected instruments that were specifically constructed to assess the lethality of suicide attempts (see Weissman & Worden, 1972; Smith et al., 1984). Simply put, the less likely that someone is able to intervene, the greater the risk. Under the heading of rescue, the reversibility of a chosen method and the discoverability of an attempt must be differentially evaluated. A much higher level of suicidal intent and lethality is reflected in an attempter who plans to use an irreversible method (e.g., a gun) in a place with little likelihood of discovery (e.g., a remote forest). For example, suicide risk may be assessed as low in a case of a vague plan involving the ingestion of pills in front of parents but high in a case where an individual has access to a large quantity of barbiturates and plans to ingest them after the parents leave the house.

In summarizing various elements of the assessment of a suicide plan, the clinician must evaluate the lethality and availability of the proposed method and the specificity of the self-harm strategy. Moreover, the clinician must evaluate the probability of postattempt discovery and whether efforts could be made to reverse the effects of the potential suicide act (e.g., stomach pumping after an overdose). Assessment of the various aspects of a potential plan is perhaps the best means of evaluating suicidal intent and imminent risk of self-destructive behavior.

It should be noted that perhaps the majority of suicidal acts by youth are impulsive and unplanned. That does not in any way decrease their potential lethality, particularly if the youth has a lethal weapon accessible at the time of urge and impulse. In the context of the other levels of assessment, the absence of a plan simply means that the clinician is lacking but one significant source of information.

Assessing Suicide History   Another variable that bears significantly on suicide risk is the presence or absence of a suicidal history. The risk and danger increase significantly when there is *any* previous history of suicidal ideation, gestures, or, particularly, previous attempts. Risk is increased if a previous attempt was recent, if a potentially lethal method was used, or if an effort was made to avoid rescue. Multiple past attempts, particularly if these occurred within the preceding 12 months and if one or more was potentially lethal, significantly increase the risk of further suicide attempts and of ultimate completion. The clinician should note the contingent reinforcers to prior behaviors to determine what the client learned consequent to these events. In addition, the history of suicidal events in the client's family is an important area of inquiry in order to assess the level of exposure to suicide the client has had and its legacies of possible imitation and modeling or possible biologically based suicidal vulnerability.

Assessing Psychological Pain   As Shneidman (1985) has discussed, the suicidal person fundamentally seeks to escape unendurable psychological pain. Critically, the pain that drives the suicidal situation must be understood idiosyncratically—what is painful to one person may not be to the next. Therefore, it is essential that the clinician be empathically connected to the youth's subjective experience of pain. However, as Curran (1987) has discussed, a suicidal youth may be unwilling or unable to communicate painful feelings. This, of course, is a formidable problem for the accurate assessment of risk. It may be necessary in emergency situations to confer with friends and family who may be aware of the youth's recent emotional status. A teacher or best friend may be able to provide critical information concerning recent behaviors, changes in mood, and potential losses in the young person's life. Whether the information comes directly from the young person or from a friend, parent, or teacher, it is important to try to infer an accurate assessment of the subjective pain experienced by the young person. It should be noted, however, that such contacts may adversely affect the therapeutic relationship after the crisis is resolved.

Even though emotional pain is difficult at any age, young people may experience it especially intensely. It is critical that the clinician respect the depth and degree of pain reported. Self-reports of extreme emotional pain and trauma should not be dismissed as adolescent melodrama. The experience of pain is acutely real to adolescents and potentially life-threatening. As discussed earlier, young people tend to be present-oriented and lack the years of life experience that may provide the perspective needed to endure a painful period. It is therefore critical that the clinician appreciate this characteristically limited world view.

Plainly stated, the risk of suicide increases as subjectively perceived psychological pain increases. Accordingly, it may be useful to have a suicidal youth actually rate his or her pain or hopelessness (e.g., ranging from zero equaling absolutely no pain to 10 equaling absolutely unendurable pain). Subjective ratings can be especially useful in helping to understand the young person's degree of pain. The rating can also help make the suicidal experience more concrete and less abstract for both the youth and the clinician. Moreover, the subjective rating can provide a barometer of suicide risk as changes and improvements can be tracked beyond the initial crisis and throughout the course of treatment.

Assessing Clinical Risk Variables It is helpful for the clinician to have a working knowledge of additional risk variables for suicide that have been identified in the empirical literature. Research conducted since the 1960s has provided practitioners with valuable information concerning various correlates of increased suicide risk.

As described by Beck and his colleagues (e.g., Kovacs et al., 1975), for example, hopelessness may be the single best indicator of suicide risk. A profound sense of hopelessness and helplessness about oneself, others, and the future has been closely linked to depressive conditions and suicide (Rush & Beck, 1978). Other clinical indicators of suicide may include dramatic and inexplicable affective change; affect that is depressed, flat, or blunted; the experience of recent or multiple negative environment changes or losses; feelings of isolation or emptiness; the experience of extreme stress; free-floating rage; agitation; and fatigue.

Young people can be very sensitive to the various interpersonal pressures and expectations of others, including parents, siblings, peers, coaches, teachers, and romantic partners. Murray's (1938) construct of "presses" may be applied to suicidal youth to identify a range of additional pressures that may be less socioculturally bound, such as genetic factors, physical danger, chance events, alcohol or substance abuse, and psychopathology. As Berman and Jobes (in press) have noted, it is important to examine predisposing conditions, precipitating factors, and psychopathology in the assessment of forces that might affect the suicidal youth.

Biological and sociocultural forces create a range of predisposing conditions that bear on the suicidal adolescent. The suicidal youth often experiences blows to self-esteem, sense of self, and ability to cope (Berman & Jobes, in press). These may be the direct result of growing up in stressful families and having conflicted interpersonal relationships. Research has indicated that parents of suicidal

adolescents experience more overt conflict and a greater threat of separation or divorce, often resulting in the early loss of a parent (Stanley & Barter, 1970; Corder et al., 1974). Further, suicidal youth have more frequent and more serious interpersonal problems with peers, are more interpersonally sensitive, and are less likely to have a close confidant (McKenry et al., 1982; Tishler & McKenry, 1982).

Adolescent suicides are often linked to a significant precipitating event, particularly an acute disciplinary crisis or a rejection or humiliation (Shaffer, 1988). It is important to note that these events, such as a fight with one's parents, the breakup of a relationship, or being teased, are common to the experience of all adolescents and thus must be considered within the broader context of each adolescent's vulnerability to respond with increased suicidality to such stressors.

The crisis clinician must be attentive to evidence of psychopathology, since perhaps as many as 90 percent of adolescent suicide completions are by youth with retrospectively diagnosable mental disorders (see Berman & Jobes, in press; Shaffer, 1988). Empirical research has confirmed that certain types of psychopathology are correlated with suicidal behavior. This is true for mood disorders, particularly manic-depressive illness or bipolar spectrum disorders (Garfinkel et al., 1982; Robbins & Alessi, 1985; Brent et al., 1988). Increased rates of suicide and attempted suicide have also been linked to schizophrenia (McIntire et al., 1977) and personality disorders, particularly borderline and antisocial (or conduct) disorders (Alessi et al., 1984; Berman & Jobes, in press). The clinician must therefore be particularly sensitive to young people with these disorders who are in distress but who may not overtly and directly reveal suicidal intent.

Imminent risk for self-harm behavior appears most reactive to conditions that threaten a breakdown in the usual coping mechanisms and consequently diminish control. In addition to a variety of psychopathological disorders, as noted, the clinician needs to be alert for significant changes in behavior, particularly if they involve an increased reliance on alcohol or drugs. Levels of rage and anxiety as well are good measures of the adolescent's ability to maintain control. In addition, behavioral change or loss of control often alienates the adolescent from significant others who could otherwise serve to buffer or protect the youth from the untoward consequences of thinking designed simply to end painful feelings impulsively. Again, hopelessness tends to be increased or reinforced under such interactional conditions.

Assessing Strengths and Weaknesses During the assessment interview, it is useful to account for and evaluate the presence and strength of negative pressures in the young person's life, counterbalanced against positive influences. Various expectations and pressures can become overwhelming to the young person in the midst of a suicidal crisis, making effective action difficult, if not impossible. The strength of one particularly salient pressure can potentially outweigh other objective strengths and abilities. For example, among adolescents who complete suicide, there is a subgroup of seemingly outstanding victims who "seemed to have it all." In such cases, various abilities, skills, and strengths may be irrelevant when the individual's self-worth is rigidly defined by extraordinarily high standards and expectations of academic perfection. Such a compulsive demand may defend against an underlying fragile sense of self. Accordingly, an unacceptable performance such as a C grade on an exam, easily interpreted as the equivalent of an F, could actually precipitate a suicide attempt to thwart the experience of feelings of unacceptability that result.

Treatment and Intervention

Having thoroughly assessed the risk of suicide, the clinician is in a position to intervene. As described by Hoff (1984) and others, a series of strategic steps needs to be initiated to ensure the client's immediate safety, effect immediate change, and shift the client's focus from crisis to resolution.

1. *Removing the Means.* The first goal should be an immediate reduction in the lethality of the situation. This is best accomplished by literally removing the means from the client's access or, at a minimum, delaying access to available means. Pills should be flushed down the toilet or given to others to monitor and dispense; guns and other weapons should be removed from the home. Where available, parents or significant others need to be involved in all efforts to safeguard the adolescent's environment (Berman, 1986).

2. *No-Suicide Contract.* One of the clinician's most effective interventive tools involves a verbal or written contract between the clinician and the client. Generally, the concrete goal of contracting is to ensure the client's safety by establishing that the client will not hurt himself or herself for a specific period of time. The more concrete and specific the contract, the better. A typical verbal contract requires that the client commit to personal safety until the next contact with the clinician, at which time a new contract will be negotiated. The clinician must remember to keep these agreements time-limited and renewable.

3. *Future Linkage.* The clinician and the client must create a "crisis game plan" that orients the client toward the future. Long-term goals should be established and operationalized with the client in short-term steps. This may be accomplished by identifying when the next clinical contacts will occur. Plans for activities and social contacts may be made as well. Scheduling possible phone contacts with the clinician can also be planned. It is critical that the suicidal client have something to which they can look forward. Future linkage helps orient the client to a different and hopefully better future, creating a distance from the immediate crisis.

4. *Decreasing Isolation.* The client must not be left alone in the midst of a suicidal crisis. It is critical that a friend or family member be with the client through the crisis phase. Efforts must be made to mobilize friends, family, and neighbors, making them aware of the importance of continual contact with the suicidal youth. In cases where friends or family are unavailable (or unwilling), hospitalization may be indicated until the immediate crisis has been resolved.

5. *Decreasing Anxiety and Sleep Loss.* If the suicidal youth is acutely anxious or unable to sleep, the suicidal crisis may become worse. Medication may be indi-

cated as an emergency intervention. However, dosages must be closely monitored and linked to psychotherapy such that the medication will not be used to attempt an overdose. Other symptoms that may exacerbate the client's ability to benefit from verbal intervention or threaten the client's ability to maintain control must be continuously monitored and treated accordingly.

6. *Hospitalization.* If the risk of suicide remains high and the client is unable to contract or commit to his or her safety, the necessary intervention is hospitalization. Stabilization through hospitalization can provide the client with a safe environment and a chance to get away from the environment that produced the suicidal crisis.

Follow-up Counseling and Psychotherapy

Beyond medical treatment and crisis intervention, follow-up to counseling and psychotherapy is essential. The absence or amelioration of a crisis does not eliminate the need for psychotherapy. It is important for the clinician to remember that people who have used suicidal behavior to respond to life crises in the past are prone to use such behaviors in future life crises. As the final phase of crisis resolution, the clinician must ensure that follow-up evaluation and treatment are arranged and that a strategic, preventive plan is in place to circumvent potential future suicidal crises.

Various treatment modalities with suicidal clients have been discussed in the literature. These modalities range from longer-term individual treatment (Hendin, 1981; Toolin, 1962) to shorter-term individual models (Beck & Beck, 1978; Getz et al., 1983) to group treatment (Comstock & McDermott, 1975; Farberow, 1976; Hipple, 1982). Family therapy may be particularly helpful with youthful populations (Lewis, Walker & Mehr, 1990; Richman, 1979, 1986). In addition, pharmacotherapy may be useful to stabilize mood, particularly in the presence of depressive or other intrusive symptoms.

It is beyond the scope of this chapter to delineate the many aspects and variants of inpatient and outpatient psychotherapy with the suicidal adolescent. However, it is imperative that the clinician be familiar with the increasing array of effective short-term and long-term intervention strategies available to treat the depressed and suicidal adolescent if the alarming increase in self-inflicted mortality among adolescents is to be halted and reversed.

SUMMARY

This chapter has examined the complexities of youthful suicide, a phenomenon that has exhibited notable increases over the past three decades. Although valid and reliable clinical prediction of suicide is virtually impossible, practitioners can nevertheless optimize their capacity to respond effectively to youthful suicide crises by informing themselves of suicide risk assessment and interventive strategies and developing skills in these areas.

The crisis intervention model described in this chapter outlines three distinct clinical services needed for effective response to the full range of suicidal crises. The first service is *emergency medical treatment* (first aid), which may be required after an actual suicide attempt has occurred. The second service is *crisis intervention,* which may be needed to respond to a suicide crisis in which an attempt has not yet been made but could occur in the near or immediate future. Crisis intervention involves the thorough assessment of suicide risk, which leads to the implementation of appropriate interventive strategies that decrease the immediate lethality, stabilize the situation, and set the stage for treatment. After resolution of the crisis, the third service, *follow-up counseling or psychotherapy,* is required to help prevent future suicidal crises and begin the therapeutic process. A variety of short-term and long-term therapies, as well as multiple treatment modalities, can be used to help create more viable and life-affirming solutions to youthful stress and pain.

REFERENCES

ALANEN, Y. O., R. RINNE, and P. PAUKKONEN. (1981). "On Family Dynamics and Family Therapy in Suicidal Attempts." *Crisis, 2,* 20–26.

ALBERTS, F. L. (1988). Psychological assessment. In D. CAPUZZI and L. GOLDEN (Eds.), *Preventing Adolescent Suicide.* Muncie, Indiana: Accelerated Development, Inc.

ALESSI, N. E., M. McMANUS, A. BRICKMAN, and L. GRAPENTINE. (1984). "Suicidal Behavior among Series Juvenile Offenders." *American Journal of Psychotherapy, 141,* 286–287.

BECK, A. J., and A. T. BECK. (1978). "Cognitive Therapy of Depression and Suicide." *American Journal of Psychotherapy, 32,* 201–219.

BECK, A. T., A. J. RUSH, B. F. SHAW and G. EMERY. (1979). *Cognitive Therapy of Depression.* New York: Guilford Press.

BERMAN, A. L. (1984). "The Problem of Teenage Suicide." Testimony presented to the United States Senate Committee on the Judiciary Subcommittee on Juvenile Justice.

BERMAN, A. L. (1986). "Adolescent Suicide: Issues and Challenges." *Seminars in Adolescent Medicine, 2,* 269–277.

BERMAN, A. L., and D. A. JOBES (in press). *Adolescent Suicide: Assessment and Intervention.* Washington, D.C.: American Psychological Association.

BRENT, D. A. (1987). "Correlates of the Medical Lethality of Suicide Attempts in Children and Adolescents." *Journal of the American Academy of Child and Adolescent Psychiatry, 26,* 87–91.

BRENT D. A., J. A. PERPER, C. E. GOLDSTEIN, D. J. KOLKO, M. J. ALLAN, C. J. ALLMAN, and J. P. ZELENAK. (1988). "Risk Factors for Adolescent Suicide." *Archives of General Psychiatry, 45,* 581–588.

CANTOR, P. (1976). "Personality Characteristics among Youthful Female Suicide Attempters." *Journal of Abnormal Psychology, 85,* 324–329.

COCORES, J. A. and M. S. Gold. (1990) "Recognition and Crisis Intervention with Cocaine Abusers." In A. R. Roberts (Ed.), *Crisis Intervention Handbook: Assessment, Treatment, and Research.* Belmont, Cal.: Wadsworth Publishing Co.

COMSTOCK, B., and M. McDERMOTT. (1975). "Group Therapy for Patients Who Attempt Suicide." *International Journal of Group Psychotherapy, 25,* 44–49.

CORDER, B. F., W. SHORR, and R. F. CORDER. (1974). "A Study of Social and Psychological Characteristics of Adolescent Suicide Attempters in an Urban, Disadvantaged Area." *Adolescence, 9,* 1–16.

CURRAN, D. K. (1987). *Adolescent Suicidal Behavior.* Washington, D. C.: Hemisphere.

FARBEROW, N. L. (1970). "The Suicidal Crisis in Psychotherapy." In E. S. SHNEIDMAN, N. L. FARBEROW, and R. LITMAN (Eds.), *The Psychology of Suicide.* New York: Science House.

FARBEROW, N. L. (1976). "Group Therapy for Self-destructive Persons." In J. J. PARAD, H. L. P. RESNICK, and L. G. PARAD (Eds.), *Emergency and Disaster Management: A Mental Health Sourcebook.* Bowie, Md.: Charles Press.

GARFINKEL, B. D., A. FROESE, and J. HOOD. (1982). "Suicide Attempts in Children and Adolescents." *American Journal of Psychiatry, 139,* 1257–1261.

GETZ, W. L., D. B. ALLEN, R. K. MYERS, and K. C. LINDER (1983). *Brief Counseling with Suicidal Persons.* Lexington, Mass.: Lexington Books.

HENDIN, H. (1981). "Psychotherapy and Suicide." *American Journal of Psychotherapy, 35,* 469–480.

HIPPLE, J. (1982). "Group Treatment of Suicidal Clients." *Journal for Specialists in Group Work, 7,* 245–250.

HIPPLE, J., and P. CIMBOLIC. (1979). *The Counselor and Suicidal Crisis.* Springfield, Ill.: Thomas.

HOFF, L. A. (1984). *People in Crisis*. Reading, Mass.: Addison-Wesley.

JOBES, D. A., A. L. BERMAN, and A. R. JOSSELSON. (1987). "Improving the Validity and Reliability of Medical-Legal Certifications of Suicide." *Suicide and Life-threatening Behavior, 17*, 310–325.

JOBES, D. A., J. O. CASEY, A. L. BERMAN, and D. G. WRIGHT (in press). "Empirical Criteria for the Determination of Suicide." *Journal of Forensic Sciences.*

KOVACS, M., A. T. BECK, and A. WEISSMAN. (1975). "The Use of Suicidal Motives in the Psychotherapy of Attempted Suicides." *American Journal of Psychotherapy, 29*, 363–368.

LEWIS, R., B. A. WALKER, and M. MEHR. (1990). "Counseling with Adolescent Suicidal Clients and Their Families." In A. R. Roberts (Ed.), *Crisis Intervention Handbook: Assessment, Treatment, and Research*. Belmont, Cal.: Wadsworth Publishing Co.

MCINTIRE, M. S., C. R. ANGLE, R. L. WIKOFF, and M. L. SCHLICHT. (1977). "Recurrent Adolescent Suicidal Behavior." *Pediatrics, 60*, 605–608.

MCKENRY, P., C. TISHLER, and C. KELLEY. (1982). "Adolescent Suicide: A Comparison of Attempters and Non-attempters in an Emergency Room Population." *Clinical Pediatrics, 21*, 266–270.

MURRAY, H. A. (1938). *Explorations in Personality*. New York: Oxford University Press.

National Center for Health Statistics. (1987). *Vital Statistics of the United States. Volume 2: Mortality*, part A. Washington, D.C.: U.S. Government Printing Office.

POPE, K. S. (1986). "Assessment and Management of Suicidal Risk: Clinical and Legal Standards of Care." *Independent Practitioner, 6*, 17–23.

RICHMAN, J. (1979). "Family Therapy of Attempted Suicide." *Family Process, 18*, 131–142.

RICHMAN, J. (1986). *Family Therapy for Suicidal People.* New York: Springer.

ROBBINS, D., and N. E. ALESSI. (1985). "Depressive Symptoms and Suicidal Behavior in Adolescents." *American Journal of Psychiatry, 142*, 588–592.

ROSENBERG, M. L., L. E. DAVIDSON, J. C. SMITH, A. L. BERMAN, H. BUZBEE, G. GANTNER, G. A. GAY, B. MOORE-LEWIS, D. H. MILLS, D. MURRAY, P. W. O'CARROLL, and D. JOBES. (1988). "Operational Criteria for the Determination of Suicide." *Journal of Forensic Sciences, 32*, 1445–1455.

ROSENBERG, M. L., J. C. SMITH, L. E. DAVIDSON, and J. M. CONN. (1987). "The Emergence of Youth Suicide: An Epidemiological Analysis and Public Health Perspective." *Annual Review of Public Health, 8*, 417–440.

RUSH, A. J., and A. T. BECK (1978). "Cognitive Therapy of Depression and Suicide." *American Journal of Psychotherapy, 32*, 201–219.

SCHEIN, H. M. (1976). "Suicide Care: Obstacles in the Education of Psychiatric Residents." *Omega, 7*, 75–82.

SHAFFER, D. (1988). "The Epidemiology of Teen Suicide: An Examination of Risk Factors." *Journal of Clinical Psychiatry, 49*, 36–41.

SHAFII, M., S. CARRIGAN, J. R. WHITTINGHILL, and A. DERRICK. (1985). "A Psychological Autopsy of Completed Suicide in Children and Adolescents." *American Journal of Psychiatry, 142*, 1061–1064.

SHNEIDMAN, E. S. (1980). "Psychotherapy with Suicidal Patients." In T. B. KARASU and L. BELLAK (Eds.), *Specialized Techniques in Individual Psychotherapy*. New York: Brunner/Mazel.

SHNEIDMAN, E. S. (1985). *Definition of Suicide*. New York: Wiley.

SMITH, K., R. W. CONROY, and B. D. EHLER. (1984). "Lethality of Suicide Attempt Rating Scale." *Suicide and Life-threatening Behavior, 14*, 215–242.

SMITH, K., and S. CRAWFORD. (1984). "Suicidal Behavior among 'Normal' High School Students." *Suicide and Life-threatening Behavior, 16*, 313–325.

STANLEY, E. J., and J. J. BARTER. (1970). "Adolescent Suicidal Behavior." *American Journal of Orthopsychiatry, 40*, 87–96.

TISHLER, C., and P. MCKENRY. (1982). "Parental Negative Self and Adolescent Suicide Attempters." *Journal of the American Academy of Child Psychiatry, 21*, 404–408.

TOOLIN, J. M. (1962). "Suicide and Suicide Attempts in Children and Adolescents." *American Journal of Psychiatry, 118*, 719–724.

VLASAK, G. J. (1975). "Medical Sociology." In S. PERLIN (Ed.), *A Handbook for the Study of Suicide*. New York: Oxford University Press.

WEISSMAN, A., and W. WORDEN. (1972). "Risk-Rescue Rating in Suicide Assessment." *Archives of General Psychiatry, 26*, 553–560.

Human Immunodeficiency Virus and Crisis Intervention
A Task-focused Approach

Grace H. Christ, Rosemary T. Moynihan, and Les Gallo-Silver

5

INTRODUCTION

Acquired immunodeficiency syndrome (AIDS) generates a spectrum of events marked by five major crises: (1) perception of personal risk, (2) confirmation of human immunodeficiency virus (HIV)–positive status, (3) onset of HIV-related symptoms, (4) diagnosis of AIDS, and (5) terminal illness. With each new crisis, people must confront and master predictable psychosocial tasks to maintain their psychological and even physical equilibrium. Effective crisis intervention—helping people to develop the cognitive and emotional strategies needed to master the crisis—requires an understanding of the psychosocial tasks that must be completed at each stage of disease (Christ, Siegel, & Moynihan, 1988). This chapter highlights the social conditions related to transmission of HIV and describes the reactions, psychosocial tasks, and interventions associated with the five major crises in the progression of AIDS.

Social Conditions Related to HIV Transmission

Effective crisis intervention requires familiarity with the complex social conditions affecting the groups most frequently diagnosed with AIDS. Many of the stresses experienced by people in each major group relate to how HIV is transmitted.

Homosexual and Bisexual Men

The largest group of patients with AIDS, accounting for 66 percent of those diagnosed, consists of homosexual and bisexual men (Goedert & Blattner, 1988). Although the gay community has developed a culture, network, and language to protect its members from general public hostility, gay patients lose this protection when asked to share intimate personal information with clinicians, who are usually heterosexuals influenced by dominant cultural values. The often unconscious prejudices of clinicians may make them emotionally distant at a time when gay patients are struggling with guilt, shame, and fear. Bisexual men may experience even greater stress because they tend to be secretive about their homosexual behavior and may feel tremendous conflict about revealing it to their partner or spouse.

Because AIDS has become epidemic, most gay men know many people with the disease. The cumulative effects of watching friends and acquaintances deteriorate and die can be as great as the effects of the death of a family member. As a result, the anxiety many newly diagnosed patients feel is often increased by fears that their disease will progress in the same way. Thus patients should be encouraged to focus on how their disease differs from that of others and how new treatments may postpone progression of the disease.

Intravenous Drug Users

The second largest group of AIDS patients, intravenous (IV) drug users, make up 24 percent of all AIDS patients (Goedert & Blattner, 1988). Unlike gay men, IV drug users have no organized community to rally to their support. Many are only marginally functional and have limited support and a minimal ability to cope with the stresses of AIDS and its treatment (Christ, Siegel, & Moynihan, 1988). Clinicians must avoid acting on stereotypic views and work with IV drug users as people whose different backgrounds, vocations, and life situations have led them to choose drugs as a means of solving life's problems. Despite the stereotypic belief that drug users are personally and socially irresponsible, we find that many express deep concern about sexual relations and about endangering future children.

Addictive illegal drugs can affect the efficacy of drugs prescribed for the pain, depression, anxiety, and nausea associated with AIDS. Methadone maintenance is also difficult during drug therapy for AIDS or the pain associated with the disease. Because effective AIDS treatment requires strict compliance in return for only limited benefits, patients with a limited ability to cope with emotional and physical frustration have difficulty complying with treatment. Moreover, recovering addicts may have difficulty staying off drugs while coping with physical deterioration, energy loss, neurologic impairment, ambiguity, rigorous treatment, and inactivity.

A long, debilitating illness often depletes a patient's personal and financial resources, and IV drug use magnifies this problem. Therefore, health care providers must maintain liaisons with drug rehabilitation programs and self-help groups composed of former addicts. These resources are essential for ongoing consultation about drug-related difficulties and referrals for further counseling or specialized intervention.

Heterosexual Women Who Do Not Use Drugs

The incidence of AIDS among heterosexual women has increased with the increasing prevalence of AIDS among IV drug users (Goedert & Blattner, 1988). Some women are unaware of the risk of sexual intercourse with IV drug users. However, many others are aware but unable to protect themselves because of their own or their partner's unwillingness to practice safer sex, economic dependence on their sexual partner, or a limited ability to change their current relationship or behavior (Siegel & Gibson, 1988).

Patients Infected by Blood Transfusions

Patients with hemophilia and others exposed to HIV in blood transfusions are likely to exhibit seemingly unjustified anger and mistrust toward physicians and other health care professionals. Clinicians need to help these patients and their families deal openly with these feelings, which are often related to their intense struggle with an already debilitating disease that evokes subtle but real social prejudice.

CRISES EXPERIENCED BY AIDS PATIENTS

1. Perception of Personal Risk

The first crisis in the spectrum of AIDS occurs when people perceive themselves as being at risk. Risky behaviors or situations include unprotected homosexual or bisexual contacts, anonymous sexual contacts, sexual contacts with present or former IV drug users, IV drug use with needle sharing, blood transfusions, or exposure to body fluids of people infected with HIV.

Most adults in the United States are aware of how AIDS is transmitted and are eager to minimize their own risk. However, those who have been involved in high-risk behaviors or situations may become so immobilized by anxiety or so preoccupied with their bodies that they require intervention. For example, a midwestern salesman went to his physician's office frantically seeking treatment for AIDS. While traveling, he had sexual relations with women he did not know, and he felt guilty and frightened after hearing repeated media warnings. When he developed a cold, he became convinced he had AIDS.

Clinicians helping clients with other problems may need to educate them about their risky behavior. For example, a social worker in an urban mental health clinic became deeply concerned about a young client being counseled for depression. The client expressed growing anger that a sexual partner engaged in prostitution to obtain money for drugs. This statement made the social worker aware that the client was unaware of his own risk of exposure to HIV.

Reactions to Concerns about HIV Infection

Psychosocial Symptoms   People who have engaged in actual or perceived high-risk behavior may present with high anxiety about their well-being or health status and be preoccupied with bodily changes. Others present with concerns about the well-being of their needle-sharing partners, sexual partners, or unborn children.

Those who are actively involved in high-risk behavior may exhibit various levels of denial about the riskiness of their acts. Denial is most often seen among IV drug users engaged in compulsive or addictive behavior and among female partners of present or former IV drug users who believe that they cannot obtain emotional, financial, or practical support outside these relationships (Siegel & Gibson, 1988). Some gay men rationalize their risky behavior by relying on their own perceptions of what constitutes risk (Siegel et al., 1989). If a client appears to be placing self or others at risk, the clinician may need to increase the client's level of anxiety by challenging the denial.

Cognitive Reactions   New scientific information constantly alters facts about HIV infection and perceptions of personal risk. Several barriers to understanding or to changing risky sexual behavior have been identified (Siegel & Gibson, 1988). These barriers include misperceptions about the risk of infection or the magnitude of that risk, cultural or personal antipathy toward condoms, the stigma associated with AIDS, confusion about the value of modifying one's sexual behavior, conflicting values, and idiosyncratic health beliefs.

Emotional Reactions   Recognition of personal risk of HIV infection produces a broad range of emotional reactions. These include immobilizing anxiety, fear, and guilt; anger and suspicion; and denial of personal risk or responsibility. For example, a young pregnant woman who transferred from Chicago to Ireland with her husband received transfusions during delivery of her first child. She was extremely anxious about the safety of the blood supply in Ireland and about being far away from home and family during this medical crisis. No amount of reassurance helped; she became so preoccupied about the risk of HIV infection to herself, her husband, and her baby that she finally returned to the United States for HIV testing.

The fear of inflicting harm on others may cause people who believe they are at risk to retreat from all sexual contact or all physical contact of any kind. People with a history of IV drug use may return to using drugs to manage their anxiety, fear, or hopelessness about treatment.

Assessment

The initial assessment of a person at risk for HIV infection should be both expeditious and comprehensive. Counseling may need to be directed toward increasing a client's anxiety rather than toward the usual mental health goal of reducing it. Two goals must be balanced: maintaining a sufficient degree of anxiety in clients to force them into assessing their risky behavior and its possible danger to others, and preventing them from becoming overwhelmed and immobilized. Thus the initial assessment should include all of the following:

> A history of the client's sexual identity and activity
>
> A description of the client's present sexual activities and relationships
>
> A history of any blood transfusions the client has received and any other situations that involve the exchange of blood or body fluids
>
> The client's history of drug use
>
> An evaluation of the personal, familial, cultural, and religious contexts of the client's high-risk sexual and drug-taking behavior
>
> A history of the client's crisis management skills and ego strengths
>
> A history of any previous psychiatric problems
>
> A description of the client's social, practical, and financial resources

An effective assessment depends on the attitudes of the clinician who seeks to obtain this personal, highly sensitive information. The potential for countertransference reactions to material that a client reveals is enormous. To be effective, the clinician's approach must reflect nonjudgmental acceptance, empathy for the client's emotional distress, reassuring interest and concern, and support for the client's positive efforts to cope with the crisis.

Because primary prevention of a life-threatening illness requires extensive assessment and planning, at least two follow-up sessions should be scheduled with clients in crisis about their risk of HIV infection. Their sexual behavior and chemical dependency should be discussed in depth, a plan should be developed for maintaining their health and for receiving regular health monitoring, and they should be helped to decide whether to be tested for HIV infection.

Crisis Intervention Model

People who are at obvious or perceived risk for AIDS usually need help in confronting multiple psychosocial tasks. Therefore, crisis intervention will not be effective unless all these criteria are met:

> Their sexual behavior and sexual dependency must be discussed with them in detail.
>
> Their actual and perceived risk must be assessed.
>
> They must receive assurance of professional support and help.
>
> They must receive help in managing—but not eliminating—their anxiety, stress, and guilt through individual or group treatment, self-help referrals, and accurate information.
>
> Their myths and misconceptions about risk must be eradicated.
>
> They must understand how HIV is transmitted.
>
> They must develop plans for altering their risky behaviors and for managing changes in their relationships resulting from these alterations.
>
> They must formulate plans for appropriate medical care.

They must direct their energies toward such positive goals as health maintenance and self-care.

They must receive information about HIV testing and help in making a decision about testing.

HIV Testing

The recent development of medical treatments that may postpone the onset of symptoms in people who test HIV-positive has significantly changed attitudes toward HIV testing (Lambert, 1989). In the past, many people who engaged in risky behavior refused testing to avoid confronting a definite diagnosis of a life-threatening illness with no known treatment. Even then, however, some people chose to be tested to eliminate ambiguity, although no medical treatments were available. HIV testing, with counseling both before and after, is now recommended as a first step toward the treatment of people at risk.

Counseling before Testing   The decision to undergo HIV testing may lead to intense anxiety and depression and thus represents a critical time for professional support and education. The purpose of pretest counseling is to help clients (1) realistically assess their risk, (2) make informed decisions, (3) anticipate their own negative psychological reactions and those of others if the test results are positive, and (4) develop plans to maximize the benefits of testing while minimizing its psychological and social costs. The clinician must inform clients about the significance of both negative and positive results and the problems of confidentiality and consequent vulnerability to discrimination. In addition, the clinician should emphasize that counseling is available while clients are awaiting the test results.

The following questions may be useful in guiding a client's thinking before testing:

How would you feel if you learned that you are infected?

How would you have to change the way you have sex?

How would you tell your sex partner or partners?

How would you feel if you learned that you may have transmitted the virus to someone?

How would you deal with discrimination in seeking or maintaining employment or insurance?

Would you have to change your pattern of IV drug use?

Would an HIV-positive result change your feelings about having children?

Whom could you talk with about the results of the test?

Counseling after Testing   Clients also need counseling after HIV testing, regardless of whether the results are negative or positive. For those with negative tests, counseling can prevent false perceptions of immunity to the infection and emphasize the likelihood of infection if their high-risk behavior continues. For those with positive tests, yet another crisis obviously looms.

2. Confirmation of HIV-positive Status

Reactions to the Crisis

Psychosocial Symptoms Even people who strongly suspected that they were HIV-positive tend to experience tremendous anxiety and depression when the test results confirm their suspicions. Because extreme reactions such as suicidal or homicidal ideation and behaviors are not uncommon, immediate reassurance of professional support and concern is essential. People who test positive must be aware from the beginning that they must control the disclosure of information about their condition to avoid discrimination and social rejection yet be able to share their concerns. Some people feel pressured to relieve their anxiety by telling everyone they know, thus exposing themselves to social rejection and other destructive losses. At the other extreme, some people have difficulty telling anyone about their condition, even those who need to know because they shared in the risky behavior that led to the disease.

In addition, people who test positive must change their sexual and drug-using behaviors to avoid infecting others and becoming more infected themselves. Some withdraw from all physical intimacy, even hugging and kissing, to avoid transmitting the virus. Others have difficulty changing even their risky behaviors for various reasons (Siegel et al., 1988). Thus HIV-positive status becomes a major barrier to continuing or developing the intimate relationships that are so vital to people under stress.

Cognitive Reactions Many people who test positive find the ambiguity of their medical condition—of not knowing if or when they will develop AIDS—difficult to tolerate. Because they initially fear that any physical symptom is related to AIDS, they need to be taught how to distinguish the symptoms of AIDS from the symptoms of other, less threatening illnesses. They also need continuous access to health care, not only to receive optimal treatment but also to maintain an optimal degree of concern about their condition and to receive support for efforts to change their risky behavior without experiencing excessive, immobilizing anxiety.

Emotional Reactions When people learn that they are HIV-positive, they are often overcome with a sense of helplessness and hopelessness even if they had strongly suspected their condition. Helping such people find a way of managing their overwhelming emotions must be a major focus of crisis intervention.

Assessment

A psychosocial assessment of a person who is HIV-positive can provide a baseline description of functioning that may help the clinician identify later symptoms of AIDS such as dementia. This assessment should determine the person's (1) knowledge of the difference between being HIV-positive and having AIDS, (2) awareness of how to avoid transmitting the infection, (3) history of emotional problems or psychiatric illness, (4) ability to cope with stress, (5) access to social networks for emotional and practical support, and (6) plans for medical evaluation and ongoing monitoring.

Because people who are HIV-positive are stressed by the ambiguous diagnosis, the chronic nature of the condition, and their potential to infect others, they require one to three extended sessions—or even more—so that the clinician can develop a support network for them or engage them in a formal, ongoing support program. The primary goals are to preserve their functioning, contain their anxiety, and encourage them to change their behavior and refocus their lives.

Crisis Intervention Model

Crisis intervention after a person tests positive for HIV should include the following components: (1) a psychosocial assessment, (2) advice about how and with whom to share information, (3) suggestions about how to maintain confidentiality and manage legal, employment, and insurance problems, (4) development of plans for medical care, (5) engagement of at least one person in the social network to provide support, and (6) initiation of the process of thinking through decisions about drug use, childbearing, and communicating with sexual partners. The clinician can often assist these people by helping them establish priorities on the basis that they may have a limited life span.

3. Onset of HIV-related Symptoms

Because people who are HIV-positive often develop an acute sensitivity to their bodies, become hypervigilant about any potential AIDS symptom, and do not know when a medical crisis will develop, they often say they feel like they are in state of constant alarm—that they feel like a time bomb. This chronic stress may diminish their capacity to cope with the onset of HIV-related symptoms. For example, a young lawyer wept as he rocked gently back and forth in his chair trying to control and comfort himself. His physician had just told him that although he could not yet be diagnosed as having AIDS, his recent fatigue and weight loss were caused by progression of the HIV infection.

Reactions to the Crisis

Psychosocial Symptoms   Many patients experience the onset of AIDS-related symptoms as the onset of the "sick role" associated with a life-threatening disease. That is, they begin to deal with some of the realities of their situation while clinging to the hope that their current condition will not progress to a full diagnosis of AIDS. Their need to cope with aggressive medical management of symptoms often leads to a preoccupation with health and treatment problems. If they are experiencing overwhelming anxiety, they may withdraw from work, child-rearing activities, and important supportive relationships. Thus the progression of the illness introduces the risk that they will lose existing sources of support.

Cognitive Reactions   As patients with HIV-related symptoms struggle with emotional reactions to their changed medical status, they must also integrate complex information about the potential effects of this change on their life span and their quality of life. Patients with AIDS-related complex (ARC) often become seriously ill. For example, IV drug users frequently die of ARC without ever having been diagnosed with AIDS. Therefore, patients often need to have their medical status clarified. Have they been diagnosed as having ARC? How long will this stage of the disease continue before they are diagnosed as having AIDS? What specific changes constitute an AIDS diagnosis?

Patients may cope with their fears of progressive disease by engaging in ritualized or even obsessive behavior, such as insisting on a specific amount of sleep each night, taking large doses of vitamins and minerals, or rigidly curtailing their daily activities and relationships. Many attempt to avoid stress and "negative" emotions.

Maladaptive or obsessive efforts to take control of preserving health are illustrated by two examples. An advertising executive who complained of insomnia revealed that he believed he could prevent becoming run down and developing AIDS by sleeping for ten hours each night. He became so anxious about his need to sleep ten hours that he had difficulty falling asleep. A computer operator was chronically late for work in the morning because he had to count the exact number of vitamin C, zinc, and garlic pills he thought he needed to take during the day.

Emotional Reactions   When confronted with the symptoms of progressive disease, patients often experience a resurgence of the immobilizing anxiety, guilt, and fear they felt when they first learned they were HIV-positive. Some patients express these feelings in sudden emotional outbursts that are often directed toward coworkers, neighbors, salespeople, or others with whom they do not have a close relationship. These outbursts often represent efforts to ventilate their fear and anger about death and dying. Their families of origin, children, and others they are close to may be unable to provide comfort because the patient has not told them about their HIV status or high-risk behavior. As a 22-year-old college student asked, "How can I tell my parents I'm gay and I'm sick at the same time?"

With the onset of symptoms, patients must reevaluate decisions about who should know about their medical status. They often worry about how to tell their employer about their need to take time off for medical appointments or about disabilities caused by new symptoms. A textile worker said, "I'm always tired. Every morning I'm late for work, and my boss yells at me. But how can I tell him what's happening to me?"

To prevent their employers from learning they have AIDS, many patients choose not to use their medical insurance. However, symptoms that require more intensive medical treatment may force them to reverse this decision. By disclosing serious health problems to their employer, patients often confront the loss of their career momentum because of an inability to compete, to be involved in special projects, or to be promoted. These losses cause many young adults to lose their sense of purpose, which heightens their fears of being unable to function independently and of death. As a cosmetics salesman said, "After I told my boss why I needed time off, I knew I'd lost the promotion I'd been striving for years to get. When someone else got it, I felt like I died a little." At such times, former IV drug users may return to drugs to cope with powerful feelings of sadness and anger.

Assessment

Assessment after the onset of HIV-related symptoms should include (1) clarification of the patient's responses to the previous crises of HIV testing and HIV-positive status, (2) an evaluation of the patient's support network, including identification of people who have already helped and those who may help as the disease progresses, (3) possible abuse of alcohol or illegal or prescription drugs in response to emotional stress, and (4) an appraisal of the patient's ability to maintain health. Patients may neglect their medical care or avoid follow-up care. For example, a patient with hemophilia said, "For five days, I've known I had an infection in my mouth, but I was so upset I forgot to call my doctor for an appointment to get medicine for it."

Two or three sessions may be needed to develop strategies that will enable a patient to stay employed, engage in creative endeavors and child-rearing activities, and increase sources of social support by disclosing the diagnosis. Joint counseling of the patient and the person identified as the key source of emotional support may help to strengthen and clarify that relationship. The clinician may need to maintain daily telephone contact with the patient if counseling sessions are scheduled several days apart.

Crisis Intervention Model

Several important steps make up the crisis intervention model for patients who develop the symptoms of progressive illness. First, the clinician should help patients disclose their condition. Selective disclosure allows them to negotiate the changes necessary in their functional responsibilities and to increase their sources of social support. Role playing and other specialized techniques can help them search for the "right words" to use when approaching others for support and comfort. Because patients are appropriately concerned about the potential for rejection and abandonment, the clinician plays a key role in helping them identify the most likely sources of support.

Second, the clinician should help patients reinvest their energy in the tasks of daily living and in setting priorities. A task-focused approach can help them feel more normal and in control of their lives. Patients need to determine which activities need to be changed or curtailed in response to such symptoms as fatigue. However, some patients may not have the flexibility to alter their work schedules to accommodate reduced stamina. For example, a plastic surgeon with HIV-related symptoms said, "I can't practice anymore. Some days are good, but some are bad. That's just not acceptable to me or fair to my patients."

Third, the clinician should evaluate patients' needs for more intense specialized services. Patients often benefit from referrals for practical, financial, and psychological services from clinicians who are knowledgeable about AIDS and its progression.

4. Diagnosis of AIDS

AIDS is a syndrome comprised of two categories of illnesses: *opportunistic infections,* which usually affect the lungs, brain, genitourinary tract, eyes, colon, or central nervous system, and *cancers,* most commonly Kaposi's sarcoma and certain lymphomas. The diagnosis of AIDS is made when the patient presents with one of these opportunistic infections or cancers.

Treatment of most opportunistic infections requires an acute hospital admission. For instance, a waiter who had been HIV-positive for several years came to the emergency room because he was short of breath. After having a chest X-ray, he was told he probably had pneumocystis carinii pneumonia, an indication that his condition had progressed to AIDS. (Further tests were required to confirm the diagnosis.) His fear and sadness made him cry, which in turn made it even harder for him to breathe.

Unlike most opportunistic infections, some cancers can initially be treated on an outpatient basis. Kaposi's sarcoma, for example, proceeds slowly, and its first symptoms are often superficial.

Reactions to the Crisis

Psychosocial Symptoms   Patients diagnosed with AIDS may not experience the emotional impact of the diagnosis immediately because of their need to focus on the immediate medical crisis. Only when their acute symptoms subside do they confront the reality of their diagnosis and their mortality, a reality that becomes more apparent with each successive hospital admission. As a postal clerk said, "This is my fourth bout of pneumonia. Each time I have to be admitted to the hospital, I think, 'This is it—I'm not getting out alive.'"

Although patients with Kaposi's sarcoma already know they have AIDS, they may not actually confront the diagnosis until they are hospitalized for the first time with an opportunistic infection. When a bookkeeper who had had Kaposi's sarcoma lesions on his face and arms for several years was admitted to the hospital with pneumonia, he said, "I've had AIDS for years, but it's only now that I'm in the hospital that I think it's going to kill me."

Cognitive Reactions   Because patients recently diagnosed with AIDS are plagued by fears of imminent death, even though many people live several years after the diagnosis, they often focus on mortality statistics and media coverage emphasizing that AIDS is a terminal illness. The fear of imminent death may induce anger and emotional withdrawal from others. For example, a young female patient, the wife of a man with hemophilia, said, "I don't talk to anyone. No one can help me."

Even when patients are doing well (e.g., after recovering from an opportunistic infection), they may prematurely contemplate resigning from their job and making funeral arrangements. The lover of a man hospitalized for AIDS-defining meningitis said to the nurses, "He seems to get better each day, but he keeps telling me to donate all his clothes to the church."

Emotional Reactions   AIDS patients, who are usually young, fear becoming debilitated, neurologically impaired, and unable to function independently almost more than they fear death. These fears become intense when they are hospitalized for treatment of advancing disease. Some react with feelings of helplessness, hopelessness, and even suicidal ideation.

The diagnosis of AIDS increases the pressure on patients who have not yet disclosed their situation to families of origin, spouses, children, and friends. Overwhelming panic, sadness, and fear of rejection may make it difficult for them to communicate with people close to them. As a middle-aged businessman said, "After all these years, how can I tell my children that their mother and I divorced because I'm bisexual? But how can I avoid telling them now that I'm sick?" Repressed fears of having transmitted the disease to sexual partners may resurface when the disease is diagnosed.

Assessment

When AIDS is formally diagnosed, the assessment focuses on (1) clarifying distortions or misunderstandings of medical information by determining how the patient views the illness and the prognosis, (2) evaluating the patient's physical frailty, possible dementia, and environmental instability, including unresolved financial, housing, or insurance problems, and (3) appraising the patient's ability to cope with future stresses as the illness progresses, which includes identification of the patient's sources of social support and previous coping abilities.

Two or three sessions are usually required to help patients cope with the crisis of the formal diagnosis. Patients must be helped to move from denial and panic to constructive processing of medical information and planning for self-care. The goal is to continue to reduce their social isolation by helping them disclose information to appropriate individuals and agencies to maintain ongoing support. Clinicians must ensure that patients' formal and informal supports are adequate to sustain them through acute medical episodes over what may be a period of years.

Crisis Intervention Model

Interventions with newly diagnosed patients should be directed toward reducing their negative identification with other AIDS patients, containing their anxiety, and increasing their realistic feelings of hope and sense of control. The clinician can assist them in achieving these goals in the following ways:

> Help them to understand the medical information they are given and to organize their lives around their new status. Asking them to write down questions and concerns may help to identify misunderstandings and gaps in information about prognosis and treatment that are caused by confusing reports in the media. The clinician also can help them formulate additional questions and learn to anticipate their reactions to new information.

Help them develop and maintain as normal a daily schedule as possible. Mastery of life-focused tasks promotes a sense of control and normalcy and helps prevent an immobilizing preoccupation with the threat of death.

Ensure that they have adequate home care, financial assistance, and other support services. Patients often experience a loss of self-esteem when they recognize that they need support services. Therefore, the clinician should offer them the opportunity to grieve over their losses of work, income, and independence and encourage them to view support services as resources for promoting an optimal degree of personal control and quality of life rather than as reasons for feeling helpless and dependent. This approach helps prepare them to accept home care and nursing if these services are needed.

5. Terminal Illness

Patients diagnosed with AIDS can live many years with the disease under control. However, when treatment fails, they enter the final stage of the disease, terminal illness, which presents another series of tasks. At this stage, they are faced with maintaining a meaningful quality of life despite the disease and the threat of death, coping with disfigurement and loss of function, and attempting to answer complicated existential and spiritual questions related to lifestyle, unmet responsibilities, and potential separation and loss (Moynihan et al., 1988).

CONCLUSION

The psychosocial tasks confronting people who are affected by AIDS will continue to evolve as more effective treatments are developed. In addition, changes in the social context of the disease will have powerful effects on these patients. Thus clinicians involved in interventions at each stage of the crisis must be aware of these changes and integrate that knowledge into their interactions with patients.

REFERENCES

CHRIST, G. H., K. SIEGEL, and R. T. MOYNIHAN. (1988). "Psychosocial Issues: Prevention and Treatment." In V. T. De VITA, Jr., S. HELLMAN, and S. A. ROSENBERG (Eds.), *AIDS: Etiology, Diagnosis, Treatment, and Prevention* (2d ed.). Philadelphia: Lippincott.

GOEDERT, J. J., and W. A. BLATTNER. (1988). "The Epidemiology and Natural History of Human Immunodeficiency Virus." In V. T. De VITA, Jr., S. HELLMAN, and S. A. ROSENBERG (Eds.), *AIDS: Etiology, Diagnosis, Treatment, and Prevention* (2d ed.). Philadelphia: Lippincott.

LAMBERT, B. (1989, August 16). "In Shift, Gay Men's Health Group Endorses Testing for the AIDS Virus." *New York Times,* p. 32.

MOYNIHAN, R. T., G. H. CHRIST, and L. GALLO-SILVER. (1988). "AIDS and Terminal Illness." *Social Casework, 68,* 380–387.

SIEGEL, K., L. BAUMAN, G. H. CHRIST, and S. KROWN. (1988). "Patterns of Change in Sexual Behavior among Men in New York City." *Archives of Sexual Behavior, 17,* 481–497.

SIEGEL, K., and W. GIBSON. (1988). "Barriers to the Adoption of Modifications in Sexual Behavior among Heterosexuals at Risk for AIDS." *New York State Journal of Medicine, 88*(2), 66–70.

SIEGEL, K., F. P. MESAGNO, J. Y. CHEN, and G. H. CHRIST. (1989). "Factors Distinguishing Homosexual Males Practicing Risky and Safe Sex." *Social Science and Medicine, 28,* 561–569.

Crisis Intervention
and the Aftermath of Disaster

Marlene A. Young

6

INTRODUCTION

On the morning of August 20, 1986, the National Organization for Victim Assistance (NOVA) received a telephone call from Michael C. Turpen, then attorney general of the state of Oklahoma. Earlier that day, he reported, Patrick Sherrill had entered the Edmond, Oklahoma, post office and killed 14 people before he killed himself. He left a community in chaos, and Attorney General Turpen was calling for help.

While NOVA had never provided communitywide crisis intervention before, Attorney General Turpen knew of its work with individual crime victims and hoped that NOVA's staff and volunteers could fashion a response to a tragedy of this magnitude. Within 24 hours, NOVA had organized and dispatched a team of seven volunteer crisis interveners to provide assistance as needed.

On the night of July 29, 1988, NOVA received a call from a citizen of Rapid City, South Dakota. Fire had been raging around the community for four days. Fourteen homes had been destroyed, and thousands had been evacuated. Although there was no identified suspect yet, most people thought the fire had been caused by arson. After discussions with the governor's office and the attorney general's office, NOVA sent a team of six volunteer crisis interveners to Rapid City on August 4.

Two kinds of tragedy, two different communities, two kinds of response, but each illustrates the kind of work NOVA has undertaken in its National Crisis Response Project. It is work that is designed to address the emotional aftermath of communitywide disasters. The project is based on the premise that disasters cause individual and communitywide crisis reactions and that immediate intervention can provide communities with tools that are useful in mitigating long-term distress.

In its first 2 ½ years of offering this service, NOVA helped 16 communities, one of them twice (Table 6-1). Most of these disasters were precipitated by criminal events. Though there are some important differences between natural and man-made disasters and between those caused on purpose and those caused by accident or recklessness, the commonalities of widespread emotional trauma appear to be more significant than their differences.

This chapter will review the features of crisis and stress reactions in individuals and special issues that are helpful in analyzing crisis situations; explain NOVA's guidelines in providing crisis intervention to such individuals; and describe how those guidelines are applied and adapted in a communitywide disaster.

Though readers may be familiar with the crisis reaction, a detailed understanding of its pattern is essential to NOVA's crisis intervention methodology. Teaching survivors and their caregivers elements of the reaction helps them to understand the normalities of what is experienced as abnormal.

CRISIS, STRESS, AND DISASTER SITUATIONS

Crisis Reaction

Individuals exist in a state of emotional equilibrium in their everyday lives. They establish their own boundaries for experiencing and expressing happiness, sadness, anger, excitement, and the like. Occasional stressors will stretch an individual's sense of equilibrium, but even then, those stressors are usually predictable within the individual's frame of reference, and they can mobilize what are for them adequate coping mechanisms to deal with the stress.

Trauma, by contrast, throws people so far out of their range of equilibrium that it is difficult for them to restore a sense of balance in life. And when they do establish a new equilibrium, it will almost always be different than before the trauma, with new boundaries and new definitions.

Trauma may be precipitated by an "acute" stressor or a "chronic" stressor. Acute, trauma-inducing stressors are usually sudden, arbitrary, and often random events. They include many types of crime, terrorism, and man-made and natural disasters.

Among the most common trauma-inducing chronic stressors are interpersonal abuse, developmental stress caused by life transitions, long-term illness, and continuing exposure to disease, famine, or war. Chronic stressors may cause crisis reactions similar to those caused by acute stressors, with significant differences that cannot be discussed here. However, they should be noted since they often affect the preexisting equilibrium, and individuals suffering chronic stressors are often at higher risk for emotional trauma after an acute stressor occurs.

The normal human response to trauma follows a general pattern. That

Table 6-1 NOVA National Crisis Response Project Interventions, August 1986–February 1989

DATE	COMMUNITY	DISASTER
August 20, 1986	Edmond, Oklahoma	Murder of 14 people in the post office before slayer, Patrick Sherill, committed suicide.
December 8, 1986	Mt. Pleasant, Iowa	Murder of the mayor of Mt. Pleasant and injury of two city council members by a man upset over sewer problems.
January 4, 1987	Baltimore County, Maryland	Amtrak/Conrail train crash (later found to have been caused by criminal misconduct), killing 16 people and injuring hundreds.
March 26, 1987	Oxford, Mississippi	University of Mississippi "walkathon" in which a truck crashed into a car that catapulted into the walkers. Five died, and several others were injured.
April 23, 1987	Palm Bay, Florida	Random murders of six individuals in a shopping mall and injuries to several others. Two police officers were killed.
July 7, 1987	Inkster, Michigan	Hostage-taking and killing of three police officers.
August 10, 1987	Winter Park, Colorado	Boulder dislodged from mountainside smashed into a tour bus, killing six people and injuring 16.
August 16, 1987	Romulus, Michigan	Plane crash near Detroit airport, killing 154 people. One survivor.
August 25, 1987	Lockport, New York	Aftermath of plane crash in Romulus. Of the 154 dead, five were engineers from the Harrison Radiator plant, a division of General Motors based in Lockport.
September 9, 1987	Point of Rocks, Maryland	Electrocution of a 10-year-old boy who rode his bicycle over a power line. Community members witnessed the tragedy.
October 20, 1987	Indianapolis, Indiana	Air Force plane crash into Ramada Inn. Nine people died immediately, one later.
November 15, 1987	Denver, Colorado	Plane crash killing 26 people. NOVA's response was to Boise, Idaho, hometown of the victims.
February 25, 1988	Washington, D.C.	Sexual assault in a counseling center.
May 10, 1988	Washington, D.C.	Stabbing of a teacher in front of her students on a school playground.
May 14, 1988	Carrollton, Kentucky	Highway crash of a car into a school bus, killing 24 children and three adults. Response was to Radcliff, Kentucky, victims' hometown.
July 26, 1988	Rapid City, South Dakota	Weeklong arson-caused fire that destroyed 15 homes, 42 outbuildings, and more than 40 vehicles and caused $1.3 million in damage.
February 14, 1989	Chevy Chase, Maryland	Shooting spree in a bank. Three employees killed, one wounded. Slayer committed suicide after attack.

pattern is characterized by both a physical response and an emotional or psychological response. The physical response is based on biological instinct and is often not within the individual's control.

Physical reactions usually begin with a sense of shock, disorientation, and numbness. That is followed by a state of physical arousal that is triggered by a fight-or-flight instinct. Epinephrine begins to pump through the body. The body may relieve itself of excess materials through regurgitation, defecation, or urination. The heart rate increases. Individuals may begin to breathe rapidly and perspire. Often one sense—sight, hearing, taste, touch, or smell—becomes pronounced (often to the detriment of the other senses). This extraordinary sensory experience may well become an intensely vivid memory that, when rearoused, can trigger a reexperiencing of the initial crisis reaction.

Finally, the immediate physical reaction is typically ended by exhaustion. The body simply cannot sustain the state of extreme arousal for a long period of time. If individuals fail to sleep or rest, they may simply collapse with exhaustion.

The cognitive and emotional reactions to crises are very similar to the physical reaction. The first response is usually one of shock, disbelief, and denial of the trauma, with the mind trying to frame an unthreatening interpretation of the evidence it perceives. There is a sense of a suspension of reality. Not only does the mind refuse to believe what the body is experiencing, but many individuals also feel as though time stops or the world is in slow motion around them.

Shock may last for minutes or weeks. It is usually followed by a turmoil of emotions as time goes on. The turmoil often engages emotions such as anger or rage, fear or terror, confusion and frustration, guilt and self-blame, and grief over losses suffered as a result of the crisis.

This emotional chaos often precipitates regression to a childlike state in survivors. They are, after all, in a helpless state of dependency on others or on outside forces, a circumstance that they may not have experienced since childhood. This, coupled with the intensity of feelings, is overwhelming, and survivors may want a parent or parent figure to take care of things—to "kiss it and make it better."

Just as the physical reaction results in exhaustion, so does the emotional reaction. Survivors often feel as though they are on a roller coaster of extremes. At one moment they are besieged with emotion, the next they may simply feel a void or nothingness. In defense, many survivors constrict the range of their emotional reactions to life events, warding off pleasure and pain equally. For many, over time, they open themselves up to more emotional risks and gains, evolving from traumatized to triumphant, establishing a new equilibrium, and constructing a new sense of self. But some face a lifetime of debilitating stress reactions as a result of the trauma.

Long-term Stress Reactions

Long-term stress reactions tend to take one of four forms: pathological, character changes, posttraumatic stress disorder, or long-term crisis reaction. Although pathological reactions may occur in a small percentage of cases, most crises resulting from trauma-specific events do not result in pathological reactions. Such reactions may include the development of severe phobias, clinical depression, multiple personality disorder, or the like. Psychotherapy is usually suggested in such cases.

The second type of long-term stress reaction may be the development of posttraumatic character changes. Again, these are not common reactions, but they may occur, particularly in survivors of extremely shocking tragedies. Such character changes are exemplified in overcontrolling personalities, rigidity of personality, posttraumatic character decline, extreme behavior change, and the like.

The third type is posttraumatic stress disorder (PTSD). The symptoms of PTSD are often seen in the loved ones of homicide victims, victims of chronic child sexual abuse, survivors of sexual assault, and survivors of catastrophic physical injury.

A final type of long-term stress reaction is one that is not often discussed by mental health practitioners but has been most often observed in NOVA's work. Referred to as long-term crisis reaction, it simply describes the fact that many victims do not present symptoms of PTSD or other disorders but are prone to reexperience feelings of the crisis reaction when trigger events recall the trauma in their life. Trigger events may include the following situations: experiencing a physical sensation that is similar to the intense sensory perception that accompanied the initial physical reaction; anniversaries of the trauma; holidays or birthdays; developmental crises or stages of significant life events such as graduations, marriages, divorces, births, or deaths; involvement in the criminal or civil justice system as a result of the event; media events or broadcasts that are similar to the trauma; and memorials of the trauma.

Issues Surrounding Disasters

Four points of analysis are helpful in determining whether an event places an individual or a community at high risk for trauma. These points also can be useful in determining the key issues that should be addressed in strategies for intervention.

Time Dimension

The first issue is an analysis of the time dimension of the event itself. Time can be broken down into eight phases that may affect the response of a survivor:

Preevent equilibrium
Threat of the event
Warning of the event
The event's impact
Inventory after the event
Time of rescue
Time of remedial work
Reconstruction

The preevent equilibrium is important because the more stressful that equilibrium, the greater the potential of an additional stressful event precipitating another crisis. If a trauma is preceded by a period of threat or warning to which the survivors have an opportunity to respond, there is a greater possibility of guilt or self-blame if they did not respond to protect themselves or loved ones. (Conversely, if the victim can take pride in the way he or she used the warning to mitigate the harm, that can be helpful in the reconstruction process.) If there is no warning, anger may be a dominant emotion in the immediate aftermath because of feelings of injustice and unfairness.

The time immediately following a crisis is when survivors will take inventory of damage and injuries suffered. There is always a stage of inventory taking, even when rescuers appear immediately on the scene. In a medical model, that stage is called triage. If a survivor or rescuer thinks that he or she has made a mistake or an inappropriate assessment during the inventory stage, it may contribute to guilt or blame. And such mistakes are not uncommon; under the influence of stress hormones, humans can become oblivious to physical injuries, even life-threatening ones.

Actions during the rescue stage or the remedy stage may also lead to guilt or anger. Rescue attempts that fail contribute to frustration and despair. The remedy stage refers to the time after the physical rescue of survivors when additional resources and services may be provided to help survivors begin to reconstruct their lives. Although it is very common for such assistance to be available in the first hours or days after a traumatic event, it is also general practice for such help to be withdrawn thereafter. This may contribute to feelings of disillusionment and outrage by survivors.

Spatial Dimension

The second issue for analysis is the spatial dimension of the tragedy. This is particularly critical in a communitywide trauma, for it defines and describes the community itself. One factor in the spatial dimension is the proximity of individuals or survivors to the event itself.

A tragedy may be visualized as the center point in a series of concentric circles. The general guideline is that the closer any individual is to the center of the tragedy, the higher the risk for a crisis reaction and for long-term stress reactions. However, there is a key exception to this guideline. Loved ones of victims who are killed due to the disaster must be considered to be central to the tragedy even if they were not present at the time of the event. The core of their tragedy is different. The death notification is the event of impact, not the actual disaster. The second spatial dimension is the phenomenon of convergence. Convergence describes the actions of individuals who come to the scene of the tragedy. The larger the number of people who converge on the event, the greater the likelihood that the event will be felt as a communitywide trauma. Conversely, when a smaller number of individuals are involved, it is more likely that it will be experienced as a trauma that happened to specific individuals.

In addition, it is important to examine whether the convergence was positive or negative. In the most obvious terms, positive convergence occurs when those who arrive come to rescue or to help, while negative convergence occurs when voyeurs, vandals, or looters come and contribute to the chaos and damage. Negative convergence may add to feelings of anger, frustration, and loss of faith or trust in humanity. One sometimes encounters these reactions among those who came to the scene as rescuers but rescued no one, serving only to tend to the dead and dying.

Role of Survivors

A third issue to address in the aftermath of tragedy is the roles played by survivors. The more roles the survivors are forced to assume, the higher the risk of trauma.

A victim of a street mugging may have only one role in the event, that of victim of predatory crime—and sometimes without even an eyewitness, as is the case in many purse snatches. However, in a communitywide trauma, it is likely that many survivors will have played multiple roles. A victim may be injured or not, an important differential in itself, but may also be a loved one of someone who was killed in the tragedy, a witness to the event, a rescuer who helped save others, a resident of the neighborhood where it happened, and a caregiver who is responsible for responding to the emotional aftermath of the tragedy in the community. The roles may be further complicated by the survivor's self-perception of how well he or she performed or is performing in any of these roles; obviously, there are almost always major differences in the reactions of rescuers who failed in the rescue attempt and those who were successful. The most dominant role from the survivors' perspective is important because it may help to assess the most dominant feelings they have about the event.

Uniqueness of Trauma

A fourth issue in the analysis of tragedy is the elements that define the uniqueness of the trauma. In examining this issue, there are several features to consider: the extent of personal impact, the type of tragedy, the duration of the trauma, the potential for recurrence, and the ability of individuals to control the impact of the trauma in its aftermath.

Extent   The extent of personal impact can be roughly measured by answering six questions:

> How many people are dead?
> Was there a great deal of carnage, or were a great many people severely injured?
> How much property was destroyed?
> Were many people dislocated or relocated from homes, jobs, or schools?
> What was the amount of financial loss, both from the immediate disaster and due to consequent expenses and losses?
> How many people were eyewitnesses to the disaster?

Type   The type of tragedy is defined in several ways, each of which contributes to the understanding of its impact. The cause of the tragedy is one definitive dimension. A natural disaster may cause anger at God but may also be more easily accepted because of the lack of human control over the outcome. An event seen as a man-made accident may raise concerns about human fallibility, blame, and standards for prevention or regulation. A criminal act may cause anger or outrage at human cruelty or, as when drugged or drunk driving leads to multiple deaths, at the driver's wanton, reckless disregard of human life.

The type of destruction experienced in the tragedy is another definitive dimension. Disasters accompanied by flooding or drowning raise concerns about property destruction and bodily disfigurement of victims who have died. Fear of water and suffocation may develop in survivors. Catastrophes that have involved fire often leave survivors with intense memories of the smell of burning wood or flesh. Burn victims suffer excruciating pain and, at times, awful mutilation or maiming. Bodies of burn victims who die are disfigured and are many times unrecognizable. Survivors may become preoccupied with thoughts of hell or damnation.

Duration   A third issue is the duration of the tragedy. Duration is experienced in three ways, each running on the "subjective time clock" of each victim. The first kind of duration is defined by the length of time a victim or survivor was at the point of impact of the disaster at the time it happened. Hence a victim who is trapped in the wreckage of a train may be at the point of impact for hours, while a victim who was thrown free of the train during the crash may only be at the point of impact for a few minutes before being taken to a hospital or an emergency shelter.

The second kind of duration defines how long survivors' senses are engaged by the disaster. Survivors of arson may have been at the scene of the fire for several hours, but the smell of the burnt building may remain with them for weeks or months after the tragedy if they continue to occupy the premises.

The third kind of duration is defined by the length of time that survivors are involved in the aftermath of the disaster due to the response of society. Thus a survivor of a disaster caused by criminal attack may be involved in the disaster for years as it works its way through the criminal justice system.

The general guideline is that the longer the survivor is engaged in the disaster in any of these ways, the greater the likelihood for experiencing severe crisis reaction or long-term stress reactions.

Recurrence Potential   The fourth issue of impact is the likelihood of the disaster's recurring. The greater the perceived chance of recurrence, the more likely it is that survivors will suffer fear as a dominant emotion in the emotional turmoil. The more impossible recurrence seems, the more likely it is that anger will be a dominant emotion.

Control   Finally, it is important to examine the extent to which the survivors have control over the impact of the disaster on their own lives and futures. Catastrophes throw the world of an individual or community out of control. The survivors must confront the chaos of destruction, of the rescue response, and of lost and interrupted time. The need to reestablish a sense of control is critical to the efforts to reconstruct a new equilibrium. Though the disaster itself cannot be controlled, survivors who feel that they are able to control the aftermath and the events that accompany it seem better able to cope.

CRISIS INTERVENTION GUIDELINES

Crisis Intervention with Individuals

This understanding of crisis reactions, long-term stress, and special issues in analyzing the emotional impact of disaster helps to structure NOVA's guidelines for crisis intervention. These guidelines address five goals as shown in Table 6-2. The first three goals are directed at intervention in immediate crisis reactions, the last two at interventions in long-term crisis reactions.

Table 6-2 Goals for Crisis Intervention

1. Safety and security
2. Ventilation and validation
3. Prediction and preparation
4. Rehearsal and reassurance
5. Education and expertise

1. Safety and Security

The first goal of crisis intervention should be to help the victim reestablish a sense of safety and security. For victims who survive a disaster, there is a need to provide safety from physical harm. There is also a need to protect survivors from unwanted invasions of personal space such as their homes—to make sure, for example, that a mob of reporters and camera crews does not trespass literally or figuratively on the property of people in distress.

In addition, safety concerns include avoidance of certain sensory perceptions that might increase the severity of the crisis reaction and the provision of aid to meet basic needs for food, shelter, and clothes. All of these safety and security activities respond to the victims' need for nurturing in their state of childlike aggression.

If safety is not an issue for survivors of loved ones who have died in a disaster, security is still a concern. Security should be provided by ensuring privacy and confidentiality for survivors during death notification or while they await news of the destruction.

Here are some hints for caregivers who seek to establish safety and security for victims:

Make sure that the victims or survivors feel safe or secure at the present moment of intervention. Do not assume that victims feel safe just because they are safe. Respond to the need for nurturing. Though victims or survivors do need to begin to make small decisions or take responsibility for some issues that they face in order to regain a sense of self-determination, they also need to be cared for. Encourage victims or survivors to relax. Just as physical rest is recommended to deal with physical injury, emotional injury calls for some emotional rest.

2. Ventilation and Validation

The second goal of crisis intervention is to give the victim an opportunity to express other feelings and reactions—to "ventilate"—and to have those reactions validated. Victims or survivors often experience such intense emotional turmoil that they fear they are going crazy. It is important to help them identify the often competing emotions that make up their turmoil and to give those emotions concrete names and descriptions. Diagramming the normal pattern of a crisis reaction is very useful because it normalizes the feelings and lets the victims or survivors know that such reactions are legitimate. Some emotions are overwhelming in part because they are perceived as socially unacceptable. Examples are anger that is expressed as hatred and a desire for revenge. But such feelings are common, and victims and survivors should be reassured that they are normal.

To help victims ventilate and to provide validation, caregivers can employ the following tools:

Ask the victims or survivors to describe the disaster.
Ask them to describe where they were when it happened or when they heard about it.
Ask them to describe their reactions and their response to the tragedy. Avoid asking them to describe or to share their feelings. Words like "sharing feelings" or discussing "emotions" alienates many individuals. However, most people can describe reactions, and those reactions will reveal feelings.
List the elements of the crisis reaction (the initial response of shock, disbelief, and denial; the following emotional turmoil and its common components; the eventual reconstruction of a new equilibrium), and have individuals identify where they think they are in the crisis pattern. Draw an emotional roller coaster in which the high points are times of extreme turmoil and the low points are the times of exhaustion and feelings of numbness and depression; ask individuals to identify where they are within those ranges.
Validate common crisis reactions and useful coping reactions.

3. Prediction and Preparation

The third goal of crisis intervention is to predict for the victims or survivors the problems, issues, and concerns they will face in the future and to help them prepare for dealing with these matters. Such prediction and preparation help victims and survivors regain control over their lives and are particularly responsive to the need to restore order in the midst of chaos.

Prediction should include all practical issues that seem relevant: relocation possibilities, financial concerns, legal issues that might arise in the criminal or civil justice system, medical issues, body identification procedures, funeral concerns, media interventions, religious problems, and so forth. When the caregiver has no answers, offer to help the survivor get them.

Prediction should also include giving the survivor a road map of normal crisis and stress reactions (as described earlier) while emphasizing that the survivor may experience none of the symptoms described. Prediction should involve the possible reactions of significant others and casual acquaintances (including the common experience of finding warmth and sympathy initially but see that give way to the attitude "you should be over that by now"). And prediction should address the problems that might be caused by normal triggering events.

Activities that help victims and survivors prepare for the practical and emotional future contribute to their sense of control.

> Encourage them to take one day at a time. Plan routines for dealing with each day, and schedule small goals for achievement.
>
> A helpful problem-solving technique is asking victims to identify the three most critical problems they face at the moment and then assisting them in thinking through what they can or cannot do to address them. Some interveners develop a short contract with victims or survivors that if they will take on one task toward the solution of one problem, the intervener will take on a related task, and together they will reach at least a temporary resolution.
>
> Survivors and victims should be encouraged to talk and write about the disaster. Even if they cannot find someone to talk to, keeping a written or oral diary of problems, reactions, and triumphs in the aftermath can be very useful.
>
> Time for memories and memorials should be planned into daily routines.
>
> Identify a person to whom the victim or survivor can turn when special problems arise (sometimes the person a victim instinctively, and wisely, turns to is not a close friend or relative).
>
> Encourage victims and survivors to eat, sleep, and exercise regularly. Physical exhaustion precipitates emotional exhaustion and further crises.

The last two intervention goals may be used in some cases immediately after a trauma but are more useful as additional strategies in the days or weeks after a disaster.

4. Rehearsal and Reassurance

Victims and survivors should be encouraged to rehearse the event or expected event in the aftermath both mentally and physically and to practice reactions or behaviors that help in coping. Mental rehearsal is a matter of visualizing the event or the expected event and then visualizing reactions. Following those thoughts, individuals are asked to visualize and practice response behaviors that are comfortable for them. At each stage of visualization, the intervener provides comfort and reassurance.

In physical rehearsal, individuals actually role-play their reactions or planned behaviors. In some cases, they may want or need to visit the site of the disaster to role-play or to think through their responses more completely. Rehearsal and reassurance are not proposed as mental health therapy but rather as a practical way to plan for difficult events. It is similar to the mental and behavioral rehearsal that has been suggested for job candidates prior to an interview.

5. Education and Expertise

The final goal of crisis intervention strategies is to provide education and a sense of expertise to the victims and survivors. It has been NOVA's experience that information is a critical need in the aftermath of a disaster. Part of that information should address practical issues or strategies of response and potential involvement with institutions with which victims may become involved. However, ongoing education and the development of new skills may be very useful in minimizing stress and crisis over time.

One means to providing education for victims and survivors is through assigning homework such as reading and writing. Articles and books on victimization, crisis, stress, and the like are often read eagerly. If victims or survivors are illiterate, an optional method is to provide them with audiotapes or videotapes that cover similar materials. For some victims and survivors, it is useful to encourage them to write letters to institutions that have caused them inconvenience, pain, or grief in the aftermath.

A variety of skills can be helpful to survivors. Self-assessment skills that may include stress tests, analysis of thinking patterns, aptitude tests, and the like are often revealing and interesting exercises. Relaxation skills can aid survivors in sleeping and maintaining energy. Communication skills such as active listening, organization of thoughts, presentation of ideas, and expressing feelings usually make ventilation more productive. Problem-solving exercises are also useful. And many survivors find the development of new physical activities such as swimming, dancing, or jogging both physically and emotionally relieving. Not all survivors will respond to these suggestions, but they are worthwhile for caregivers to offer.

In providing crisis intervention and supportive counseling, caregivers should involve family members, friends, or neighbors where appropriate. Support networks usually provide the most effective interventions unless they are impaired by the disaster as well—and even then, it is helpful to urge the members to be patient with one another, knowing that they may not be able to give or get the support they would normally expect of one another.

Finally, the encouragement of peer support group meetings for survivors is advised. The best source of validation of emotional reactions is the knowledge that others exposed to similar horrors reacted in similar ways.

Table 6-3 presents a sample list of phrases that should and should not be used by caregivers as they work toward the goals of crisis intervention. It is important to note that the sooner intervention is provided, the more likely it will be effective. It is suggested that crisis intervention take place within the first 24 to 48 hours after a disaster.

Crisis Intervention in Community Crises

The principles of crisis intervention can be applied in community crisis situations in a similar way as they are used with individuals. NOVA's Crisis Response Project is based on that premise.

Both the process used in sending a crisis response team to a community

Table 6-3 Caregiver Vocalizations in Crisis Intervention

Do Say:

I am sorry this happened to you.
You're safe now (if the person is, indeed, safe).
I'm glad you're here with me now.
I'm glad you're talking to me now.
It wasn't your fault.
Your reaction is a normal response to an abnormal event.
It's understandable that you feel that way.
It must have been upsetting/distressing to see/hear/feel/smell that.
You're not going crazy.
Things may never be the same, but they can get better, and you can get better.
Your imagination can make a horrible reality worse than it is.
Its OK to cry, to want revenge, to hate . . .

Don't Say:

I know how you feel.
I understand.
You're lucky that you're alive.
You're lucky that you were able to save something.
You're lucky that you have other children/siblings/etc.
You are young and can go on with your life/find someone else.
Your loved one didn't suffer when he/she died.
She/he led a good and full life before she/he died.
It was God's will.
He/she is better off/in a better place/happier now.
Out of tragedies, good things happen.
You'll get over it.
Everything is going to be all right.
You shouldn't feel that way.
Time heals all wounds.
You should get on with your life.

and the procedures that the team follows are designed to address the goals of crisis intervention.

When a disaster occurs, NOVA is placed in contact with the community in one of two ways: either the community calls NOVA, or NOVA, on hearing of the tragedy, calls the community and offers assistance.

When NOVA makes the contact, it does so through a local victim assistance program or, if there is none, through other agencies (e.g., police department, sheriff's office, district attorney's office, mayor's office, county commissioner's office, attorney general's office).

No matter how the contact is made, NOVA offers three types of service: sending written materials on how to deal with the aftermath of disaster, sending the materials and providing telephone consultation to leading caregivers in the community, or sending a trained team of volunteer crisis interveners to assist the community.

Should the community decide that it wants to have a crisis response team come, NOVA will send a team only if all community leaders are in agreement that the service will be useful. These initial protocols for outreach are designed to provide the community with a sense of control over its destiny and to affirm that whatever happens will be guided by leadership from the community, not from the outside.

Arrival of Crisis Response Team

The team that is sent to a community will arrive within 24 hours of the disaster, if the community so wishes. That team has three goals:

> To help the community develop an action plan for dealing with the emotional aftermath of the disaster
> To train caregivers in crisis theory as it applies to disaster
> To provide immediate care for populations that are at high risk for severe crisis reaction or long-term stress reactions

The arrival of a team is usually perceived as an act of support and reassurance. The team is seen as an expression of security amid the chaos. The team's role is to serve as adviser to the community and to teach how to conduct group interventions when necessary. The team (including the local hosts) helps mobilize the community just as an individual intervener attempts to help an individual in crisis to regain control.

The general pattern for the team's activity is to stay in the community for no more than 48 hours. This two-day period allows time to accomplish the team's goals but does not promote bonding between community members and team members. In individual crisis intervention there is a danger that the victim may become dependent on the intervener unless certain boundaries are established; this danger also exists in a community crisis situation.

Whether it presents a danger or a problem, two days together under those intense circumstances does produce bonds that last—which reaffirms the sad usefulness of the 48-hour limitation.

Within that period, ideally, the team will work to complete a clear-cut agenda in conjunction with its community hosts. First, the team will visit the site of the disaster, if possible. It has been NOVA's experience that the site visit is important to the team's understanding of the logistics involved in the disaster and also its understanding of the kind of devastation that occurred. For example, when NOVA's team went to Indianapolis in the aftermath of the Air Force plane crash into the Ramada Inn, they became aware that the destruction involved not only the Ramada Inn but also a bank building nearby. This meant that the bank employees as well were at risk for severe crisis reactions.

Second, at some point early on, it is recommended that the team hold a news conference. This conference serves three purposes: it lets the community at large know of the arrival of assistance, it provides an opportunity to communicate basic information about the emotional aftermath of tragedy, and it may provide an opportunity to advertise when group discussions will take place to address some of the immediate issues, as well as advertise which agencies are inviting calls for assistance. The news conference is important because many community members may not understand why they are feeling distressed if they were not at the scene of the disaster or its direct victims. Information from the media can help them understand that their reactions are normal.

Third, the team will meet with community leaders and policymakers to plan the remainder of the two days. This planning session is critical because it symbolizes the control the community has over its immediate future. The community identifies who will be the lead and auxiliary caregivers to be trained by the team. It plans when and where any community debriefing sessions will take place. It identifies high-risk population groups. It designs an outreach strategy for communicating with all such groups. And it addresses any other urgent issues or concerns such as immediate memorial services or funeral services.

Team Planning Session

The only assertive role that NOVA's team takes during the planning session is to insist that there be a training session for all caregivers who will be involved with the NOVA team over the two-day period and for any caregivers who will be involved in follow-up care after the team leaves the community. That training session, usually three hours long, covers basic crisis and stress theory and crisis intervention guidelines as outlined earlier in this chapter.

The training session has four purposes. The first is that it provides a forum for caregivers who have been exposed to the disaster to express their feelings in a safe context. Second, by reviewing crisis and stress theory, it provides validation for those feelings. Third, it usually provides validation for the services they have already provided. They learn that their natural reactions have been "correct." Fourth, even if the caregivers are familiar with crisis intervention, they may have forgotten their knowledge in the shock of the disaster or may have learned such theories in a different context. It is important that all caregivers use similar words and phrases in communicating to survivors of the disaster. If they do not, they often contribute to the sense of chaos.

The planning session will generate a list of population groups that are at risk for crisis and stress. From that list, the planners will identify those with whom the team will be able to meet while they are in the community. Usually, the team tries to meet with groups such as rescuers who have been at the scene of the disaster, victims or survivors, and eyewitnesses. This may include a wide variety of groups: firefighters, law enforcement officers, Red Cross workers, paramedics, emergency medical teams, clergy, teachers, neighbors, and so forth.

Much of the remaining agenda after the training session is spent conducting debriefing sessions of those groups. In addition, the planning session usually results in at least one scheduled communitywide debriefing session. The session is an open-to-all session aimed at attracting individuals who have recognized their own distress and their need for help.

NOVA team members generally lead the debriefing sessions, but in most cases, the local caregivers are urged to attend and to serve as immediate and long-term referrals. Team members lead the sessions so that they can model the debriefing process for the caregivers.

Finally, just before the team leaves the community, NOVA recommends that there be another news conference to review what has been done in the community and to convey any lessons learned. In addition, there is usually a final session with local hosts and caregivers to help develop recommendations and strategies for the community to pursue in the weeks, months, and years to come.

The group debriefing sessions are designed to provide the participants an opportunity to express their reactions to the disaster. Group members help to validate each other's reactions. For some, the debriefings may be sufficient to mitigate severe reactions. Others may need additional sessions or individual help as well. The local caregivers will be the source for that follow-up. The sessions are also designed to begin the process of predicting problems that may arise in the future and to help individuals begin to prepare for them.

The final planning session is devoted to predicting and preparing the community as a whole for the future. For the most part, the team's role is simply one of adviser and resource to community leaders.

Group Debriefing Process

The debriefing process in a group follows the steps of individual crisis intervention with a few variations. Because it is a process of intervening in crisis, special attention must be paid to the logistics and the environment as well as the procedures used.

It is important to try to arrange debriefings so that they do not conflict with aftermath events such as funerals and memorials. Clearly, the goal is to encourage as many individuals to attend as possible. Night debriefings are usually better for communitywide group meetings, and day debriefings are generally better for people who are employed outside of the home, homemakers, and children. It is advisable to encourage employers to give at-risk employees time off to attend debriefing sessions. Generally, immediate postdisaster group debriefings do not take more than two hours each, although in some cases other debriefings may be done as a follow-up.

The location of the debriefing sessions should be designed to promote feelings of safety and security. It is generally imprudent to use for debriefing sessions a site that triggers reactions to or memories of the disaster (for example, an airport conference room following a plane crash or a school gymnasium following the slaying of a student at the school).

The room for the debriefing should be accessible and comfortable for the group. Seating should be arranged in a horseshoe or a circle, and local caregivers or other team members should be spread around the room. Water should be available since the intake of water can mitigate physical stress reactions. Boxes of tissues should be available in case there are tears.

NOVA encourages the use of a flipchart to record the phrases used by participants as the group interaction proceeds. These records will be given to the group at the end of the session or destroyed, depending on the group's will to preserve confidentiality. No individual's name will be attached to any reactions recorded.

Debriefing sessions should be conducted by a debriefing team of two, a leader and an assistant. The leader's role is to conduct the debriefing. The debriefing assistant's role is to provide emotional support to the debriefing leader, to record notes on the flipcharts, to take over if the debriefing leader cannot continue, and to assist individuals who may go into a crisis reaction as a result of the debriefing session itself (although it is better if local caregivers assume this role). The assistant should never be involved in conducting the debriefing unless the leader specifically requests assistance.

Once a group is assembled, the debriefing leader should begin the meeting by introducing the debriefing team and reviewing ground rules for the session. The following rules are essential for preserving the sense of safety and security.

The group is pledged to confidentiality so that people feel they can discuss reactions freely.

While expressions of any feelings are legitimate, there will be no physical violence during the session. (At times, individuals may react so strongly that they may try to take out their rage on another group member.)

Individuals may leave the group as they need to, although they are encouraged to stay from beginning to end, and those who leave can expect someone to accompany them for support if they want it. Further, if they do leave, they are encouraged to rejoin the group when they feel they are ready.

The group session is not a critique of how any individuals or institutions behaved during the disaster; rather it is a discussion of individual reactions.

The team's agenda is to help the group define the crisis reaction, to provide some crisis intervention, and to predict and prepare the group for possible future events. The goal is not to provide individual or group therapy. However, that agenda is presented to the participants in a different form. The announced agenda is to review three things: how the participants reacted or are reacting, how their family or loved ones are reacting, and what they expect in the future.

Opening the Session   To accomplish the aforementioned agenda, the team leader should begin the session with the following type of introduction. The introduction is accompanied by commentary to better explain its use of crisis intervention strategies.

"I am sorry that this plane crash happened here in Midville."

[This statement of sympathy is almost a mandatory introductory phrase in the NOVA protocol. It indicates to the listener that the intervener is concerned about the listener and the tragedy. Even though it may seem trivial, many victims have said that the statement of sorrow is very important.]

"I know that if I lived here, it would be terribly distressing to me. And even though I live in Center City, it is still upsetting to think that 24 people were killed."

[These introductory words are designed to validate in advance feelings of turmoil and to acknowledge the extent of the disaster and destruction.]

"I'm John Jones, a victim advocate with the National Organization for Victim Assistance, or NOVA. With me are Susan Brown, a crisis intervener from Medford, Oregon; and Larry Little, Mary Mays, and Sarah Smith from Midville's Victim Assistance Program. Susan and I are here as members of NOVA's Crisis Response Team Project, which sends volunteer crisis interveners to help communities in the aftermath of disaster. We have assisted 18 communities since our first response in the aftermath of the Edmond, Oklahoma, post office murders in 1986. Larry, Mary, and Sarah are here to provide follow-up assistance if needed in Midville."

> [This part is an introduction of the individuals in the debriefing session who will be active and the organization sponsoring them. It includes just enough information to establish the credibility of the project and the intervention.]

"I want to talk to you today about the impact of this plane crash on Midville. But before we begin our discussion, it is important that everyone here understand some basic ground rules for our talk. First, I think it is important that everyone agrees that this discussion will be confidential between us. That means that no one will report to others what any named individual said about anything. You may want to tell your spouse or a friend that certain things were discussed or even that someone in the group made a certain remark that you agree or disagree with. But I'm asking you to agree that any such commentary will make no references to names or to specific characteristics that might reveal a person's identity. If you agree with this rule, please nod your head in affirmation."

> [This rule is very important for ensuring privacy. The experience of NOVA's team debriefing leaders is that when group members are asked to underscore their agreement by nodding their heads, they feel more accountable for maintaining confidentiality, and others feel more trust in their peers.]

"The second rule is that no matter what your reactions are, you should feel free to tell us about them. But there is an exception to this rule, and that is that you should not express your reactions through physical violence. That may sound humorous, but I have found that sometimes a tragedy like this can trigger strong anger or a desire for vengeance. Occasionally, that kind of reaction causes individuals to lash out at others without meaning to."

> [This rule of nonviolence is very difficult to present. NOVA's experience has been that if the rule is presented in the positive manner as a rule of total expression with one exception, it is better received. In addition, the rule against physical violence often brings snickers or laughter because no one thinks that such a reaction would happen, but it can, so giving a caution and a reasonable explanation of the caution is a preventive strategy.]

"The third rule is that you should feel free to go and come as you please. Sometimes people need to get away from the group for a while to collect their thoughts or to think through certain things. If you want to leave for a few minutes, do so. One of our team members will follow you out just to make sure you don't need anything or that if you do, we can help you. We'd like you to return because we think your thoughts and reactions to this disaster are important, but you are not obliged to do so."

> [Some people have expressed the thought that group debriefings should require that individuals who participate in them must stay for the full length of the session. It has been NOVA's experience that it is better to provide participants with the fullest amount of freedom. Any restriction takes away their sense of control. This is a time to help them reestablish their own ability to function as they see fit. At the same time, it is good practice to tell them that someone will be available to talk to them or assist them so that they do not feel stranded if they leave and still need help.]

"Those are our guidelines; now let me give you some more information that may be helpful. There are water, coffee, and soft drinks on the back table if you would like some refreshments during the session. The bathrooms are located down the hall and to the right. And if you need to smoke, please feel free to do so over in that end of the room. If any of you cannot tolerate smoke, we suggest that you sit over at this end."

[Note that in this section, the rules are referred to as guidelines. This softens the impact of the regulation. Also note that permission is given to move about the room to get refreshments, to go to the bathroom, and to smoke. Once again, this expands the sense of control the group members have over their behavior. At some training sessions, individuals have asked why NOVA allows smoking in debriefing groups. The answer is simple. Although there are good reasons to promote nonsmoking among our general population, we have observed that even reformed smokers may have a need to smoke during intense emotional sessions. We are not encouraging smoking, but it is our view that the time of a disaster is not a time to curb an addiction.]

"Now, let me say once again that I'm sorry that the plane crash happened in Midville. It is terrible that so many people were killed and injured. It is terrible that the destruction was so immense. But what I would like you to do at this moment is to think back over the past 48 hours and try to remember the moment—the instant—when you first saw, heard, or learned of the plane crash. I want you to try to remember where you were, whom you were with, and what your reactions were. What do you remember seeing, hearing, smelling, tasting, or even touching at that time?"

[This is the critical transition to the group crisis work. There are several important factors to this transition. After suggesting that the group think back and remember, the leader should allow a few moments for that to happen. For some, this may be the first time they have allowed themselves to do such thinking. For others, it may be something that has been remembered over and over again. After allowing those few moments, the leader helps to structure those thoughts by stating what the group should think about. It is important to use the word *reactions* and to talk about physical reactions. These will serve as a lead to other discussions.]

"Now, I want to ask for anyone who would be willing to tell me about his or her experience. Where were you? Whom were you with? And what were your reactions?"

[Repeating the questions is useful while someone in the group prepares to respond. In most cases, the leader will not have to wait for a response. However, in the cases where no one responds immediately, the leader should be aware that silence is an ally, not an enemy.]

Working with the Group   After the leader has set up the introduction, the group work begins. Usually a number of people will be ready to tell their stories. The normal progression of events will include a description of shock and disbelief, followed by a wide range of conflicting and congruent emotions. It is useful for the group leader gently to interrupt individuals in their discussion of reactions after they describe the shock-and-disbelief stage and their physical reactions and then proceed to the next person. That type of interruption and progression assists the validation process.

However, if an individual seems so consumed by the experience that he or she must continue to describe events up to that very day, the leader should allow that. That judgment is subject to the intervener's common sense.

Once the discussion is under way, it is important for the leader to validate all key reactions. Underscore any statements that fit within the crisis reaction framework. For example, if a person says, "I was stunned. I could not believe that it happened," a validating comment would be, "Shock is common in a disaster. How could anyone believe that such a disaster was happening to them?" It is ideal if the group itself does the validation, so that group members say, "I couldn't believe my eyes" or "I felt numb and couldn't move or think." This is the most effective validation because it comes from one peer to another. However, the leader should not be seduced into thinking that she or he should not provide validation if the group does not. Every statement that reflects normal crisis reaction should be validated.

The leader should keep an eye on the time. After about 30 minutes of introduction and descriptions of shock and disbelief, the leader should move on to reactions of emotional turmoil. If the discussion does not naturally flow in this direction, the leader should ask participants to describe what has happened to them in the aftermath. Again, validate anger, fear, confusion, grief, self-blame, and other strong emotions.

The second segment of the discussion usually takes longer than the first. One reason for that is that there are more reactions and the emotional content of those reactions is often more intense. After about an hour, the leader should lead the discussion toward questions such as "What do you think will happen tomorrow or next week in your life, and how do you think you will handle it?" This last segment of the session is the predict-and-prepare segment.

In most cases, group participants will accurately predict problems and concerns. In some cases, the leader may have to describe unexpected obstacles. Those obstacles may range from involvement in the criminal justice system (because the disaster involved criminal intent) to media sensationalism.

The leader should remember that an important part of the content at this stage of the discussion is to help survivors to prepare for such issues. As a result, the leader should validate good proposed coping techniques and give them a safety net for the future. In most communities, that safety net will have developed from the community's mobilization of emotional aftercare. Perhaps there will already be a plan in place for the future. No matter what the stage of preparedness is, the group participants need to know there is a place to turn for help. That is the safety net for their next 24 hours and, sometimes, for the rest of their lives.

In the group debriefing process, the leader needs to be fully prepared for emotional reactions and behavioral symptoms of trauma. Participants may manifest confusion or physical and mental agitation. They may begin to cry or may become withdrawn. They may become angry and irritated. The leader needs to know that such reactions are not directed at him or her personally. The reactions are directed at the disaster. But the disaster is not controllable, and the leader is.

The leader should also be prepared for the unexplainable. In most disasters, there are stories of supernatural physical feats, messages from the dead or dying, visions of death or dying. It is not important whether such events have an explanation; it is important that the individual believes what she or he is describing.

At the conclusion of the group process, the leader should go over the agenda briefly and indicate how it was accomplished. If a flipchart was used to record reactions, it should be used to review them in the context of normal crisis reactions. Group members will then have confirmed that their statements were reasonable. The leader should ask for any final concerns or questions from the group.

Then the leader should distribute handouts on crisis reactions, long-term stress reactions, and special issues. Participants need to have something to take home with them. The group should be thanked for their participation. The confidentiality of the discussion should be repeated. And the ongoing support and interest of the host or leader's organization should be emphasized.

THE FUTURE

Understanding the crisis and stress reactions, strategies for crisis intervention, and NOVA's approach to community crisis intervention should demonstrate how closely the theory of crisis and stress can translate into practice.

Disaster occurs far too often in modern life—the disaster of an individual tragedy such as a sexual assault or murder or the massive destruction of lives and property in a plane crash or multiple slayings. The impact of disasters is exponentially increased by each death, each eyewitness, each injury, each loss.

Thus it is critical that mental health professionals, clergy, victim assistance workers, and others be prepared to respond to the emotional dimension of disaster. Without appropriate interventions, many individuals may face a lifetime of severe stress reactions. With effective help, most individuals can reconstruct a new life, one that forever carries painful memories of their losses but one into which they build new hope, pride, and gratification.

SUGGESTED READINGS

ANDERSON, J. & WOODARD, L. (1985). "Victim and witness assistance: new state laws and the system's response." *Judicature.* 68(6):223–226.

Bureau of Justice Statistics. (1987). *Lifetime Likelihood of Victimization.* U.S. Government Printing Office, Washington, D.C. (Technical Report #NCJ 104274.)

BURGESS, A. & HOLSTROM, L. (1979). "Adaptive strategies and recovery from rape." *American Journal of Psychiatry. 136:*1278–1282.

COHEN, RAQUEL E. (1990). "Post-Disaster Mobilization and Crisis Counseling: Guidelines and Techniques for Developing Crisis-Oriented Services for Disaster Victims." In A. R. Roberts (Ed.). *Crisis Intervention Handbook: Assessment, Treatment and Research* (Belmont, CA.: Wadsworth). pp. 279–299.

KAHN, A. (1984). *Final Report of the American Psychological Association Task Force on the Victims of Crime and Violence.* (American Psychological Association, November 30) Washington, D.C.

LEE, J. & ROSENTHAL, S. (1983). "Working with victims of violent assault." *Social Casework. (64)*593–601.

U.S. Department of Justice, Office of Justice Programs. (1986). *A Report on the President's Task Force of Crime: Four Years Later.* U.S. Government Printing Office, Washington, D.C.

ROBERTS, ALBERT R. (1990). *Helping Crime Victims: Research, Policy and Practice.* Newbury Park, CA: Sage Publications, Inc.

ROBERTS, ALBERT R. (Ed.) (1990). *Crisis Intervention Handbook: Assessment, Treatment, and Research.* Belmont, CA: Wadsworth Publishing Co.

SHULMAN, NORMAN M. "Crisis Intervention in a High School: Lessons from the Concord High School Experiences," in A. R. Roberts (Ed.). *Crisis Intervention Handbook, op.cit.* pp. 66–77.

Crisis Intervention
with Victims of Hostage Situations

Thomas Strentz

Thomas Strentz

7

INTRODUCTION

The Federal Bureau of Investigation does not engage in the direct delivery of social work services. Yet the Bureau and other law enforcement agencies around the world are directly involved in crisis intervention and thus provide some form of psychological support to people encountered at the crisis site. Most "code three," "red light," and siren responses are calls to a crisis. Personal crimes, such as rape and robbery, involve victims of a personal crisis. In addition, responses to an ongoing hostage situation also qualify as responses to personal crisis.

Case Study

At 10:20 A.M. on a Friday morning in 1974, a lone gunman entered a branch of the Home Savings and Loan Association office in a western city. He approached an experienced, mature, and emotionally stable teller and announced a robbery. She quickly initiated the police response by activating the silent alarm system. The police response was immediate. When two plain-clothes units entered the bank, the subject placed his gun to the teller's head and ordered the police out of the building. During this initial withdrawal, the police were able to take the other employees and the customers with them. The reaction of the now trapped armed robber was typical: he added abduction charges to his offense. When negotiations were initiated, he demanded a much larger sum of money from the police than he ever expected to obtain from the robbery. He threatened to kill the teller, whom he called by name, if his demands were not met by a specified time. The negotiator gained an extension of this initial deadline and several subsequent ones. As time passed, the subject was identified as JD, and his therapist from a local psychological counseling service was located. In an attempt to gain additional time and to create a less tense atmosphere, the negotiator agreed to some of JD's demands. Money was delivered, and an opportunity to view JD and confirm his identity was created. His counselor agreed to speak with him on the telephone. When she called JD by name, he denied his identity and became more violent in his threats against his hostage. The counselor told the negotiator that JD had been diagnosed as an antisocial personality and was on parole for the second time after a series of rapes, an attempted murder, and several burglaries. As morning turned into afternoon, a subtle change was noted in the subject's threats. JD was now threatening to kill "the girl" rather than the teller he had previously called by name. He then said that if the rest of the money and the car were not delivered by 4:00, he would kill the girl. For emphasis he added that he was looking her in the eye as he said this. JD told the negotiator that the FBI could explain to her children why Mommy would not be coming home anymore. His counselor agreed that this was a bad sign. She said that it appeared that JD was de-humanizing this victim as he had his other female victims. As late afternoon arrived and the evening rush hour approached, the subject became adamant that he be allowed to leave with his hostage. He promised to release her once he was sure that no one was following him. His counselor agreed that the life of the hostage meant nothing to JD and that allowing her to leave with him would be sentencing her to death. Shortly after 4:00, JD was shot and killed as he attempted to leave with the teller. She was not physically injured and after some counseling returned to work. She was the victim of two more armed robberies and now works in the personnel office at the same bank.

Today a quiet surrender of the subject is a more common conclusion to such a siege. But emotional levels are high during the early hours of any such incident. It is during this traumatic period that the initial law enforcement response is achieved. Local police units are the first to arrive. During this time, the crisis is still very real. By using proper crisis intervention techniques, law enforcement can, and frequently does, begin the psychological healing process for the people involved. The first to arrive engage in ego support and family and individual counseling, encourage ventilation, clarify issues, and provide facts and a reality orientation for all of the victims. The major players are the hostages, the subject, and the responding interveners. To some degree, all of these individuals are or can be victims in the hostage-taking crisis. Of these three primary players, the responding interveners, the law enforcement officers, are the most prepared and certainly the best trained. Many preparation programs also exist for people who have a high potential for victimization as a hostage. Generally, these private programs are attended by executives who have applied for kidnap insurance and must attend a program that focuses on prevention and survival. In the public sector, the government provides programs for airline cockpit and cabin crews, bank employees, and people assigned to our embassies (Strentz, 1987; Bolz, 1987; McKinnon, 1986; Third U.S. Army, 1985).

Many of the federal felonies investigated by the FBI are white-collar crimes. The FBI is charged with the responsibility for the enforcement of over 200 federal laws ranging from a violation of the Migratory Bird Act to violations of copyright laws and extortion of federally insured banks and savings and loan associations. However, matters that may include personal crisis are also of concern to the FBI.

Some of these more dramatic crimes are hijacking of a commercial aircraft, robbery of a federally insured institution, and kidnapping and other forms of hostage taking. Many of these violations involve people who have been held hostage. To deal with these crises, the FBI has developed a local, regional, and national response network that includes special weapons and tactics (SWAT) teams, technical support units, and a command post to coordinate the use of these assets. This crisis response team also includes hostage negotiators who comprise a large cadre of multilingual, carefully selected and trained male and female special agents of every race, color, and creed in 58 field offices around the country.

ORIGIN OF THE FBI'S CRISIS MANAGEMENT PROCEDURES

Like so many other innovative law enforcement methods, hostage negotiations, SWAT, and crisis management practices are domestic forms of the so-called Pearl Harbor syndrome. Many of us tend to be more reactive than proactive. After the fire at the Cocoanut Grove nighclub in Boston in 1943, cities enacted ordinances covering the outward opening of doors, and mental health professionals saw the need for crisis intervention. Similarly, the FBI crisis management program grew out of a disaster. At 4:00 A.M. on October 4, 1971, special agents of the FBI responded to the hijacking of a commercial aircraft in Jacksonville, Florida. The plane had left Memphis, Tennessee, with two armed male hijackers, the hysterical estranged wife of one hostage taker, and a crew of two commercial pilots. A refueling stop in Jacksonville was scheduled. The twin-engine Aero Commander Hawk 681 landed at 5:10 A.M. at the Jacksonville International Airport, and a confrontation developed over the request for additional fuel.

The following is taken from the Federal Aviation Administration transcript of the conversation between the FBI in the tower (T) and the pilot of the hijacked airplane (P):

P: 58 November. This is the captain speaking. We're going to cut engines and we're gonna need some fuel, but I request that everyone stay away.

T: 58 November. Advise when your engines have been cut.

T: 58 November?

P: This is 58 November. Uh, this gentleman has about 12.5 pounds of plastic explosives back here, [not true] and . . . uh, I got no . . uh, yen to join it right now so I would please expr, uh, appreciate it if you would stay away from this airplane.

T: That's a roger, 58 November. Are your engines cut?

P: Negative.

T: Stand by.

P: Where's the fuel truck?

T: 58 November?

P: 58 November. Go ahead.

T: This is the FBI. There will be no fuel. Repeat, there will be no fuel. There will be no starter. Have you cut your engines?

P: Uh, look, I don't think this fellow's kiddin' . . . I wish you'd get the fuel truck out there.

T: 58 November. There will be no fuel. I repeat. There will be no fuel.

P: This is 58 November. You're endangering lives by doing this, and, uh, we have no other choice but to go along, and, uh, uh, for the sake of some lives we request some fuel out here, please.

T: 58 November. What is the status of your passengers?

P: Ah, uh, well, they're OK, if that's what you mean.

T: Are they monitoring this conversation?

P: Yes, they are.

T: Do you have two passengers aboard?

T: 58 November. What's your present fuel status on that aircraft?

P: We're down to about thirty minutes.

T: 58 November. The decision will be no fuel for that aircraft. No starter. Run it out, any way you want it. Passengers, if you are listening . . . the only alternative in this aircraft is to depart the aircraft, to depart the aircraft.

Within an hour the discussion escalated into an argument between the hijackers and the FBI. The copilot was allowed to exit the aircraft, and he confirmed the lack of explosives as he argued for additional fuel. One hijacker also exited the aircraft to argue for additional fuel. Neither was allowed to return to the plane. Fearing that the lone hijacker was suicidal and would force the remaining pilot to crash the aircraft if it were refueled and allowed to take off, the FBI remained adamant in its refusal to provide additional fuel. The aircraft was then disabled by the FBI. Shortly thereafter, the remaining hijacker shot and killed his estranged wife and the pilot and then killed himself. Four years later, on August 8, 1975, the Sixth Circuit United States Court of Appeals decided that the FBI had not acted correctly and awarded a large settlement to the widow and children of the pilot.

FBI Director Clarence Kelley, in anticipation of the court's decision and in keeping with the newest trend in law enforcement, had already ordered the FBI's Training Division to develop a program to instruct its agents in the skills and strategies of hostage negotiations. Supervisory special agents of the recently formed Behavioral Science Unit attended the New York City Police Department's (NYPD) hostage negotiation course. Other agents were developing the special weapons and tactics (SWAT) alternative, which was a modification of the Los Angeles Police Department's SWAT program. Additional crisis response resources were developed as the FBI's Training Division identified the need to deal more effectively with the developing complexities of the FBI's investigative responsibilities.

The NYPD, under the direction of Commissioner Patrick Murphy and in response to the tragedy at the Twentieth Olympiad at Munich in September 1972, had just developed a hostage negotiations program for police. The NYPD recognized that terrorist groups could strike and kill in New York with the same impunity they had demonstrated in Munich. Sergeant Frank Bolz and Officer Harvey Schlossberg, Ph.D., had been tasked to create this first hostage negotiations program (Bolz & Hershey, 1979). They shared their expertise with the FBI and other police departments around the world. The NYPD's hostage negotiations guidelines, as they were called, were altered slightly to fit the national jurisdiction of the FBI, and training in this skill was begun at the FBI Academy. The first priority of the FBI and the NYPD was then, and is now, the preservation of human life. In other words, every decision made by the commander during a hostage siege rests on the premise that the selected course of action will do the most to preserve human life. Property damage and arrest of the hostage taker are secondary concerns. Thus the options of negotiating, using a sniper or chemical agents, or assaulting are all considered with the goal of resolution with preservation of life as the primary concern.

TRAINING SPECIAL AGENTS IN CRISIS INTERVENTION

As a supervisory special agent who was an instructor in the Behavioral Science Unit and later in the Special Operations and Research Unit at the FBI Academy, I was given the responsibility of creating a hostage negotiators' course. At that time I had been a special agent in the FBI for eight years and had a Masters of Social Work degree. The development of this course required a wide range of information, to include social work and mental health practices, philosophies, and techniques. The FBI was assisted in this developmental process by two sworn officers from New Scotland Yard who spent a month at our academy in Quantico, Virginia, and in our homes guiding us in the creation of this program.

Research into hostage situations revealed that most hostage takers in the United States were suffering from paranoid schizophrenia or extreme depression. In addition, a large number could be classified as having antisocial or inadequate personality disorders. The number of so-called political terrorists taking hostages in the United States was then, and is now, statistically insignificant (Strentz, 1984). Further, the programs developed with hostage takers who are mentally ill or monetarily motivated are easily adapted to fit the terrorist. Thus the instruction included several hours on the symptoms of the most common mental disorders of hostage takers, with law enforcement examples of these maladies. Woven into this instruction were the guidelines for negotiators with ample time for closely critiqued role playing.

GUIDELINES FOR CRISIS NEGOTIATIONS

The basis for the decision-making process for FBI executives during a hostage crisis is the preservation of human life. Preservation of property, even an expensive aircraft, is secondary. Over the years, countless lives have been saved by following several tenets that have proved their value in saving lives. Time is the most important ally of the crisis interveners. As time passes, the authorities gain intelligence, improve their tactical position, and incur countless other benefits from the fatigue induced in the perpetrator. His basic human needs increase and provide the crisis team with additional negotiation points.* As he speaks with the negotiator, his anxiety level diminishes, and he tends to become more rational. His expectations and demands tend to lower as trust and rapport develop with the negotiator. Although the passage of time can have some negative effects—for example, an unrealistic level of complacency and boredom can develop in the command post—overall, time has a much more beneficial effect on the crisis interveners than it has on the initiator of the crisis. Additional guidelines include the general refusal of the authorities to provide weapons or mobility to the subject as well as some reluctance to exchange hostages (Fuselier, 1981a, 1981b).

Because hostage negotiation is a skill, a widely practiced teaching technique is the use of role playing or simulations. This application of action models is a common technique in teaching skills that cannot be learned from a lecture. One of the early leaders in the field of role playing was J. L. Moreno (Moreno & Whitin, 1932), who is credited by many as being the founder of psychodrama. Yablonsky (1980) has discussed this technique in mental health settings. Other applications include football teams engaging in scrimmages, public speaking courses using speeches, and future negotiators practicing their skills in controlled crisis settings called field training exercises or classroom scenarios. These scenarios are simulated hostage situations based on actual incidents where role players familiar with the case play the roles of the subject, to train the new negotiators. Hostage crisis cases that are representative of typical situations are used to provide realistic training. The negotiation process is evaluated by instructors who work with the trainees during the exercise and critique them afterward. At the FBI Academy, this process is observed by the rest of the class on closed-circuit TV, which enables everyone to learn from the role playing and to participate in the critique.

Since 1976, this type of instruction, with advanced classes for experienced negotiators, has been provided to over 1,000 domestic and foreign police officers at the FBI Academy as well as in seminars conducted at police department facilities around the world. As New Scotland Yard assisted the FBI in developing its program, the FBI assisted law enforcement agencies in Australia, Canada, Israel, New Zealand, Norway, and other democracies in Europe, Asia, and South America. Today most nations of the free world exchange hostage negotiations staff and students regularly.

The research conducted by the FBI and other law enforcement organizations enables everyone to remain up to date on hostage-taking trends. This research indicates that over 95 percent of American hostage situations are successfully resolved by negotiations, usually without a shot being fired by law enforcement (Strentz, 1983b). This is accomplished through the purposeful use of crisis intervention theory and techniques by well-trained law enforcement personnel.

---

*According to the *Hostage Incident Report,* 98 percent of American hostage takers are male (Strentz, 1983b). Males also appear to predominate as subjects overseas (Jenkins et al., 1977). Hence our assumption throughout this chapter that the hostage taker, or subject, is a male.

CRISIS COUNSELING STRATEGIES

The taking of hostages represents a crisis for the hostage taker as well as for the hostages. All the elements of a crisis are present: an unsolved problem, disequilibrium and stress, attitudes of panic or defeat, and feelings of frustration. Efficiency is decreased, and hostage situations, like other periods of emotional crisis, are of limited duration (Puryear, 1980). Research has shown that over 92 percent of American hostage situations are resolved within nine hours (Strentz, 1983b).

The procedural steps, or crisis counseling strategies, used to defuse a hostage situation are similar to those used for intervention in other crises as discussed throughout this book. For instance, in a hostage situation, contact is made as soon as possible with the subject. This may be via a telephone call or by calling out to him if a phone is not immediately available. A telephone call is preferred to a face-to-face discussion. Very few negotiators are shot by subjects while talking to them on the telephone. The caller usually says something like, "Hello, this is John Smith of the FBI." Although it is important to identify oneself as an officer of the law, the use of rank tends to be counterproductive.

The following is an example of this initial rapport-developing process in the early discussions between an FBI negotiator, TS, and the subject, Jamie, who has taken hostages in a federal prison. Since this is a prison setting, the name of the subject is known, and quite a bit of intelligence is available on him.

TS: Hello, Jamie? This is TS of the Federal Bureau of Investigation.
Jamie: What the . . . is the FBI doing here?
TS: Well, I'll tell you Jamie. Like you, we want to see that no one gets hurt.
Jamie: Where the . . . is the warden?
TS: Beats me. Nothing but chaos out here; this place is a zoo. I think you and I are the only sane ones around.
Jamie: You have to be crazy to work here. I sure ain't here 'cause I want to be. Why are you here?
TS: They always call us in on an important case.
Jamie: Well this is an important case all right. I'm innocent and they been holding me here against my will for too long. I got my rights.
TS: Why don't you fill me in on what's been happening?
Jamie: Didn't they tell you?
TS: I want to hear it from you. . . . That way I get it straight. You know what I mean?
Jamie: Well, first off, . . .

Eventually, as rapport and trust develop, the negotiation process reaches the point where the subject begins calling the negotiator and asking for advice. The negotiation process is reflective, and the negotiator tries to keep the subject in the role of decision maker.

Ventilation is encouraged so that the negotiator can determine the subject's view of the siege. This process also allows a full exploration of the subject's emotions and some insight into his mental state by the negotiator and, in some instances, an on-scene psychological consultant. It is rare that a subject will have been involved in previous hostage situations, yet past experience in "sticky situations" is explored. Every attempt is made to discuss the various alternative courses of action in a very nondirective and nonjudgmental mode. The subject is encouraged to do most of the talking, thinking, planning, and coping with the stress of the siege. The subject is asked to provide his views on what is happening and how he would resolve the siege. The negotiator remains nonjudgmental and discusses the various options at length. Finally, he or she will say something like "Let me run that by the boss and see what happens." This is said even if the subject wants something that the negotiator knows is unlikely to be provided, like weapons or an escape vehicle. The negotiator plays the role of arguing the case for the subject with the boss who makes the decisions. The negotiator never says no. The negotiator says maybe later or not right now, but never no, even if the boss has made it clear that the demands will not be met. By talking about each demand in detail, the negotiator stresses the importance of what the subject wants, and thus the importance of the subject, in this siege. In this way, the negotiator gains time and induces fatigue in the subject. Eventually, the subject is convinced of the logic of a face-saving resolution that may involve "walking out like a man." This crisis intervention process is woven into several stages of the typical siege.

FOUR STAGES OF THE CRISIS EVENT

Most authorities agree that hostage situations have stages (Strentz, 1984; Derrer, 1985; Rahe & Genender, 1983). They tend to differ on the specific number of stages, with counts ranging from three to seven. I see most hostage situations as having four steps: alarm, crisis, accommodation, and resolution. Each stage is different for each of the participants and from each other stage, although there is some overlap. Also, it is important to realize that each hostage situation, like each crisis, is of limited duration. It has a beginning, an end, and a time in the middle when lots of things happen. It is during these middle hours that the crisis is being worked toward a successful resolution.

Alarm

The first, and probably most traumatic, period in a hostage situation is the alarm stage, and it can last for an hour or more. In many ways, particularly in the case of an armed robbery gone sour, the abductor, hostage, and police are going through similar emotional experiences. Though injury to hostages is rare, research shows that most of the hostages who are injured during the siege sustain these injuries in the opening moments when the armed robber is trying to consolidate his position or when the terrorist is intimidating his hostages to ensure control or domination of them (Jenkins et al., 1977). In his desperation, the armed robber compounds his dilemma by adding kidnapping and assault charges to his list of offenses. These considerations are initially minimal to him. His emotions are running high: he wants to buy time, and in this he succeeds. A trapped armed robber usually tries to gain additional money and project the blame for the situation onto the police.

The opening moments of negotiations are usually very emotional, and generally little is achieved until the subject has settled down. It takes time for the negotiators to arrive, get the right phone number, and make the first call. Thus the initial contact may be after the alarm phase has passed. In fact, other people—the press or relatives of the hostages—may have called the subject before the negotiator arrives. In some situations, to add to the confusion, a bank of telephone lines lead into a siege site. It takes time for law enforcement to locate all the lines and obtain legal authority to cut other forms of contact. In some situations, the subject is asked to answer only one number or phone because the others are being used by people who are not authorized to call. The initial phase of negotiations may involve convincing the subject that the negotiator is the legitimate representative of law enforcement. At this point, the subject commonly vents his anger at the police, threatens to kill hostages, and demands money, transportation, and, at times, the release of friends from prison.

Contact between the negotiator and the hostage taker may be initiated by either party. Eventually, as the negotiator gains control of the crisis, the subject calls the negotiator more and more frequently. During the early contacts, the negotiator attempts to develop a relationship of trust. This trusting relationship is crucial to the successful resolution of the crisis. Although no law requires total truthfulness on the part of the negotiators, they make every attempt to be completely honest. Through discussion of the issues at hand—identity of the hostages, location, demands—the negotiator is able to engage in an initial psychological assessment of the subject.

Without taking the focus away from the subject, efforts are made to identify the hostages. In some situations, negotiations go on for hours before it is verified that there are in fact no hostages.

The subject is encouraged to tell his side of the story in as much detail as he deems necessary—in other words, to ventilate. To assist him in this process, most successful negotiators use the Carl Rogers model of active listening while negotiating. This nondirective, client-centered approach has proved most effective. Through working and carefully critiquing many foreign and domestic hostage situations, law enforcement has learned how to defuse a hostage situation. Experience has demonstrated the importance of paying close attention to the subject and his needs, desires, and dreams. It has become clear that if the negotiator does not pay close attention to the subject, the subject frequently does something to remind everyone that he thinks he is in charge of this crisis. He wants this to remain his show of force. If and when the negotiator strays from keeping him at center stage, the subject may respond by making threats against hostages, firing a shot, or injuring a hostage. Therefore, more than most crisis experiences, the hostage taker maintains "ownership" of the siege, and negotiators endeavor to help him in this activity. He makes the decisions. The negotiator works with him in a role similar to that of a defense attorney working with a client. Because of the relationship that tends to develop between the subject and the negotiator, the negotiator is generally isolated from the command post operation. Thus the negotiator is able to focus on the subject while working with him toward a non-violent solution to the dilemma.

To assist the negotiator, an excellent backup system of other negotiators, a psychological assessment of the subject, and many other resources are made available to ensure a tranquil termination of the incident. Thus the negotiator can concentrate on the subject and encourage him to talk about his problems.

While talking with the subject or listening to him ventilate, the negotiator must pay close attention so as to hear not only the subject's expressed demands but also those that are instrumental. While the subject may be talking about money and an automobile to make good his escape, one must remember that he is enjoying all the attention his demands and this crisis are garnering him. The granting of his instrumental demands, allowing escape from center stage, may be the last thing he really wants. A review of hundreds of hostage situations indicates that the hostage taker really wants a quiet conclusion. If he really wanted to kill people, he probably would have already done so. Most hostage takers want an audience for their performance (Schlossberg, 1980). Like most terrorists, they want a lot of people watching, not a lot of people dead (Jenkins, 1986). Thus simple demands should not be met quickly because the need for the audience is such that the hostage taker may then dream up new and more difficult demands to retain the undivided attention of his audience.

The subject is in a difficult situation. He wants to surrender but may not know how. To quit would cause him to lose face; he cannot admit failure. The process of hostage negotiations enables him to find an honorable solution to his dilemma. Thus a relationship between the negotiator and the subject is slowly developed by concentrating on the subject's favorite topic, himself—what he wants, how he feels, and so on. Furthermore, the negotiator insists that the subject make the decisions on as many points of discussion as possible. Every attempt is made to keep him in a decision-making mode. This may remind some people of the practice of self-determination and the client's right to fail, but law enforcement has learned that it also provides many tactical advantages. The subject is in the center of the stage during this crisis, and every attempt is made to keep him there. Making all the decisions is a fatiguing process. His fatigue is crucial as the authorities move him toward a quiet conclusion of his crisis.

During this discussion called hostage negotiations, the negotiator helps the subject talk about his problem, how and why he came to be in this situation, and, of course, his plan for its resolution. In the process, he is encouraged to talk about whatever is on his mind. Law enforcement has all the time in the world, and the most important person in the siege is the hostage taker. Interestingly enough, this process has also worked in those rare situations where a person trained as a negotiator has taken hostages and issued demands (Lanceley, 1988).

Hostage negotiators, because of the careful selection and training process, have a high level of confidence in their ability to resolve the crisis peacefully. This level of confidence is shared by the SWAT team. When called on to fire, they do so with the confidence that all other alternatives to end this situation in a manner designed to preserve human life have been tried and have not succeeded. This attitude is evident when the SWAT agent is debriefed in the post-traumatic incident interview and his or her psychological reactions are compared with those of others who have been involved in an equally justifiable but more spontaneous shooting. The SWAT team member has a much lower stress level. This tends to be true even when the same SWAT team member is involved in a spontaneous shooting.

Another major player in this siege is the hostage, the unsuspecting citizen who is the bargaining chip, the pawn in this dangerous dilemma. While the basis of the hostage negotiating guidelines is the preservation of human life, and the life of the hostage is of primary importance, this value should not be communicated to the hostage taker. It is a very poor bargaining tactic to escalate the value of what you want to the person who possesses this item. The reason for the police presence is the hostage, yet the hostage taker must believe that he, not the hostage, is of primary importance to the police.

Generally, law enforcement's contact with hostages during this first phase is limited. However, if contact can be made, the negotiator tries to reassure the hostages with frequent words and expressions of concern and sympathy to help them deal with their very high level of anxiety. The alarm phase is traumatic for unprepared law-abiding citizens forced into this life-and-death situation. Suddenly their world is turned around, and they may experience near-paralyzing fear (Rahe & Genender, 1983). The police, whom one expects to help, seem to be doing nothing and could give the impression of being confused. The hostage feels let down; it all seems so unreal (Derrer, 1988). Diego Asencio, U.S. ambassador to Colombia, was taken hostage with other diplomats in the Chilean embassy. He described well the reaction to the first few minutes of a hostage situation from the victim's perspective: "The worst aspect of the ordeal was the initial trauma. In the first few minutes, all you can do to ensure survival is to lie very close to the floor." Although he was to alter his behavior later and play a more comfortable role, his most enthusiastic advice to victims of any hostage situation during the alarm stage is to disregard any notion of heroics or curiosity. "Unarmed, untrained and poorly conditioned civilians can best ensure survival by maintaining low profiles," he advised (Asencio, 1983).

Many hostages, while lying close to the floor in those hectic opening moments, seek immediate psychological refuge in the denial of reality. Denial is a very primitive but effective psychological defense mechanism that is put into use when the mind is overloaded with trauma it cannot handle. Each victim who copes effectively has a strong will to survive. Some may deal with the stress by believing they are dreaming and will soon wake up and it will all be over. Some deal with the stress by sleeping—somnolent withdrawal. I have interviewed hostages who have slept for over 90 percent of their time in captivity. Some have fainted, although this is rare. Thus one encounters a variety of responses to the trauma of captivity. In time, some of this trauma may abate; however, some individuals, like some prisoners of war, carry the psychological scars of captivity for the rest of their lives.

Contact with family members of the hostages and the subject is common throughout the siege. From them we obtain information about their relative to assist us in the siege and assist them in dealing with the anxiety they are feeling by providing information. We also remain available to them throughout the siege. Though the FBI does not engage in the direct delivery of social work services, an informal referral to a minister, mental health professional, or significant other is common. In some situations, like the Hanafi Muslim siege at the Washington, D.C., B'nai B'rith headquarters in 1977 and in most prison sieges, family members are provided with shelter near the site and regular briefings throughout their ordeal.

Crisis

Although this phase marks the beginning of reason for the hostage taker, many similarities to the alarm phase remain. During this phase, most subjects begin to feel a sense of growing frustration. This is particularly true if the siege is the result of a poorly planned robbery. Generally, the subject's initial demands reflect his frustration. His early dialogue may be marked by emotional outbursts and excessive demands. His level of frustration is best indicated by the amount of money demanded. A subject may have expected a few thousand dollars from his efforts at robbery. Now that the police have trapped him in the bank, he may believe that he can punish them by making them pay a large amount of money. Initial demands for hundreds of thousands of dollars are not unusual. In fact, an evaluation of the demands can provide insight into the subject's mental processes. Demands for money and other creature comforts or a car indicate a criminal orientation that generally means an antisocial or inadequate personality. Demands for impossible action, like Corey Moore's insistence in Warrensville Heights, Ohio, that all white people vacate the earth in 24 hours, suggests some mental problems. The absence of clear demands or the refusal of the subject to talk with the negotiator suggest depression and suicidal ideation.

Evidence of this pattern has emerged over the years. The subject may insist on negotiating through one of his hostages. Or he may not answer the phone or respond to other attempts at negotiation, as with the Symbionese Liberation Army in Los Angeles and many other less dramatic sieges. This lack of direct communication usually results in a violent termination of the incident. Instead of talking, he may shoot at police. Another ploy is to run from the location while threatening to shoot police. A third is suddenly to shoot a hostage and then stand by a window. One theory attempts to explain this behavior by suggesting that the subject fears that he will be talked out of suicide. He uses this passive-aggressive behavior pattern to force the authorities to do to him what he cannot do to himself.

Another method of evaluating the emotional state of the subject is to identify his hostages. Since most normal people do not take their spouse or children hostage, information on the identity of his hostages may also provide psychological data.

The crisis phase is of critical importance to the survival of the hostage. The behavior pattern exhibited now creates the precedent for hostage-subject interaction that can maximize the chance of survival or ensure the demise of the victim. The stress hostages experience during this phase may be due to their personal fears of isolation, claustrophobia, the loss of a sense of time, and the clear and present danger they face. These and other hostage problems are discussed at length by several authors.*

Accommodation

This is the longest phase and can be the most tranquil. The personality of the hostage taker will become more evident as he talks with the negotiator. The mental stability of the hostage taker is evaluated continuously throughout the siege. While the more normal criminal subject may bargain with authorities, the mentally ill hostage taker will engage in rambling ventilation. The depressed individual will contact the negotiator less frequently than the other types of hostage takers, and his mental state will be very clear during discussions. Some suicidal subjects insist that hostages negotiate for them.

The following is an example of an inadequate type of hostage taker. Recently, a subject took his counselor hostage in a midwestern prison. The FBI negotiator was able to delay satisfying most of the subject's wants by blaming prison bureaucracy and shift changes. During this time, the negotiator made some judgments on the personality of the subject and the likelihood of his injuring his female hostage. Part of this process involved delaying the meeting of simple demands to evaluate the subject's reaction to this type of stress. Although one may not always want to delay the gratification of a simple request, it is an excellent tactic to be prepared to negotiate the substitution of satisfying a simple demand for a difficult one when the subject seems likely to injure the hostage.

A recent example of such a transaction comes from the negotiations conducted by an FBI special agent (JD) while negotiating in Knoxville, Tennessee. The subject (Tommy) had taken his hostage at 3:00 P.M. and demanded a shotgun with a box of shells, a loaded .38-caliber revolver with extra ammunition, and an automobile. At 7:00 P.M. he also mentioned the need for coffee. The following negotiations took place at 10:45 P.M. the same day (Strentz, 1983a):

TOMMY: It's been over eight hours since I requested what I requested: the car, the shotgun, and the piece.

JD: Yeah.

TOMMY: The car.

JD: Just a minute, Tommy. (Talking to someone nearby yet heard by Tommy.) Did you get that coffee in to him? Dammit, you'd think you could

---

*In doing this reading, one should differentiate among the reactions of prisoners of war, concentration camp inmates, and hostages (Rahe & Genender, 1983; Symonds, 1980; Wesselius & Desarno, 1983; Eitinger, 1980; Ford & Spaulding, 1973; Kentsmith, 1982; Ochberg & Soskis, 1982; Derrer, 1988; Strentz, 1979, 1983a, 1987).

handle something simple like that, he wants some coffee. The man needs some hot coffee.

TOMMY: I want . . .

JD: A damn cup of coffee.

TOMMY: Hey!

JD: Sorry, Tommy. What is it?

TOMMY: We want a pot of percolating coffee. With a lot of cream and sugar. Send a coffee pot down here.

JD: Coffee pot.

TOMMY: We're going to need it. If you are going to keep holding out this long . . .

Eventually, the subject was distracted and taken into custody while his hostage was being rescued. It is important to note that it took eight hours to address his demands. The subject was aware of this delay and acquiesced to this tactic. This delay allowed time for the negotiator to assess the subject, induced fatigue, and enabled the SWAT team to effect a rescue without injury to anyone.

This negotiating sequence, conducted by a trained negotiator, stands in contrast to those in Jacksonville a few years before.*

Resolution

This final phase may be one of trauma or tranquillity. The mood in and outside the siege site depends on whether the siege is broken by an assault or resolved by a quiet surrender.

In the majority of situations, the subject will be fatigued by the negotiation process and will have reluctantly resigned himself to his fate, an honorable solution, not surrender.

One hostage siege in Los Angeles was resolved when the subject exited a jewelry store pushing a shopping cart he had filled with watches. It was his plan to trade these items, which he had stolen, fair and square, for a United Airlines 747 with a crew for a flight to the South Pacific, where he wanted to buy an island. He envisioned living happily ever after as he bartered with the natives for the necessities of life. His knowledge of history provided him with the Dutch precedent in Manhattan. Though he did not call himself Peter Minuit, he tried to duplicate this 1626 effort. Yet as he exited the jewelry store with his booty, as out of touch with reality as he was, he was not ignorant of what might happen. Suddenly, on a smooth sidewalk, he accidentally tripped, and the cart of jewelry and his weapons went rolling down the sidewalk as he fell to the ground, unarmed, with his hands in full view. As the police rushed to arrest him, he remained quite still. While he was being handcuffed, he looked over at the arresting officer and said, "Hell of a way to make a living, isn't it?" This situation in May 1978 contrasted

*Information on the mechanics of hostage negotiations is available in several articles on this subject written by instructors at the FBI Academy (Lanceley, 1981; Soskis and Van Zandt, 1986; Fuselier, 1981a, 1981b; Strentz, 1983a, 1986). Additional information is available in the books written by Schlossberg and Freeman (1974) and Bolz and Hershey (1979).

sharply with a Beverly Hills jewelry store siege a few years later during which several hostages were killed. Thus while some generalizations can be made about typical subject and hostage behavior, each situation is a different crisis and must be treated as such to ensure a successful resolution.

It is during the process of resolution that law enforcement has the greatest and most positive psychological impact on the hostages. During the debriefing interview, law enforcement wants them to tell all they can about their experience. Most victims ventilate for some time before a sequential pattern of events can be obtained. Time is of no consequence. The postincident interview continues until all participants are satisfied that it is over, and it is usually conducted prior to hostage contact with anyone else. This is necessary to obtain their version of the incident before it is contaminated by the media and others. Rarely is a former hostage too disturbed to conduct such an interview. If some psychological or physical problems are present, the negotiator probably knew about them prior to the release, and the appropriate community resources are alerted and available at the site. Police officers and FBI agents are genuinely interested in what the released hostages have to say. One reason for this interest is the distinct possibility that the listener will have to tell a judge and a jury all about the siege. Thus the law enforcement officer needs to know what happened.

The very positive reaction of victims to the postincident interview was especially clear when the Americans who had been hijacked on TWA 847 in June 1985 were interviewed in Germany by a number of mental health, intelligence, and law enforcement professionals. According to Dr. Robert Sokal, who was the Army psychiatrist in charge of the processing of the hostages, they said that as victims, they felt best about their interview with the FBI agents who were so interested in their story. Certainly one reason for their reaction was the fact that talking to the FBI gave them a chance to get even with the terrorists who had held them for so long and killed one of their fellow passengers. According to Sokal (1988), the former hostages felt that by talking to the FBI, they were telling someone about their suffering who could do something to correct the wrongs they had experienced.

While many of the hostages on TWA 847 expressed hostility toward their captors, a sympathetic reaction called the Stockholm syndrome is also common. This is a positive reciprocal relationship that frequently develops between hostage and subject as well as between negotiator and subject. It was first identified during a bank robbery in Stockholm, Sweden, that turned into a 131-hour siege in August 1973. One definition of this reaction takes into account three phases of the experience and describes it as the positive feelings of the captives toward their captors that are accompanied by negative feelings toward the police. These feelings are frequently reciprocated by the captors (Strentz, 1979). A hostile former hostage may be the price that law enforcement must pay for a living hostage. Anti–law enforcement feelings are not new to the police. But in a hostage situation, such feelings are encouraged to ensure the development of the Stockholm syndrome. Hostility from people whose lives law enforcement has mustered its resources to save seems inconsistent. However, a human life is an irreplaceable treasure and worth some hostility. A poor or hostile witness for the prosecution is a small price to pay for this human life.

CONCLUSION

The process of hostage negotiations, as engaged in by trained professionals in a variety of settings, ranging from a domestic dispute or a foiled armed robbery to a group of political terrorists who have hijacked an aircraft, is a very practical application of crisis intervention theory. Hundreds of hostage situations around the world have been successfully resolved by the application of these principles in a time-limited, traumatic event in the lives of otherwise normal human beings who just happened to be in the wrong place at the wrong time.

It is said that the Chinese character for crisis is a combination of the symbols for danger and opportunity (Puryear, 1980). In a hostage situation, the element of danger coexists with the opportunity for successful resolution and personal growth. With good mental health counseling to deal with the effects of posttraumatic stress disorders, people victimized by this trauma can grow in positive directions. They can view their captivity as a test that they passed, not a crisis that they failed.

REFERENCES

ASENCIO, D., and N. ASENCIO. (1983). *Our Man Is Inside.* Boston: Little, Brown.

BOLZ, F., and E. HERSHEY. (1979). *Hostage Cop.* New York: Rawson Wade.

BOLZ, F. (1987). *How to Be a Hostage and Live.* Secaucus, N.J.: Lyle Stuart.

DERRER, D. (1985, May). "Terrorism." *Proceedings/ Naval Review*, p. 198.

DERRER, D. (1988, May). Victim training session, Camp Pendleton, California.

EITINGER, L. (1980). "The Concentration Camp Syndrome and Its Late Sequelae." In J. E. DIMSDALE (Ed.), *Survivors, Victims and Perpetrators.* Washington, D.C.: Hemisphere.

FORD, C. V., and R. C. SPAULDING. (1973). "The Pueblo Incident." *Archives of General Psychiatry, 29,* 340–343.

FUSELIER, G. D. (1981a). "A Practical Overview of Hostage Negotiations." *Law Enforcement Bulletin, 50*(6): 2–6.

FUSELIER, G. D. (1981b). "A Practical Overview of Hostage Negotiations: Conclusion." *Law Enforcement Bulletin, 50*(7): 10–15.

JENKINS, B. M. (1986). Lecture to *Fortune* 500 vice-presidents. Los Angeles.

JENKINS, B. M., J. JOHNSON, and D. RONFELT. (1977). "Numbered Lives: Some Statistical Observations from Seventy-seven International Hostage Episodes." Santa Monica, Calif.: Rand Corp.

KENTSMITH, D. K. (1982). "Hostages and Other Prisoners of War." *Military Medicine, 147,* 969–971.

LANCELEY, F. (1981). "The Antisocial Personality as a Hostage Taker." *Journal of Police Science and Administration, 9,* 28–34.

LANCELEY, F. (1988). Lecture to FBI hostage negotiators course. FBI Academy, Quantico, Virginia.

McKINNON D. (1986). *Everything You Need to Know before You're Hijacked.* San Diego, Calif.: House of Hints.

MORENO, J. L., and E. S. WHITIN. (1932). *Plan and Technique of Developing a Prison into a Socialized Community.* New York: National Committee on Prisons and Prison Labor.

OCHBERG, F. M., and D. A. SOSKIS (Eds.). (1982). *Victims of Terrorism.* Boulder, Colo.: Westview Press.

PURYEAR, D. A. (1980). *Helping People in Crisis.* San Francisco: Jossey-Bass.

RAHE, R. H., and E. GENENDER. (1983). "Adaptation to and Recovery from Captivity Stress." *Military Medicine, 148,* 577–585.

SCHLOSSBERG, H. (1980). "Values and Organization in Hostage Crisis Negotiation Teams." *Annals of the New York Academy of Sciences, 347,* 113–116.

SCHLOSSBERG, H., and L. FREEMAN. (1974). *Psychologist with a Gun.* New York: Coward, McCann & Geoghegan.

SOKAL, R. (1988). Personal interview. San Francisco.

SOSKIS, D. A., and C. R. VAN ZANDT. (1986). "Hostage Negotiation: Law Enforcement's Most Effective

Nonlethal Weapon." *Behavioral Science and the Law, 4,* 423–435.

STRENTZ, T. (1979). "The Stockholm Syndrome: Law Enforcement Policy and the Ego Defenses of the Hostage." *Law Enforcement Bulletin, 48,* 2–12.

STRENTZ, T. (1983a). "The Inadequate Personality as a Hostage Taker." *Journal of Police Science and Administration, 11,* 363–368.

STRENTZ, T. (1983b). "A Statistical Analysis of American Hostage Situations." Unpublished handout, FBI Academy, Quantico, Virginia.

STRENTZ, T. (1984). "Preparing the Person with High Potential for Victimization as a Hostage." In J. T. TURNER (Ed.), *Violence in the Medical Care Setting.* Rockville, Md.: Aspen.

STRENTZ, T. (1986). "Negotiating with the Hostage Taker Exhibiting Paranoid Schizophrenic Symptoms." *Journal of Police Science and Administration, 14,* 12–16.

STRENTZ, T. (1987). "A Hostage Psychological Survival Guide." *Law Enforcement Bulletin, 58,* 2–10.

STRENTZ, T. (1988). "A Terrorist Psychosocial Profile: Past and Present." *Law Enforcement Bulletin, 57,* 13–19.

SYMONDS, M. (1980). "The Second Injury to Victims." *Evaluation and Change,* special issue, 36–38.

Third U.S. Army. (1985). *Terrorism, Security, Survival Handbook.* Washington, D.C.: U.S. Government Printing Office.

WESSELIUS C. L., and J. V. DESARNO. (1983). "The Anatomy of a Hostage Situation." *Behavioral Science and the Law, 1,* 33–45.

YABLONSKY, L. (1980). *Psychodrama: Resolving Emotional Problems through Role Playing.* New York: Basic Books.

Crisis and Recovery Services
for Family Violence Survivors*

Arlene Bowers Andrews

8

INTRODUCTION

People who are intentionally hurt or threatened with harm by family members confront exceptional challenges as they cope with the aftermath of victimization. Family violence is an extraordinary stressor, one that challenges the competencies of the survivor and erodes the support that could mediate the survivor's stress, as illustrated by this situation:

Case Study

Until she was eight years old, Rose was a cheerful child who made friends easily and maintained average grades at school. Soon after Rose's eighth birthday, her mother remarried, and within weeks physical fights began between Rose's mother and stepfather. At school, Rose began to act fidgety and withdrawn. Her grades dropped. She talked to no one, including her mother, about what was happening at home.

Rose's solitary struggle to cope with her exposure to family violence changed her healthy approach to the world. She needs help to regain her positive coping skills.

This article reviews a variety of effective crisis and recovery interventions developed to promote the individual's healthy recovery from family violence and

*Reprinted from Albert R. Roberts (Ed.). *Helping Crime Victims: Policy, Practice and Research* (Newbury Park, CA: Sage Publications) 1990, pp. 206–232; with the permission of the publisher. Case studies have been added for this edition.

reduce the risk of long-term psychosocial damage. First, a conceptual foundation is introduced that integrates stress theory and knowledge about family violence.

CONCEPTUAL FOUNDATION: STRESS AND FAMILY VIOLENCE

Synopsis: Stress Theory

The foundation for this conceptual framework lies in general stress theory (Goldberger & Breznitz, 1982) as well as in the specialized variants of stress theory known as crisis theory (Slaikeu, 1984) and traumatic stress theory (Figley, 1985).

People of all ages confront routine stressors, external events that are part of their social and physical environments. Normally, people reduce the anxiety induced by environmental stressors and maintain emotional and functional equilibrium by coping effectively with these routine stressors. Coping involves adjusting cognitions, feelings, and behaviors in response to environmental events, including changing the environment if necessary (Moos & Billings, 1982). Each person tends to have characteristic ways of coping; family systems tend to have their coping styles, too.

Examples of adaptive coping methods are acknowledging and expressing feelings, using social help, engaging in task-focused behavior, exercising, and relaxing. Maladaptive methods include chemical substance use, denial, aggression, suicide attempts, psychosomatic complaints, and social withdrawal. Any of these methods may reduce anxiety, but they also have obvious healthy or unhealthy side effects.

Consider the different coping styles of these three women, who have all come to a battered women's shelter because their husbands beat them:

Case Study

Lashonda tries to stay busy with household tasks such as cooking and cleaning. She regularly meets with her counselor, expressing pain, anger, and anxiety about what is going to happen next. She takes a daily walk and has had two long talks with her mother by phone. She actively participates in evening groups for shelter residents.

Case Study

Jean prefers to stay in her room. She snacks alone and does not join the others for meals. She avoids the counselors and appears to feel hopeless, staring into space for long periods of time.

Case Study

Sandra is chronically agitated and frequently mentions to other residents that she needs a drink. She feels too sick (mostly headaches) to help with household chores. She participates in counseling and groups, mostly to complain about problems with the shelter and other community agencies.

All three women are struggling to cope with their anxiety, and each probably feels temporary relief. Lashonda is most likely to resolve her anxiety, while

Jean and Sandra have already developed side effects that can lead to long-term problems.

If the stressor is exceptionally strong, multiple stressors are simultaneously present, or the chosen coping response is not effective, the individual may experience the subjective state of stress. Stress is manifested as an aroused physiological state and subjective feelings of tension that can lead to exhaustion. Chronic stress can have harmful, even fatal, physical and psychological effects on the individual, including coronary disease, depression, immune system deficiency, and problems in maintaining interpersonal relationships.

Stressors may be routine, extraordinary, or catastrophic. Routine stressors include such events as a child's test at school, a verbal disagreement between spouses, and a holiday celebration. Periodically all people confront extraordinary stressors, such as change in life status (e.g., marriage, divorce, retirement), loss of a loved one, or residential relocation. The cumulation of routine and/or extraordinary stressors can induce particularly intense stress. Some people will also be faced with catastrophic stressors, which include events that are "sudden, overwhelming, and often dangerous, either to one's self or significant other(s)" (Figley, 1985, p. xviii). Individuals who experience catastrophe are at risk of developing psychic trauma, "an emotional state of discomfort and stress resulting from memories of an extraordinary catastrophic experience which shattered the survivor's sense of invulnerability to harm" (p. xviii).

Family violence may occur in conjunction with routine, multiple, extraordinary, or catastrophic stressors. Family violence may itself take any one of these stressor forms. For example:

Case Study

Jeremy Jones is a seven-year-old boy who frequently defies his mother. At least every other day she grabs a leather belt and pops him on the legs four or five times, leaving temporary skin marks but no bruises. The child-parent conflict and use of physical force are *routine stressors* for Jeremy and his mother.

One day Jeremy's mother became exasperated. She started beating Jeremy with the belt and did not stop until she was exhausted. Multiple bruises appeared on Jeremy's legs and back. This event and the fear that it would happen again are *extraordinary stressors* for Jeremy.

One day Jeremy's mother beat him severely then locked him in a dark closet for two hours, telling him that she needed to get him out of her sight so she wouldn't kill him. Jeremy's stay in the closet and fear for his life became a *catastrophic stressor* for him.

A person's exposure to multiple, extraordinary, or catastrophic stressors may precipitate a temporary state of psychological crisis, depending on the coping resources of the person at the time of exposure. Slaikeu (1984) defines crisis as "a temporary state of upset and disorganization, characterized chiefly by an individual's inability to cope with a particular situation using customary methods of problem solving, and by the potential for a radically positive or negative outcome" (p. 13). People in crisis may have uncontrolled emotional expressions, disorganized thoughts, anxiety, and fatigue. They may have difficulty completing routine tasks and may withdraw from or cling to social contacts. The person in crisis is highly vulnerable to influence by others, acts helpless, and may appear to be psychopathological or suffering from chronic stress. In fact, the symptoms are temporary, typically resolved within a few weeks. The return to normalcy may be misleading, as serious residual psychological damage may have occurred. Figure 8-1 summarizes the crisis process. Crisis intervention techniques are used to facilitate crisis resolution in an adaptive direction.

Whether a person enters a state of crisis in response to a stressor depends on individual and situational characteristics. For example:

Case Study

Miguel (age 14), Tomas (age 12), and Lara (age 11) are siblings who watched their grandmother aim a gun at their father when he came to their house and started beating their mother, from whom he was divorced. Their father left. In the days following, Miguel was busy helping his mother change the locks on the door and accompanying her to appointments for arranging an order of protection. Miguel remembers earlier violence before the divorce and is able to talk about his anger toward his father. Lara became unusually clingy after the confrontation and crept in to sleep with her mother a few times, but otherwise behaved in her usual way. Tomas, however, became extremely withdrawn. He could not concentrate on his school work and awoke each night with nightmares. The incident precipitated a state of crisis for Tomas.

How a person handles stress, trauma, or crisis is influenced by personal and social factors. Personal factors that promote healthy growth include effective normal coping skills, good physical and mental health, and general self-confidence. All people have strengths and competencies; the degree to which they can master stress is apparently related to their awareness of and ability to apply their competencies. Perceived competence includes a sense of personal efficacy, freedom from self-denigration, perceived control over emotions and imagery, interpersonal trust, and a sense of wholeness and integrity. The person who acts competently will be able to communicate empathy, bond with other persons, experience pleasure, and engage in positive health and safety behaviors.

When the survivor is a child, developmental issues obviously must be considered (Mowbray, 1988; Smith, 1984; Wolfe, 1987). A child's cognitive, moral, and physical ability to master his or her environment, understand what happened, and seek help will be directly affected by maturity. The younger the child, the more social support he or she will need (Eth & Pynoos, 1985). Adolescents have particular challenges when they must cope with victimization within their families while also confronting the development of identity and sexuality. Children cope better when they have an intimate attachment to at least one adult and history of being able to trust in the reliability and support of a relationship (Zimrin, 1986). The demand of coping with trauma or extraordinary stress can interfere with a child's normal developmental tasks and thus impair the child's future development. When the child copes with maladaptive behavior, the parent's stress may be increased, leading to even higher risk for psychosocial and physical harm.

Families have competencies, too. Under routine circumstances, families

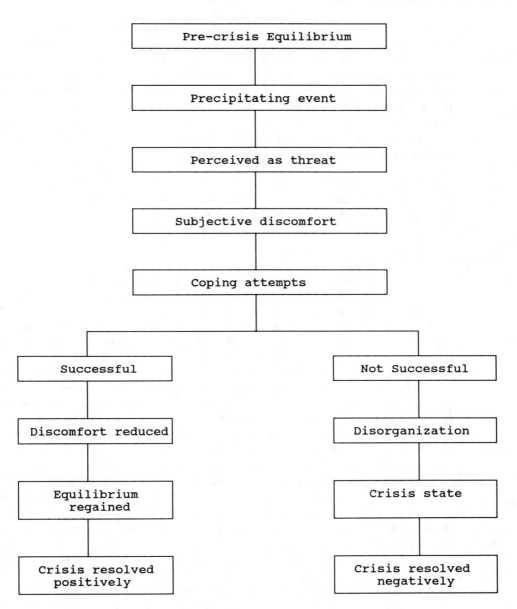

Figure 8-1 Crisis Process

can potentially provide support to members as they cope. Families can enable adaptive coping strategies, share in problem solving, encourage communication of feelings, buffer the impact of external stressors on the individual, and provide a sense of stability when other environmental factors are unstable (Dunst, Trivette, & Deal, 1988). Through its major socializing role, the family teaches coping and problem solving to its members. The strength of competence varies from one family to another, but most families play some supportive role for family members.

Social networks and community support resources also affect an individual's ability to cope. The availability of responsive helping resources can inspire the trust that is important for a person's perceived competence as well as provide material resources necessary for control of the stressor in some cases. Trained professionals and volunteers who can render crisis intervention and recovery services are part of the formal community support system of the survivor. Some survivors will master their situations without formal help, because their personal and social resources for effective coping are adequate. Other persons will look to formal helping resources for assistance as they work to regain competencies, grow through the stressful or traumatic experience with minimal residual damage, and develop new psychosocial strengths.

NATURE OF FAMILY VIOLENCE

The potency of family violence as a precipitator of psychosocial harm lies in the fact that the nature of the act is a direct affront to the competencies necesary for effective coping. That violence occurs in a family is a symptom of a family systems problem, indicating a reduced capacity for the family to function in a supportive role for the person who must cope. Thus the survivor's resources for coping are depleted by the act itself, leaving the survivor exposed and susceptible to the harmful effects of stress or the secondary effects of maladaptive coping resources.

Family violence can be broadly defined as covering a range of potentially harmful acts, including the use of physical force, sexual assault, neglect, and exploitation. The use of physical force includes direct assault, such as hitting and using a weapon on the body of the survivor, as well as indirect acts, such as restraint (e.g., locking in a closet) and destruction of pets or personal property. Sexual assault includes direct physical acts, such as rape and molestation, as well as indirect acts, such as making pornographic images, exhibitionism, and voyeurism. The threat of physical or sexual assault can induce psychosocial harm even if the act is not carried out. Neglect includes withholding food, health care, or economic resources, deprivation of rest, and failure to supervise dependent family members. Exploitation includes requiring family members to perform inappropriate roles (e.g., jobs that are illegal or unhealthy) and such acts as financial extortion. Neglect and exploitation may not be forceful acts, but the impact on the psyche and body of the survivor can be as severe as assaultive acts. A survivor is anyone who has lived through victimization by a family member or has been a vulnerable witness to another family member's victimization.

Acts of family violence may be chronic, such as chronic nutritional deprivation or repeated use of mild physical force by adults against one another or children in the family. The act may be extraordinary, as in the case of an exceptionally severe beating or near-starvation. If the act is sudden and unexpected, it may be perceived as catastrophic, particularly if it is life threatening. Any of these acts may precipitate a state of crisis or increased stress in the victim, leading to the risk of maladaptive coping responses.

The survivor's ability to cope successfully is hindered by several factors that tend to be present when victimization occurs in the family. These include the survivor's perceived isolation, violation of trust, risk of recurrence, and loss, or threat of loss, of home.

Survivors often perceive support from potential helping resources as ambivalent, leading to a pervasive feeling of isolation. The family as a whole is usually coping with the aftermath of the violence and the factors that precipitated it. Survivors often believe they cannot get help from other family members. Battered women, for example, have reported asking for help from extended family and being rejected (McEvoy, Brookings, & Brown, 1983). Abused children may perceive collusion among family members, even when only one is the perpetrator. Support through extended social networks such as friends and colleagues may be strained by family violence. For example:

Case Study

Gerhardt is a 72-year-old widower who lives with his 43-year-old daughter and her family. Gerhardt is nonambulatory since a stroke a year ago. Recently Gerhardt was left without food for a whole day. When the daughter came home, he asked for something to eat. She became verbally abusive and gave him cold soup with bread. When Gerhardt mentioned this incident to his son who lives across town, his son told him he should be grateful that the daughter takes care of him and that he should try not to bother her.

The isolation is intensified by ambivalent cultural messages from people in the family's community and formal helping resources. Family violence generally occurs within private boundaries. Cultural norms and, to some extent, legal standards in the United States dictate that a family's business is its own, that problems within the family should be resolved by the family. Survivors of all ages usually understand and accept these norms, and struggle to maintain the secrecy of the victimization. Thus disclosure of the victimization by the survivor to someone outside the family becomes a critical moment, one that can itself precipitate crisis, increased stress, or trauma. Survivors are at risk of "secondary victimization," harm that results from inappropriate responses from potential helping resources. Asking for help and not receiving it can be a crushing disappointment to someone who is already suffering intense stress related to victimization.

Disclosure may occur in many different ways. The survivor may ask for help, as when a battered woman calls the police. Someone else may recognize the indicators of family violence, as when a teacher reports child abuse or neighbors call the police about a spousal conflict. Survivors may be ill prepared for the response to the disclosure. They may feel blamed or manipulated. The type of help they want may not be the intervention that is offered, as when a sexually abused child wants her father to stop molesting her and the intervention takes her away from her home, a move she does not want. Throughout the literature on family violence, survivors' frustration with responses to requests for help and intense sense of isolation are major themes. The combination of ambivalent family and community support can be a significant deterrent to healthy coping for the family violence survivor.

Certain forms of family violence involve deception by the perpetrator. Sexual abuse of children and financial exploitation of elderly family members are two situations in which deception plays a major role. In other cases, the perpetrator may offer well-intended assurances that are subsequently violated, as when the physically abusive parent or spouse promises to stop using force but continues to do so. The violation of trust implicit in this type of interaction can have devastating consequences for the victimized family member. Asking for and accepting support are healthy coping behaviors, but when a survivor has been deceived or repeatedly disappointed, mistrust can become generalized, and the help-seeking behaviors of the survivor are restricted.

Another factor that makes family violence an extraordinary stressor is its chronicity. Neglectful families are unpredictably available as providers of physical and emotional nurturance. Violent episodes recur—sometimes with predictability, sometimes erratically. The threat of harm is ever present in the physical and social environment of the survivor, and constant vigilance is required. Survivors sometimes cope by developing extraordinary behavioral patterns as a way of exerting control over their environment, such as the child who withdraws completely, refusing ever to speak, and the battered woman who develops a ritualized schedule for herself and her children that includes cleaning house in the middle of the night to avoid irritating the perpetrator.

Stress is further accentuated in family violence by the survivor's realization that her or his attachment to home and family, the primary sanctuary despite its faults, is in jeopardy. Child and adult survivors sometimes must flee home temporarily, often against their own wills. Survivors in these situations must cope with grief as well as with the fear that the loss will become permanent. The lack of predictability and stability of the home may induce feelings of powerlessness and lack of personal control. When the loss is permanent, the survivor becomes even more vulnerable to unresolved feelings and maladaptive coping. Survivors may lose family members to death by homicide or suicide, to imprisonment, or to permanent separation.

In some unfortunate cases the loss is compounded by the phenomenon that family violence is repeated in the new family system, as when child abuse recurs in a foster home, an abused elderly person is again abused in a nursing home, or a battered woman is revictimized in a new relationship. Revictimization or adjustment problems may lead to another loss of home. Victims are at risk of developing serious attachment disorders when such loss and vulnerability are present.

As this review of selected factors unique to family violence has indicated, being victimized in one's own family not only can cause immediate physical and psychosocial harm but also drastically impedes the ability of the survivor to cope with the aftermath of victimization. Following is a summary of the damage that can result.

CONSEQUENCES OF FAMILY VIOLENCE

Research to document the consequences of family violence is fragmented, organized according to the nature of the precipitating act and the target of the abuse. While one can review studies about the impact of specific forms of child or adolescent maltreatment, spousal violence, and elder abuse on the survivor, it is difficult to draw conclusions about victims of family violence in general with precision about the nature and prevalence of the impact. However, by reviewing the fragmented literature, one can identify general themes that suggest the kinds of harm done by various forms of family violence.

Survivors obviously are at risk of physical harm, including direct injury, disability, and even death. They suffer physical stress reactions such as fatigue, insomnia, and headaches. They also suffer material losses such as loss of property, economic support, and access to basic necessities (food, shelter, clothing). These physical and material needs lead victims to require assistance and sometimes even long-term service, as in the case of permanent disability.

Some of the most damaging consequences of surviving family violence are psychological and social, which is the emphasis here. Survivors may develop negative affective, cognitive, behavioral, and social symptoms (Bolton & Bolton, 1987; Figley, 1985; Lystad, 1986; Walker, 1984; Yin, 1985). Affectively, survivors may express sadness and depression, reporting limited ability to experience pleasure. They may feel chronically anxious or "numb" or vacillate between the two feelings. Anger, including anger displaced toward persons other than the perpetrator, hopelessness, and loneliness may be persistent.

Cognitively, the survivor may develop a negative view of the world that is based on the generalized appraisal that the world is a bad place. Fearful ideation about everyday phenomena is common and may escalate to become flashbacks, nightmares, and intrusive images of death and destruction. Perceived control over environmental influences is likely to be low, causing survivors to describe themselves as "powerless." Often they minimize their perceptions of threat by denying the severity of the violence and the potential for harm as well as by denying the emotional impact on themselves. The survivor may develop a negative self-concept, including attributing self-blame for the victimization. Body image may become negative. In some cases, sexual identity may become confused. The problem-solving capacity of the survivor may be restricted by confused thoughts, disorganized consideration of various options for action, and a pervasive sense that there are no feasible solutions to life's problems. These negative and disorganized cognitions are reinforced when unsuccessful attempts are made to seek help or solve the problem, leading to a cluster of symptoms known as "learned helplessness" (Walker, 1984). These cognitive messages, when combined with the cluster of negative emotions, can lead a survivor to feel exhausted and to give up trying to stop the probability of repeated family victimization or to resolve the negative aftermath.

Behaviorally, the survivor may lead a restricted life, limiting routine activities to those over which he or she perceives some degree of control. Some survivors become highly dependent on others. Those who cope with chronic threat of harm develop ways of responding to cues that the risk of assault may be escalating. Some replicate the perpetrator's behaviors, for example, the manipulated incest survivor becomes manipulative, or the controlled wife becomes controlling of her children. Some cope with their negative emotions and cognitions by using behaviors that, at least temporarily, change their perceptions and feelings, such as use of chemical substances, thrill-seeking behavior, and aggression toward others. Suicide attempts are higher in the survivor population than in the general population. As noted earlier, these maladaptive behaviors can have negative consequences of their own.

Socially, survivors may be detached and isolated. They may have difficulty forming intimate relationships, including parent-child attachments. Their trust of others tends to be low. The potential for conflict in relationships is high when one of the parties is a family violence survivor who has not positively resolved the victimization. Some resort to shallow serial sexual relationships for attachment. Survivors are susceptible to entering exploitive relationships, leading to revictimization.

In severe cases, the survivor may develop posttraumatic stress disorder, a cluster of symptoms that may include intrusive memories causing reexperience of the stressor, numb affect or social withdrawal, hyperalertness, sleep disturbances, guilt, thought disturbances, and sensitivity to events similar to the stressor (American Psychiatric Association, 1981). For example:

Case Study

When Simon was 11, he spent a week with his 19-year-old uncle at college. The two shared his uncle's single room in the dorm. During the week, Simon was sexually fondled by his uncle. He never spoke of the incident to anyone. When Simon left for college at 18, he moved into a dorm room with a roommate he did not know. Starting with the first night, he could not sleep. As evening drew near, he would begin to sweat. As he lay in his bed, he envisioned his uncle in his roommate's bed. During the day he would have intrusive memories of the molestation. At night he was paralyzed with fear. By the end of the first week at school, he was near exhaustion. His roommate sat up and leaned forward one night, asking him what was wrong. Simon responded by punching him in the face with his fist. The dorm counselor referred Simon to the student counseling center, where he was diagnosed as suffering from post-traumatic stress disorder.

Child survivors may react in ways that are analogous to the symptoms for adults noted above, only the manifestations are developmentally linked (Ammerman, Cassisi, Hersen, & Van Hasselt, 1986; Augustinos, 1987; Browne & Finkelhor, 1985; Erickson & Egeland, 1987; Mowbray, 1988; Wolfe, 1987; Wolfe, Wolfe, & Best, 1988). Preschool children are likely to be fearful and sick, showing compulsive or restitutive play and regressed behavior (e.g., separation anxiety, enuresis). School-age children may have these symptoms as well as anger, social withdrawal or aggression, guilt, depression, underachievement, and self-deprecation. Adolescents may be fearful but otherwise unlike the preschool children. They may have many of the same symptoms as school-age children but also may be apathetic and/or anxious, express rationalizations about the victimization, and act out or exhibit personality changes if the victimization began during adolescence. Children and youth may be hindered in their efforts to attain a sense of competence and mastery when their primary environment is so controlling and unpredictable.

The probability that any of these psychosocial harms will affect a particular survivor is mediated by a number of factors. One, of course, is the general coping strength of the individual, based on personal characteristics and social support. The nature of the stressor itself makes a difference, with intrusive acts such as sexual assault, use of severe physical force, and psychological torture inducing the greatest harm, as do sudden onset and severe force. The survivor's relationship to the perpetrator makes a difference, with the most severe damage related to intimate relationships in which trust is violated. The survivor's previous victimization in another family system will affect how he or she copes; if the victimization was resolved in a positive direction, the survivor will be better prepared to handle a new assault. If it was not, serious consequences can evolve.

Some survivors develop none of the symptoms described above. Others experience the feelings, cognitions, and behaviors for a period of time and then move beyond them to a new state of being. Survivors have resolved their victimization when they are able to feel relaxed, connected to others, and in control of their anger. They can experience pleasure in a variety of ways. They have positive self-esteem, perceive themselves to be whole, and are free from intrusive negative thoughts. Their belief in their ability to exert personal power in the world is adequate, as is their confidence about their problem-solving capacity. They engage in positive health and safety behaviors and are able to form and maintain social relationships, including intimate bonds. They essentially are able to express competencies that they may have had prior to the victimization or can develop as they cope with the aftermath.

CRISIS AND RECOVERY INTERVENTIONS

No magical intervention can minimize the pain of the victimization itself. The survivor has no choice but to confront the reality of what happened. The goal of crisis and recovery interventions is to help the survivor grow through the pain and beyond, to avert residual damage and promote new strengths for coping with the memories and future similar challenges.

Any survivor should be able to ask for and receive help in coping with family violence, although not all survivors will need help. This section describes three levels of assistance. The first is psychological first aid, which is a basic helping skill that anyone with minimal interpersonal skills can learn. Public awareness efforts about all forms of family violence during the past three decades have emphasized that anyone should be able to recognize the indicators of family violence. The survivor's initial contact may be with a friend or colleague or someone from a formal agency, such as a law enforcement officer, teacher, or crisis telephone worker. Anyone may be the first help contact for a survivor, so training in how to respond is important.

The second level is survivor need assessment and empathic support, which all human service agencies should be prepared to do. Many agencies designate workers to assume survivor functions, as when police departments, mental health centers, and hospitals have victim specialists. Survivors may present for help years after the victimization, with indirect presenting problems such as depression or substance abuse. Whether the victimization is recent or distant, an appraisal of how the event(s) affected the survivor's life is important for targeted recovery intervention. Survivors also need information, advocacy, and companionship, particularly when going through legal proceedings or dealing with multiple agencies.

The third level, recovery intervention, requires greater skill in psychoeducation and psychotherapy. Examples of interventions at each level are briefly reviewed here. Ideally, survivors will receive coordinated assistance from the many specialized agencies that may be involved. Many communities have formed survivor services networks and assessment/treatment teams to promote interdisciplinary and interagency collaboration for the good of the client.

Crisis Intervention

Crisis intervention is recommended for all initial contacts between helping persons and survivors, even though many survivors will not experience crisis. The strategies are effective in establishing initial rapport, gathering sufficient information for a short-term assessment, and averting a potential state of crisis.

Whether a family violence survivor enters a state of crisis depends on such factors as how threatened the survivor feels, her or his confidence in being able to emerge safely from the situation, and the degree of social support available. The following situations are particularly intense for family violence survivors, so they may be considered indicators of potential high risk for crisis:

> physical and emotional exhaustion of the survivor due to cumulative stressors
> severity of actual or threatened harm, particularly sexual assault or use of potentially lethal force
> first-time disclosure of the violence outside the family
> high probability of leaving home or family dissolution, even if temporary
> discovery or realization by the survivor that he or she has been deceived
> initiation of court proceedings involving the survivor

People in crisis can be recognized by their expressed personal discomfort and apparent disorganization (Borgman, Edmunds, & MacDicken, 1979; Halpern, 1973; Hoff, 1984; Lazarus, 1976; Roberts, 1990; Slaikeu, 1984). Figure 8-2 describes common symptoms, using a case example of a mother in crisis due to her child's abuse. Persons in crisis tend to be emotionally aroused and highly anxious; often they are weepy. Occasionally they will act extremely controlled and noncommunicative as a way of coping with high anxiety, but most often they will express despair, grief, embarrassment, and anger. Their thoughts are disorganized, lead-

This case is based on a call to a crisis hotline.

Facts: Three days ago Doris discovered her husband in the act of sexually fondling their 4-year-old daughter. Doris immediately took the child and her 2-year-old sister to Doris's mother's house, where she and the children have stayed.

Affect: Doris is obviously upset when she calls. Her voice is trembling. She says she is afraid of what is going to happen; afraid of Murray and afraid of the future in general. She feels physically safe at her mother's, but she is irritated with her mother, who tends to fuss at the children. Doris has not told her mother what happened, she just says she and Murray had a fight. Doris wants to talk about her mother. Her affect fluctuates quickly between anger at her mother and sadness about what Murray has done. She avoids talking about the abuse, seems to be embarrassed, and says, "I can't believe it happened." She is irritated that the children are asking to see their father.

Sensations: Doris did not sleep last night and does not feel like eating.

Thoughts/ Images: Doris keeps repeating, "I don't know what to do." She believes Murray is mentally ill. Her major plan is to get bus tickets for herself and her children to flee to another state, where she will stay with her former college roommate. She does not plan to tell the roommate she is coming. She will get a job there and never see Murray again.

Behavior: Doris says she is too upset to take care of the kids. It is 1:00 p.m. and they are still in their pajamas. Her mother has been fixing their meals. Doris will not speak to her daughter about the fondling because she wants her to forget about it. Doris impulsively decides that if she calls Murray's boss, whom she has known since childhood, and tells him about what Murray has done, then maybe Murray will be shamed into getting psychiatric help.

Social / Interpersonal Behavior: Doris fluctuates between speaking harshly to her children and hugging them close to her. She and her mother argue whenever Doris comes out of the bedroom. Doris cannot remember the name of the agency she is calling, since she closed the phone book after she dialed the number. She repeatedly asks the crisis worker, whose name she cannot remember even though she has been told twice, "What should I do?"

Figure 8–2   Case Example: Crisis Precipitated by Child Abuse

ing to trouble in relating ideas, events, and actions. They may overlook important details, or may jump from one idea to another, making communication hard to follow. They may confuse fears and wishes with reality. Persons in crisis may not be able to perform routine behaviors such as basic grooming. They may avoid eye contact, and may mumble. Some persons may act impulsively. People in crisis have reported feelings of fatigue as well as appetite and sleep disruptions. They are socially vulnerable, which means that a helper can have significant influence, but so can people with exploitive motives. People in crisis act in ways similar to people with certain forms of chronic mental illness, but it must be emphasized that the crisis state is time limited, usually lasting no more than a few days to six weeks.

Depending on their developmental level, children display signs of crisis that are analogous to adult symptoms (Smith, 1984; Wolfe, Jaffe, Wilson, & Zak, 1985). They are likely to display random, manic activity, including aggressiveness. Often they have an insatiable craving for attention, and cling to caretakers. They may have sleep difficulties, including enuresis. Usually their ability to cope is directly related to the coping of the adult to whom they are primarily attached. The child who is temporarily out of home must cope with adjustment to a new environment as well as with the history of violence and the separation.

Psychological first aid is a process that anyone can learn (Slaikeu, 1984). Crisis helpers must essentially be empathic, able to listen actively, able to focus the survivor's immediate problem and to assess resources, and knowledgeable about community resources. The goals of psychological first aid are to help the survivor feel supported and able to cope and to link the survivor with resources for longer-term support. A significant point is that the goal of crisis intervention is not to solve the family violence problem; rather, it is to manage the state of crisis and promote a competent approach to the challenge of solving the broader problem. Psychological first aid is a first step, to be followed by other interventions.

Psychological first aid tends to take from 20 minutes to 3 hours. When such intervention is done with a child, the child's ability to understand, feelings of solitude, and lack of personal power should be considered. The process takes place through successive stages found in any problem-solving process (adapted from Roberts, 1990; Slaikeu, 1984; Hoff, 1984):

Stage 1: Establish psychological and emotional contact.

> *Goal:* Survivor feels heard, understood, and accepted. Intensity of emotional distress reduced. Problem-solving ability reactivated.

The worker listens actively. Most survivors have been coping remarkably well with their situations; they need to hear spoken support for their strength and courage. The focus is on how the survivor feels, not on actions that might be taken. The worker lends calm control to an intense situation. This first stage leads to establishment of rapport, the mutual feeling that the two people are interested in and understand one another.

Stage 2: Explore dimensions of the problem.

> *Goal:* Person in crisis can distinguish immediate needs and needs that can be addressed through later action.

The crisis worker inquires about the nature of the problem, asking questions, if necessary, as the survivor relates the story. Useful information includes who was involved (e.g., perpetrator, other victims, witnesses, helpers), what happened, where it happened, whether the survivor is immediately safe, how the survivor is handling the problem now, how the survivor has handled it in the past.

After gathering the information, the crisis worker ascertains what the survivor believes to be the immediate problem and then shares his or her own perception of what the immediate problem is with the survivor. In many cases, the immediate need is for safety. When the survivor minimizes the threat of harm, the worker may need to help her or him understand the danger and need for protection.

An important issue at this stage is assessment of lethality. A survivor may feel so overwhelmed by the situation that she or he believes suicide or homicide is the only way out. Scales are available to facilitate assessment of lethality (Hoff, 1978), to aid the worker in exploring such issues as whether the survivor has considered killing her- or himself or another person, has or did have a plan to do so, has the means to do so, or has a history of having attempted to do so. The crisis worker takes a directive stance if lethality risk is high.

This stage is complete when the crisis worker and the survivor have agreed about what problem needs to be addressed immediately and what can be handled later.

Stage 3: Examine possible solutions.

Goal: Survivor identifies and accepts one or more solutions to immediate and later needs.

The worker begins by asking the survivor to identify alternative actions that can be taken to address the immediate needs. Prompts may help, such as "What have you considered or done thus far?" "What can you do?" "What else can you do?" "What might happen if you try to . . .?" The worker may offer additional suggestions, using this time to educate the survivor about available resources. The worker may need to initiate a list of actions with depressed survivors who believe there are no options. The availability of social support is discussed and included in the plan for action.

Solutions to immediate and later needs should be distinguished. During crisis is no time to initiate actions such as divorce, termination of parental rights, getting a new job, or moving to another town. These are long-term solutions that require careful deliberation.

Advantages and disadvantages to various immediate actions should be discussed, and obstacles to action identified. The survivor's understanding of resources should be explored, since persons in crisis tend to have magical thinking about being rescued and may assume that a resource can help more than it can, leading to disillusionment.

This stage ends when the worker and survivor have agreed on an action plan, including safety measures, that the survivor will follow. The plan is focused on the immediate problem, appropriate for the survivor's functional level, consistent with life-style and culture, inclusive of social networks, realistic, time limited, concrete, and adaptable.

Stage 4: Assist in taking concrete action.

Goal: The survivor accomplishes what is necessary to meet immediate needs.

In a situation where lethality is not likely, the worker's role is primarily that of backup support and provider of information. The survivor is capable of acting on his or her own behalf; the worker should encourage the survivor to assume control of the action plan, avoiding the inclination to "rescue" the survivor. The worker must take care not to pass judgment on what the survivor chooses to do, even if the choice is not one the worker would have made.

In a situation where lethality is likely, the worker assumes a more directive role. In these cases, the worker actively mobilizes resources such as the police or other emergency services.

Stage 5: Prepare for follow-up.

Goal: Feedback is secured on how adequate the support to the survivor is, whether linkages to resources were made, and whether lethality was reduced.

Linkages for resources to help nonimmediate needs can begin to be made. Before the end of the psychological first aid session, the worker secures identifying information so that the survivor can be contacted again. The possibility of making a follow-up contact should be explored. Survivors sometimes ask that a fictitious name be used and specify limited availability for recontact because they do not want the perpetrator to know that a helping resource has been contacted.

These procedures operationalize the precepts that have been summarized previously; that is, people have competent ability to cope and can master their abilities when temporarily lost due to crisis if appropriate help is offered.

Assessment

After the survivor has expressed some degree of increased personal control as a result of psychological first aid, a more comprehensive assessment of need can begin. The purpose of the assessment is to determine how the crisis is affecting all parts of the survivor's life, so that a plan for recovery intervention can be developed and the survivor can begin to face the future. Comprehensive assessment covers the survivor's physical, affective, interpersonal, cognitive, behavioral, and legal situations. One goal of assessment is to differentiate normal from pathological reactions. Figure 8–3 illustrates two alternative resolutions of crisis due to battering—one adaptive, the other maladaptive. Recovery services are most effective if they are initiated during the crisis period.

In some cases of family violence, the assessment also serves the purpose of collecting evidence for legal purposes. Legal proceedings may be of long-term benefit to the survivor by increasing protection and/or promoting perpetrator treatment, but in the short term the evidentiary demands are often intrusive and can aggravate the survivor's crisis. The comprehensive collection of information requires the potential involvement of numerous individuals from various disciplines, such as medicine, social work, nursing, and law enforcement. Many emergency service settings, such as hospital emergency rooms, child protection programs, and battered women's shelters (Bross, Krugman, Lenherr, Rosenberg, & Schmitt, 1988; Klingbeil & Boyd, 1984), have developed protocols to ease the demands on the survivor while comprehensive information is collected.

A comprehensive assessment will thoroughly cover information about the precipitating event, presenting problem(s), social environmental context of the crisis, precrisis functioning of the survivor, and current functioning of the survivor. The protocol usually provides a checklist of pertinent documents to complete at this time, such as photographs/X-rays of injuries, consent forms, and forms for filing criminal charges. The protocol identifies the roles of particular professionals and agency representatives as well as appropriate agencies to be contacted on behalf of the survivor. Ideally, the survivor will be interviewed only once, either by a team or by a professional acting on behalf of the team. The protocol includes a list of possible persons (by relation) to contact on behalf of the survivor. The comprehensive assessment is the basis for developing a plan for recovery services.

Recovery Intervention

The goals of recovery intervention are to help survivors restabilize their lives and grow more healthy and to deter pathology. Recovery may require considerable

Sharon, a divorced teacher, is regarded by her friends as an independent person. Her daily routine involves household chores, going to work, watching TV at night. Her friends regard her as pleasant, though she seldom expresses her feelings.

Sharon's ex-husband Ted moves back to town. Within two days he comes to her apartment, starts an argument, and beats her.

Sharon drives herself to the emergency room and is treated for a fractured wrist. She is afraid Ted will kill her if she calls the police. She returns home, embarrassed to tell her friends or family. At work she says she was in an accident. Sharon begins to feel confused and afraid that Ted will return, even though he said she disgusted him and he never wanted to see her again.

Sharon feels alone. Her memories of former fear and beatings by Ted occupy her thoughts. She cannot concentrate on her work. She does not sleep well and does not feel like preparing meals.

Adaptive	*Maladaptive*
Sharon calls a friend. She tells her the situation and describes her past. The friend comes over and offers Sharon a place to stay for a few days.	Sharon stays home from work. She is beginning to feel paranoid, afraid Ted may come at any minute. She considers buying a gun to protect herself.
Sharon feels relieved.	Sharon feels she may be going crazy. She feels exhausted and does not want to see anyone.
Sharon feels more in control. She decides to file charges, at least having the district attorney warn Ted to stay away from her.	Sharon stays in her bedroom with the door closed. She feels like killing herself and Ted. She feels overwhelmed and alone.
Sharon has learned new skills: She can ask for and get help from friends and formal systems.	After several days, Ted does not come. Calls from the school cause Sharon to take care of herself and go back to work. She settles into a lonely routine, more withdrawn than before. She feels that her life is worthless and wonders why she bothers to live.

Figure 8-3   Case Example: Two Ways a Crisis Might Be Resolved for a Battered Woman

work—that is, time and energy—on the part of some survivors and their support systems. A variety of psychotherapeutic interventions have been demonstrated to be effective in promoting healthy recovery. Several specific methods are reviewed here.

Survivors generally have multiple recovery tasks. The crisis state must be resolved, if there is one. The survivor must adapt to immediate losses and changes created by the disclosure and protective response, when one occurs. The survivor must master the perceived state of victimization. And the fundamental family dysfunction that contributed to the victimization must be addressed.

Crisis therapy, which generally lasts only six weeks, involves the application of psychotherapeutic and educational interventions during the crisis period. The four tasks of crisis resolution are essentially as follows: to survive the crisis physically, to express feelings related to the crisis and any recent associated losses, to attain cognitive mastery of the experience, and to make behavioral and interpersonal adjustments necessary for future living (Slaikeu, 1984). Once the crisis is positively resolved, the survivor is likely to need longer-term, less intense recovery services to promote healthy long-term coping.

Information and support can help the survivor handle protective interventions. A support person or advocate can promote stability and security in a services system that may otherwise be unpredictable and manipulative. Clear information about all interventions can reduce uncertainty and promote accurate expectations. This is essential, particularly given the predictable disorganized thought and low trust of the highly stressed individual.

Recovery services are those that aid the survivor in resolving the long-term issues. Swift (1986) has noted the relevance of George Albee's (1982) prevention model to family violence prevention. This model, which can be conceptualized as an equation that summarizes the association of the major factors in stress and stress management with dysfunction, has relevance to recovery intervention as tertiary prevention. As adapted by Swift, the model is as follows:

$$\text{incidence of dysfunction} = \frac{\text{stress} + \text{risk factors}}{\text{social supports} + \text{coping skills} + \text{self-esteem}}$$

Holistic recovery intervention targets all the variables in the equation. The goal is to minimize the strength of factors in the numerator and maximize the factors in the denominator for the lowest probability of dysfunction. A description of sample interventions, using these variables as an organizing framework, follows.

Stress reduction. Interventions to reduce stress are generally of two types: those designed to help the person prevent or manage actual stress and those aimed at eliminating or reducing the potency of the stressor.

As noted above, victimization by family violence can induce some of the most intense subjective stress known to humans. A variety of techniques to promote wellness of mind, body, and spirit have been used with survivors with demonstrated effectiveness (Mervin & Smith-Kurtz, 1988). Such techniques include *physical activity,* which should be initiated as soon as possible after the victimization. The activity can help to discharge repressed energy and promotes the survivor's perceived control over body functions and positive body image. Physically injured survivors should have their activity regimes prescribed by a health professional. *Nutrition* has important physiological effects in promoting recovery, although survivors may demonstrate initial eating disturbances, such as loss of appetite or overeating. *Spiritual support,* including religious counseling for persons who value religious beliefs and activities to promote any survivor's sense of integrity with the natural world, can help to sharpen the survivor's senses and promote a cognitive framework for understanding the stressor. Bibliotherapy, art therapy, and music therapy can help promote spiritual wellness. *Relaxation* is essential for survivors, many of whom have developed hypervigilance, and can be encouraged through a variety of cognitive and physical techniques. *Pleasure activities* that promote a perceived sense of fun and humor are critical to survivor growth. Many survivors of chronic victimization cannot initially identify any source of pleasure in their lives and report no memory of ever having felt happy. Helping them to probe their memories for what has brought pleasure is an important starting point. Education about sexuality and sexual relationships may be required before survivors can perceive their sexuality to be a source of pleasure, particularly for sexual assault survivors. *Stimulating and creative activities* help the survivor to be productive, and thus to feel competent, or to experience alternative physiological sensations to the numbness and anxiety that may pervade their existence.

    Stressor abatement. Although family violence has a complex etiology, the immediate act that precipitates the survivor's stress is the violent or exploitive behavior of the perpetrator(s). Interventions to eliminate or change the behavior are thus focused on the perpetrator. Many of the interventions rely on law enforcement and *legally based protective interventions* (particularly for children, handicapped persons, and dependent elders). Unfortunately, this form of intervention is unreliable in reducing the stressor and sometimes introduces new stressors with which the survivor must cope, so the total potency of the stressor(s) is increased, at least temporarily. For example, the temporary jail detention of an assaultive family member may stop the violence, but his or her absence from the home and anticipation of long-term implications of the removal creates new stressors for the family. The external control inherent in the legal system is countertherapeutic to the needs of the survivor unless the control is carefully used to help empower the survivor. When the protective action produces long-term reduction of violent acts, then the total power of the stressor(s) is reduced. Sometimes the only resolution is permanent removal of a family member, which may occur through divorce or termination of parental rights.

    A variety of *psychoeducational and therapeutic interventions* have been developed to change *perpetrator behavior,* many of which have produced an actual decrease in violent or exploitive behavior (Bolton & Bolton, 1987; Giaretto, 1982; Goldstein, Keller, & Erne, 1985; Guerney, 1986; Isaacs, 1982; Lutzker, 1984; Sonkin, Martin, & Walker, 1985; Wodarski, 1981). Interventions tend to be designed for particular forms of maltreatment, such as neglect, use of physical force, or sexual assault. Generally, interventions include components designed to increase the knowledge and skills of the perpetrator with regard to family roles, such as spouse, parent, or caregiver to an elderly parent. Support to perpetrators in fulfilling these roles and coping with associated emotions is provided through individual and group work.

REDUCTION OF RISK FACTORS

Risk factors associated with the probability of family violence are embedded in personal characteristics of the survivor and the perpetrator, the family system, and the broader social and physical environment of the family (Belsky, 1980; Mann, Lauderdale, & Iscoe, 1983). Levy, Sheldon, & Conte (1986) offer a succinct list of the numerous factors that are hypothesized to be associated with child abuse alone. Risk is often associated with poor interactions within the family or inadequate person-environment fit. Prominent among the personal characteristics of survivors that are correlated with higher incidence of family violence are special status of children (e.g., developmental disability, stepchild) and status inconsistency for battered women (i.e., the woman's social and economic status are higher than her spouse's). The perpetrator's history of violence, neglect, or exploitation in his or her family of origin and abuse of chemical substances are major correlates of using violence in the family. The family that is isolated, has poor communication skills, and is of low socioeconomic status is at greater risk. Community and societal risk factors include low availability of formal and informal support, economic depression, high workplace demands on employed family members, tolerant attitudes toward use of aggression by members of the community, and nonassertive political leadership in addressing the problem.

Interventions to reduce the prevalence and impact of these risk factors include those that change the risk factor itself and those that prepare individuals to cope adequately with the presence of the factors. Examples are *interventions that strengthen the family,* such as economic support, health and mental health care, adequate housing, and neighborhood social organizations. *Broad-scale interventions* are those that aim to change community attitudes about family violence, influence policymakers, and persuade the public and its representatives to increase allocations for formal helping agencies. Moderating the impact of risk factors is essential for promoting a supportive recovery environment for the survivor.

Risk-reduction intervention for individuals are generally educational, designed to teach how to avoid and manage high-risk situations. Training in interpersonal and family conflict resolution, personal safety practices (including physical and verbal self-defense), and preparation for life transitions such as change in family composition or loss of job are examples of these interventions.

MAXIMIZATION OF SOCIAL SUPPORTS

People who cope alone often develop long-term physical and psychosocial stress symptoms. Cultural norms in the United States dictate that individuals receive their primary social support from families. When the family fails or struggles with this responsibility, as in the case of family violence, efforts must be made to build social support.

Family violence has an impact on all family members, even when one member is the primary target. Sometimes family members are so occupied with their own pain that they do not or cannot assist other family members. *Family systems intervention* to help the whole family cope with its stress and support the survivor is possible in some families. In some family violence cases the family dissolves, and family systems intervention is appropriate for the new fragmented units, which may be such combinations as sibling groups without parents, isolated siblings, parents without children, and parents in different households. Even when the family structure breaks down, the family violence survivor needs to receive support from other family members.

Intervention with extended family members and social networks can increase the survivor's perceived social support. Programs that train anyone in how to be supportive to a friend or family member who experiences domestic violence or how to listen when a child discloses child abuse are significant examples of how to prepare potential natural helpers to be supportive when needed. Linking survivors with social activities such as exercise groups, church groups, and craft clubs can reduce their sense of isolation. Many survivors, when emotionally ready, have become part of volunteer services to other survivors, which has the effect of further increasing their own perceived support.

The most prevalent formal intervention is probably the *peer support group,* where family violence survivors, matched by age and nature of the violence, work together on coping with their situations and supporting one another. Most large communities in the United States now have ongoing battered women's groups, adolescent incest survivors' groups, and groups for adult survivors of childhood incest.

Many communities are also able to provide *individual support to survivors* through such programs as court-appointed child advocates, victim/witness assistants, parent aides, teen companions, and child friends. Prompt protective response by law enforcement officers who are also trained to give psychological first aid provides strong social support at some of the most critical moments. Resources to provide for individual survivor counseling by mental health professionals are increasing in some areas. Certainly the number of professionals trained to provide such assistance has increased in recent years.

MAXIMIZATION OF COPING SKILLS

Survivors must learn to reduce maladaptive coping responses and increase adaptive ones in the context of a *safe, therapeutic relationship* (Berliner & Wheeler, 1987; Figley, 1985; Gentry & Eaddy, 1980; Long, 1986; Ochberg, 1988). They may need help to master negative emotions such as guilt, fear, anger, depression, and low perceived control. Cognitive-behavior therapy is a popular approach to facilitate affective control and mastery of the victimization, although a variety of psychotherapeutic techniques are used with survivors. Some survivors may need special help, such as substance abuse treatment, systematic desensitization to overcome fears, or reality therapy to overcome denial, magical thinking, and belief in negative myths about victimization.

Behaviorally, survivors also may need to learn basic social skills and how to master neglected developmental tasks. Because of pervasive family dysfunction, some have not adequately learned basic *problem solving,* that is, how to assess a problem realistically, consider alternative solutions and their consequences, choose a feasible solution, actively pursue it, and evaluate the outcome. In such people, *decision-making skills* to facilitate gathering information from those affected by a decision and selecting the most appropriate action may be weak. *Basic communication and assertiveness skills* such as sending clear messages, actively listening, and feeding back may be needed. Skill in *nonviolent conflict resolution,* including anger management and alternatives to corporal punishment as well as other conflict management skills, is deficient in many family violence survivors. *Help-seeking skills*—that is, knowing how to identify appropriate sources of help and how to ask for help—are needed by those survivors who have low trust and a history of disappointment by others.

Survivors often get stuck at immature developmental levels because they do not have the information or skill to move ahead. Many programs offer *education about family roles* to facilitate personal growth and responsibility. For example, teaching parents to be empathic to children and to fulfill roles appropriate to the age of the child is a common treatment for child abuse or neglect. Teaching spouses to appreciate gender roles within the family and to promote role flexibility where necessary is also common. Child survivors may need guidance in how to find pleasure through play; innovative programs teach formerly maltreating parents to play with their children.

Interventions for child survivors must, of course, be developmentally appropriate. For young children, whose communication is primarily behavioral rather than verbal, play and art are often used as therapeutic media. Older children are often treated in groups to reduce their sense of isolation and scapegoating.

After the recovery from victimization has been initiated for the individual survivor, the matter of long-standing personal and family problems, some of which may have precipitated the violence, must be confronted. The family might be reestablished. Even if it is not, the survivor is likely to maintain attachment and at least limited interaction. Controversy exists among professionals about how soon this intervention should take the form of couples or family therapy (Neidig & Friedman, 1984). Some programs begin recovery services with such intervention, but most await the perpetrator's acceptance of responsibility for the victimization and the survivor's attainment of some degree of perceived personal control before initiating joint therapy. In cases in which family members are temporarily or permanently removed from the home, the survivor must work on redefining the family.

MAXIMIZATION OF POSITIVE SELF-ESTEEM

Although not all survivors suffer from low self-esteem, it is prevalent among abusive parents, abused children, and the survivors and perpetrators of spouse abuse. Since it may be intrinsic in the family system, it can be resistant to change and thus difficult to treat.

Self-concept is based in one's beliefs about the characteristics one possesses. Self-concept comes partially from a realistic appraisal of information about oneself communicated by others in one's environment, such as family members (Heller & Swindle, 1983). Self-esteem is the value one places on oneself. Family violence survivors may have problems with both self-concept and self-esteem. Their self-concepts are often diffuse because repeated forced intrusion into their personal space has led them to have difficulty differentiating themselves from others and developing integrated identities. They are thus often excessively dependent on people in their environment who are sending clear negative messages to them about their worth. Survivors' self-esteem may be low in part because they have been given direct family or community messages that they have done something wrong or are "bad" or "worthless." Often survivors report feeling dirty and defiled, particularly if the violation was highly intrusive, as in sexual abuse.

Self-esteem can be enhanced by feelings of competence, but the family violence survivor has seldom received affirmation of achievements from within the family. The survivor's inability to control the family violence reinforces perceptions of weak efficacy. The survivor often focuses on failures and sometimes cannot begin to identify personal achievements and strengths. The demands of coping with victimization deplete the survivor's energy, contributing to such effects as poor school achievement for children and low work performance for adults, which further depresses their self-esteem.

Recovery services to promote positive self-esteem and integrated self-concept must be handled delicately. These perceptions are based in survivors' realistic appraisals of what other people believe about them. The message that others (e.g., recovery workers) do care about and admire them must be genuine. Survivors need to hear that they are not to blame and that they are unconditionally worthy of affection from others and themselves. Recovery workers must be able to communicate such affection and to enable others to do so, such as family members and peers in support groups.

Intervention can also focus on the survivor's negative cognitions by training the survivor to recognize personal strengths and achievements. Behavioral reinforcers, such as verbal acknowledgment of minor accomplishments and celebrations of major ones, can also be effective. Simple recognition of successful survival can have a strong impact on the survivor's self-esteem.

When the survivor has achieved a satisfactory level of adjustment, recovery services can be terminated. A periodic *psychosocial needs checkup,* depending on the developmental level of the survivor, is recommended.

CONCLUSION

As an extraordinary or catastrophic stressor, family violence imposes excessive coping demands on survivors of any age. Recovery requires a combination of the survivor's hard work and the commitment by formal and informal helpers to promote a healthy recovery environment. The societal recognition of the responsibility to be effectively supportive to survivors and their families is a critical ingredient in the reduction of stress and prevention of serious psychosocial dysfunction. Helping professionals can provide coordinated, skilled intervention for crisis resolution, needs assessment, support, and recovery. Family violence survivors can neither change nor forget their history, but they do not have to be alone as they confront the future.

REFERENCES

ALBEE, G. W. (1982). "Preventing Psychopathology and Promoting Human Potential." *American Psychologist, 37,* 1043–1050.

American Psychiatric Association. (1981). *Diagnostic and Statistical Manual of Mental Disorders* (3d ed.). Washington, D.C.

AMMERMAN, R. T., J. E. CASSISSI, M. HERSEN, and V. B. VAN HASSELT. (1986). "Consequences of Physical Abuse and Neglect in Children." *Clinical Psychology Review, 6,* 291–310.

AUGUSTINOS, M. (1987). "Developmental Effects of Child Abuse: Recent Findings." *Child Abuse and Neglect, 11,* 15–27.

BELSKY, J. (1980). "Child Maltreatment: An Ecological Integration." *American Psychologist, 35,* 320–335.

BERLINER, L., and J. R. WHEELER. (1987). "Treating the Effects of Sexual Abuse on Children." *Journal of Interpersonal Violence, 2,* 415–434.

BOLTON, F. G., and S. R. BOLTON. (1987). *Working with Violent Families: A Guide for Clinical and Legal Practitoners.* Newbury Park, Calif.: Sage.

BORGMAN, R., M. EDMUNDS, and R. A. MACDICKEN. (1979). *Crisis Intervention: A Manual for Child Protective Workers.* Washington, D.C.: U.S. Department of Health, Education and Welfare, National Center on Child Abuse and Neglect.

BROSS, D. C., R. D. KRUGMAN, M. R. LENHERR, D. A. ROSENBERG, and B. D. SCHMITT. (1988). *The New Child Protection Team Handbook.* New York: Garland.

BROWNE, A., and D. FINKELHOR. (1985). "Impact of Child Sexual Abuse: A Review of the Research." *Psychological Bulletin, 99,* 66–77.

DUNST, C., C. TRIVETTE, and A. DEAL. (1988). *Enabling and Empowering Families: Principles and Guidelines for Practice.* Cambridge, Mass.: Brookline.

ERICKSON, M. F., and B. EGELAND. (1987). "A Developmental View of the Psychological Consequences of Maltreatment." *School Psychology Review, 16,* 156–168.

ETH, S., and R. S. PYNOOS (1985). "Developmental Perspective on Psychic Trauma in Childhood." In C. R. FIGLEY (Ed.), *Trauma and Its Wake: The Study and Treatment of Post-traumatic Stress Disorder.* New York: Brunner/Mazel.

FIGLEY, C. R. (Ed.). (1985). *Trauma and Its Wake: The Study and Treatment of Post-traumatic Stress Disorder.* New York: Brunner/Mazel.

GENRY, C. E., and V. B. EADDY. (1980). "Treatment of Children in Spouse-abusive Families." *Victimology, 5,* 240–250.

GIARETTO, H. (1982). *Integrated Treatment of Child Sexual Abuse: A Treatment and Training Manual.* Palo Alto, Calif.: Science and Behavior Books.

GOLDBERGER, L., and S. BREZNITZ (Eds.). (1982). *Handbook of Stress.* New York: Free Press.

GOLDSTEIN, A. P., H. KELLER, and D. ERNE. (1985). *Changing the Abusive Parent.* Champaign, Ill.: Research Press.

GUERNEY, L. (1986). "Prospects for Intervention with Troubled Youth and Troubled Families." In J. GARBARINO, C. J. SCHELLENBACH, J. SEBES, and associates (Eds.), *Troubled Youth, Troubled Families: Understanding Families at Risk for Adolescent Maltreatment.* Hawthorne, N.Y.: Aldine.

HALPERN, H. A. (1973). "Crisis Theory: A Definitional Study." *Community Mental Health Journal, 9.*

HELLER, K., and R. W. SWINDLE (1983). "Social Networks, Perceived Social Support, and Coping with Stress." In R. D. FELNER, L. A. JASON, J. N. MORITSUGU, and S. S. FARBER (Eds.)., *Preventive Psychology: Theory, Research, and Practice.* Elmsford, N.Y.: Pergamon Press.

HOFF, L. A. (1984). *People in Crisis: Understanding and Helping.* Reading, Mass.: Addison-Wesley.

ISAACS, C. D. (1982). "Treatment of Child Abuse: A Review of the Behavioral Interventions." *Journal of Applied Behavior Analysis, 15,* 273–294.

KLINGBEIL, K. S., and V. D. BOYD. (1984). "Emergency Room Intervention: Detection, Assessment, and Treatment." In A. R. ROBERTS (Ed.), *Battered Women and Their Families: Intervention Strategies and Treatment Programs.* New York: Springer.

LAZARUS, A. A. (1976). *Multi-modal Behavior Therapy.* New York: Springer.

LEVY, H. B., S. H. SHELDON, and J. R. CONTE. (1986). "Special Intervention Programs for Child Victims of Violence." In M. LYSTAD (Ed.), *Violence in the Home: Interdisciplinary Perspectives.* New York: Brunner/Mazel.

LONG, S. (1986). "Guidelines for Treating Young Children." In K. MACFARLANE and J. WATERMAN (Eds.), *Sexual Abuse of Young Children: Evaluation and Treatment.* New York: Guilford Press.

LUTZKER, J. R. (1984). "Project 12-Ways: Treating Child Abuse and Neglect from an Ecobehavioral Perspective." In R. F. DANGEL and R. A. POLSTER (Eds.), *Parent Training: Foundations of Research and Practice.* New York: Guilford Press.

LYSTAD, M. (Ed.). (1986). *Violence in the Home: Interdisciplinary Perspectives.* New York: Brunner/Mazel.

MANN, P. A., M. LAUDERDALE, I. ISCOE. (1983). "Toward Effective Community-based Interventions in Child Abuse." *Professional Psychology: Research and Practice, 14,* 729–742.

MCEVOY, A., J. B. BROOKINGS, and C. E. BROWN (1983, February). "Responses to Battered Women: Problems and Strategies." *Social Casework,* pp. 92–96.

MERWIN, M. R., and B. SMITH-KURTZ. (1988). "Healing of the Whole Person." In F. M. OCHBERG (Ed.), *Post-traumatic Therapy and Victims of Violence.* New York: Brunner/Mazel.

MICKISH, J. E. (1985). "Elder Abuse." In J. E. HENDRICKS (Ed.), *Crisis Intervention: Contemporary Issues for On-Site Interveners.* Springfield, Ill.: Thomas.

MOOS, R. H., and A. G. BILLINGS. (1982). "Conceptualizing and Measuring Coping Resources and Processes." In L. GOLDBERGER and S. BREZNITZ (Eds.), *Handbook of Stress*. New York: Free Press.

MOWBRAY, C. T. (1988). "Post-traumatic Therapy for Children Who Are Victims of Violence." In F. M. OCHBERG (Ed.), *Post-traumatic Therapy and Victims of Violence*. New York: Brunner/Mazel.

NEIDIG, P. H., and D. H. FRIEDMAN. (1984). *Spouse Abuse: A Treatment Program for Couples*. Champaign, Ill.: Research Press.

OCHBERG, F. M. (Ed.). (1988). *Post-traumatic Therapy and Victims of Violence*. New York: Brunner/Mazel.

ROBERTS, A. R. (Ed.). (1990). *Crisis Intervention Handbook: Assessment, Treatment, and Research*. Belmont, Cal.: Wadsworth Publishing Co.

SLAIKEU, K. (1984). *Crisis Intervention: A Handbook for Practice and Research*. Boston: Allyn & Bacon.

SMITH, C. (1984). "Children in Crisis and Adolescents in Crisis." In E. H. JANOSIK (Ed.), *Crisis Counseling: A Contemporary Approach*. Belmont, Calif.: Wadsworth.

SONKIN, D. J., D. MARTIN, and L. E. A. WALKER. (1985). *The Male Batterer: A Treatment Approach*. New York: Springer.

SWIFT, C. (1986). "Preventing Family Violence: Family-focused Programs." In M. LYSTAD (Ed.), *Violence in the Home: Interdisciplinary Perspectives*. New York: Brunner/Mazel.

WALKER, L. E. (1984). *The Battered Woman Syndrome*. New York: Springer.

WODARSKI, J. S. (1981). "Comprehensive Treatment of Parents Who Abuse Their Children." *Adolescence, 16,* 959–972.

WOLFE, D. A. (1987). *Child Abuse: Implications for Child Development and Psychopathology*. Newbury Park, Calif.: Sage.

WOLFE, D. A., P. JAFFE, S. K. WILSON and L. ZAK. (1985). "Children of Battered Women: The Relation of Child Behavior to Family Violence and Maternal Stress. *Journal of Consulting and Clinical Psychology, 53,* 657–665.

WOLFE, D. A., V. V. WOLFE, and C. L. BEST. (1988). "Child Victims of Sexual Abuse." In V. B. VAN HASSELT, R. L. MORRISON, A. S. BELLACK, and M. HERSEN (Eds.), *Handbook of Family Violence*. New York: Plenum.

YIN, P. (1985). *Victimization and the Aged*. Springfield, Ill.: Thomas.

ZIMRIN, H. (1986). "A Profile of Survival." *Child Abuse and Neglect, 10,* 339–349.

Contemporary Prevention Strategies

Professionals working in the fields of public health, social work, and mental health distinguish among primary, secondary, and tertiary prevention. Tertiary prevention, known in the helping professions as crisis intervention, was the focus of Sections I and II of this book. We now turn our attention to ways in which clinicians and educators can provide services *before* individuals have such severe problems that they constitute a crisis.

Primary prevention is defined as planned activities designed and implemented to ensure that a particular problem never develops. Here are some examples of such activities:

> Primary prevention of teenage pregnancy and child abuse (before pregnancy occurs) by educating adolescent girls and boys about the many difficulties of parenthood, including information on financial burdens and loss of freedom
>
> Primary prevention of serious physical injuries resulting from certain types of automobile accidents by promoting safe, defensive driving
>
> Primary prevention of AIDS by providing age-appropriate education for all persons about safe sexual practices

Secondary prevention is defined as activities designed to stop a particular problem at a very early stage, before it has developed into a severe problem. Here are some examples of such activities:

> Secondary prevention of woman battering by providing counseling and education for men who have hit their mates for the first time

Secondary prevention of airplane crashes resulting from pilot error by identifying pilots who are under intense stress and providing them with a stress management program

In Chapter 9, Martin Bloom examines several definitions of primary prevention, which he interweaves into a general working definition of healthy and nonhealthy functioning with regard to physical and mental health and illness. Bloom then provides a discussion of preventive, treatment, and rehabilitative activities. The final section of this overview chapter illustrates the ways in which the health functioning continuum can be applied to prevent teenage pregnancy, suicide, child abuse, and AIDS.

Raising awareness of parental mistreatment and early intervention with new or at-risk parents has much potential for preventing emotional and physical abuse of children. In Chapter 10, Deborah Daro examines the research on the most effective prevention programs, including parenting enhancement programs, life skills training for children and young adults, support programs for new parents such as nurse home visitors, and child assault prevention education.

Parental mistreatment most frequently stems from an initial lack of awareness regarding the negative consequences of certain actions or inactions and a lack of knowledge or awareness of alternatives. For some number of parents, raising awareness regarding these negative consequences may be sufficient to stop unintentional abusive and neglectful behavior. For many others, however, more directed interventions are warranted to assist parents in incorporating various prevention messages into their behaviors. Recently, prevention services have also targeted the potential victims of maltreatment in an effort to help children to resist or disclose abusive situations. The main purpose of Chapter 10 is to summarize the extent of the child abuse problem nationwide and to highlight the critical need for prevention services. Two major service avenues currently dominate the child abuse prevention field: direct services to new or at-risk parents and services to the potential victims of maltreatment. The chapter identifies the program characteristics in both areas that hold the most promise for success and offers strategies for building on these prevention models to enhance future outcomes.

AIDS is a disease that is no longer confined to gay men and intravenous drug users but has an impact on all segments of society. Chapter 11, written by Joanne Mantell and Steven Schinke, discusses adolescents' increased risk for becoming infected with the human immunodeficiency virus (HIV). Many people in their twenties who have AIDS were undoubtedly infected while in their teens. The normal developmental stages of adolescence are characterized by sexual and drug experimentation and other risk-taking behaviors. High rates of sexually transmitted diseases and emotional vulnerability increase adolescents' risk of HIV infection. In addition, perceptions of invincibility and immortality contribute to denial of risk. Teens are often unable to connect sexual behaviors with their consequences. All of these factors underscore the importance of AIDS prevention activities directed toward adolescents. Chapter 11 emphasizes that education, beginning at an early age, is the front line of defense in stemming the tide of the AIDS epidemic.

Also included is an explanation of the disease's epidemiology and transmission modes. Finally, methods for limiting its spread among youth and practice frameworks for cognitive-behavioral and peer group model preventive interventions are thoroughly examined.

Prevention of adolescent suicidal behavior in the schools is the focus of Chapter 12, by John Kalafat. After a review of the scope and prevalence of this social problem, Kalafat examines the recent literature on adolescent suicide, with an emphasis on the contagion effect of a suicide on peers and fellow students. He discusses three ways in which the school system can be involved in successful secondary prevention efforts:

1. Early detection of at-risk students by recognizing warning signals (e.g., a significant decrease in student's level of performance, excessive misbehavior, fatigue)
2. Consultation with local and community mental health professionals and a coordinated response from teachers, guidance counselors, and administrators
3. Education for staff and students on the most effective ways of responding to troubled students, including the development of a peer counseling program

Also examined are Lifeline and other school prevention models, as well as recent legislation authorizing statewide school-based youth suicide prevention programs in California, New Jersey, and Wisconsin.

In Chapter 13, Laurie Schwab Zabin and Rosalie Streett describe the empirically tested teen pregnancy prevention model they implemented in an inner-city junior and senior high school in Baltimore. The educational approach was aimed at adolescents with the highest risk of pregnancy—sexually active teens in their first month of coital activity. Zabin and Streett describe the kinds of services that were useful in encouraging responsible behavior among male and female students. They address issues in staffing, referral, and confidentiality. Also discussed are the objectives that can legitimately be expected with these age groups in an educational, as opposed to a therapeutic, setting. The chapter also reports on ways in which male students were encouraged to behave responsibly and to use contraceptives regularly.

Chapter 14, written by Linda F. Little, I. C. Gaffney, and Judith Grissmer, describes the Pilot Information, Education, Resources and Referral Services (PIERRS) program, a stress management and prevention program for commercial airline pilots. During the past few years, therapists in the PIERRS program have worked with several hundred airline pilots. They often provide services to pilots employed by commercial carriers that have a history of hostile labor-management interactions, corporate instability, corporate losses, or a recent unwanted buyout. Services include a 24-hour-a-day toll-free number for counseling, a national referral network of licensed mental health professionals for local referrals, printed educational material designed to go to the homes of all pilots who work for a particular carrier, a stress resource library of educational materials that are mailed on a request basis, and tailored interventions for pilot employee groups following a major air disaster. This chapter has implications for persons working with clients in commercial aviation and for helping professionals who work with any group of employees who are experiencing distress.

Primary Prevention
Theory, Issues, Methods, and Programs

Martin Bloom

9

INTRODUCTION

Primary prevention is an idea whose time has come, to the work place (as in employee assistance programs), to the home (as in planning for nutrition, safety, interpersonal skills), and to the community (as in efforts to cut down pollution). Primary prevention reflects a fundamental human concern for well-being, reflected in the folk sayings such as an ounce of prevention being worth a pound of cure. Yet millions of people ignore the anti-smoking campaigns, practice unsafe sex, and in other ways live their lives in ways risky to their own health and to others. Clearly we must study the nature of primary prevention and the people who use, and do not use, its recommendations.

THEORETICAL PERSPECTIVES

As a working definition, let us agree to use the expression *primary prevention* to include systematic and planned activities undertaken simultaneously to prevent the occurrence of some predicted untoward event, to protect current states of health and healthy functioning, and to promote desired states for some identified target person or population (Bloom, 1987). This broad-spectrum definition is an attempt to capture the wide range of activities that go under the banner of primary prevention while excluding equally worthy near-neighbors, such as crisis intervention, that address an existent problem.

This working definition also puts the discussion on a broader plane beyond simply preventing specific problems such as AIDS, automobile accidents, or abuse, even though, obviously, practitioners work in specific areas, not in prevention in general. The more general definition will permit us to see commonalities and differences among the several specific target groups, thus encouraging advances along many fronts at the same time. This working definition is also broader than "preventing psychopathology and promoting human potential" since it also includes nonpsychological conditions such as preventing unwanted pregnancy or promoting desired pregnancy, or preventing automobile accidents or promoting safe defensive driving. The primary prevention field itself has moved from preventing problems to the combined preventive-promotive orientation. For example, employee assistance programs began as attempts to deal with preventing and treating problems of alcoholism and have now moved to include a wider array of work-related topics viewed within a multiple preventive-promotive frame of reference. Literally anything can be conceived as an object to be prevented, protected, or promoted by some group, even though other groups may hold contrary views. Primary prevention is value-laden from the start.

Interestingly, there is a deep fund of goodwill for primary prevention that stems from folk wisdom regarding "ounces of prevention" and "stitches in time" that has not been widely used by helping professionals, perhaps because of the negative image that prevention has—"don't do fun things because they are bad for you"—as contrasted with a more positive image that promotion offers—"consider these pleasurable and safer alternatives. . . ." Thus the multiple dimensions of the working definition are best viewed in systematic and simultaneous perspectives.

Consider this systemic formula, which defines both sources of problems and opportunities for fulfilling potentials:

> A preventable problem is some function of (1) organic or genetic factors, (2) psychological factors (especially stress), and (3) socioeconomic and political exploitation that can be reduced by actions directed toward (1) biologic structures and functioning, (2) psychological coping skills and self-esteem, and (3) social supports and changes in the physical environment. (cf. Albee, 1983).

The four system levels—biological, psychological, sociocultural, and physical environmental—are to be considered intrinsic aspects of any human concern. They represent points of departure for any helping activity.

Another distinctive emphasis of primary prevention concerns the time dimension. Looking at any one act requires us to observe when the event occurs in relation to other happenings. The abortion of an unwanted fetus, for example, is preventive of one set of events (not having an unwanted child), but it is the treatment of another failure event (not using an effective contraceptive in the first place). The treatment process of the abortion may also represent the promotion of a desired future for the couple (having a child at such time as they are ready and able to care for it properly). The abortion may also serve a rehabilitative function in the sense of moving them back to their preconception status. Society stands to lose from an abortion (what if da Vinci's unwed mother had opted for abortion?) as well as to gain (what if society did not have to pay for the welfare of the million plus adolescents with unplanned and unwanted pregnancies each year?) The intricate interweaving of individual and collective acts and responsibilities has made primary prevention a national priority (Public Health Service, 1979).

This same complex interweaving of events makes research in primary prevention difficult and expensive (Price and Smith, 1985; Mednick and Baert, 1981) even though the results tend to be encouraging (Bloom, 1981; 1986). It is one of the paradoxes of preventive services that to be successful means that a problem did not occur for some individual. It is almost impossible to know whether or not the untoward event would have happened to that individual naturally; thus research is largely directed toward groups or populations in which probabilities can be used to indicate successful outcomes. Rates of problem behavior (incidences) are relatively stable given stable social conditions, so that when planned changes in rates of individuals' behaviors occur, these may be used as indicators of prevention. When planned changes occur in social conditions or physical environmental factors that likely reduce risks for individuals, then we are set to look for changes in rates of individual behaviors. But the contextual changes per se are not preventive outcomes, and the causal linkages for any preventive outcome are complex.

Consider the situation where the drinking age is raised to 21, and the rate of youthful-driver auto accidents falls. It would be nice to associate the legislative action with the accident rates, but in fact there are many other factors that could also have been involved, for example, changes in driving instruction, improvements in traffic safety, engineering changes in cars, psychological awareness and raised consciousness, and altered policing or judicial sentencing. However, as Albee (1983) has noted, no significant social or health problem has been successfully controlled by treating its victims one by one. The complexity of real life must be conceptually included in any effective and humane solution of its problems and potentials.

The work of James Alexander and his colleagues represents another aspect of a systems perspective on primary prevention, in this case the interrelationship of all three major modes of helping—prevention, treatment, and rehabilitation (Klein, Alexander, and Parsons, 1977). Working with delinquents and their families, these researchers attempted to treat current problems (the existing delinquency situation), rehabilitate the involved parties (helping families learn how to communicate once again with their delinquent son), and prevent future occurrences (by working with younger siblings of the delinquent). Their data suggest that they were successful on all counts, using their broad theoretical perspective, which viewed these concerns holistically. The main lesson from this work is that tasks must be conceptualized as requiring relevant solutions on all three dimensions before the problem can be considered resolved (see Ambrosino, 1979; Germain, 1979).

This is not a common perspective of the established helping professions, who defend their turf with all the vigor of street gangs. But as the systems perspective grows in these many professions, the borders of problems and solutions blur, and the many-sided aspects of effective and humane services becomes clearer. As a contribution to this interdisciplinary service trend, I offer a working definition of healthy and nonhealthy functioning with reference to physical and mental health and illness in which, first, distinctions among prevention, treatment, and rehabilitation will be identified at biological, psychological, and sociocultural levels. Second, appropriate forms of helping are identified (see Bloom, 1990).

Using Table 9-1 to represent a health functioning continuum, we can focus on some basic definitons of the helping modalities, we can clarify the time dimension involved in the service activities, and we can recognize that biological, psychological, sociocultural, and physical environmental aspects are at work at every level of human functioning. It might be helpful in this book, which combines crisis and prevention, to offer some remarks about their relationship.

First, note that treatment has two aspects in Table 9-1: Level IV (unaware problematic functioning and advanced service activities) and Level V (crisis and acute problems with acute service activities). In both, the problem has occurred, although in the first, the victim is not aware yet. There is an important semantic problem involving Level V because the word *crisis* may appear in the sense of (a) "an impending crisis that has not yet occurred" or in the sense of (b) "an impending crisis in which the problem has occurred and is now being played out."

Table 9-1 A Working Definition of 14 Levels of Functioning Regarding Health and Illness

I. (A) HIGH LEVEL OF HEALTHY FUNCTIONING.   A person at this level is operating at or near physical and/or mental capacity and is feeling exhilarated about self and involvements with significant others and in social roles.

   (B) PROMOTIVE ACTIVITIES.   The relevant self-help or helping actions for this level are those that motivate or support the person in achieving high-level potentials or make appropriate environmental changes toward that end.

II. (A) ADEQUATE HEALTH FUNCTIONING.   This level represents operating in the middle range of physical and/or mental capacity, sufficient to deal with ordinary life demands; the person feels satisfied with his or her efforts, as well as with significant others and social roles. There may be momentary highs and lows, but the predominant feeling is one of satisfaction and adaptation to social demands.

   (B) PROTECTIVE ACTIVITIES.   At this level of functioning, the major actions are those that maintain or move a person into the zone of adequate performance regarding personal, social, and environmental demands. The environmental supports may be taken for granted because of their pervasiveness.

III. (A) AT-RISK FUNCTIONING.   This level describes a person who is engaging in behaviors or living in an environment thought to put that individual at risk for a predictable problem. Note that the person is currently functioning adequately with regard to the problem or the environment in question. The feeling states are like those of II, with satisfaction being the predominant affective tone.

   (B) PREVENTIVE ACTIVITIES.   This level identifies actions that are intended to forestall predictable untoward events from occurring either by eliminating the harmful environmental agents or by strengthening the person's resistance to the harmful agents, or both. Forestalling may include a continuum of results from outright elimination of the problem and its effects to reduction of the impact of that harmful agent.

IV. (A) UNAWARE PROBLEMATIC FUNCTIONING.   This level refers to operating at or below adequate physical and/or mental functioning but being unaware of any difficulty sufficient to induce the person to take actions with regard to a presumed problem. Or the person may be aware of the problematic feeling but not of any way to resolve the problem.

   (B) ADVANCED SERVICE ACTIVITIES.   The actions relevant to this level would include those that screen, detect, and treat subclinical problems through the use of technological devices. Likewise, epi-

Table 9-1 *(Continued)*   A Working Definition of 14 Levels of Functioning Regarding Health and Illness

demiological or environmental problems may also be the subject of advanced service activities when the specific hosts of the problems may not be aware of their condition.

V. (A) CRISIS AND ACUTE PROBLEMS.   The person is operating below adequate levels of physical and/or mental functioning but is aware of the difficulty and takes some actions with regard to it. This awareness is expressed as unhappiness and/or pain with regard to self and reduced effectiveness with regard to interactions with significant others and the environment.

(B) ACUTE SERVICE ACTIVITIES.   These actions include services to treat observable problems promptly through standard medical, psychiatric, engineering, or other relevant methods, as well as to observe for other problems that may not be observable (level IV). The target of helping action is both toward the causal agent (if known) and the host.

VI. (A) CHRONIC PROBLEM ZONE.   After the crisis problem (level V) has been resolved as far as possible, the person may still be operating at or below ordinary levels of functioning. This is the measure of the chronic problem. Feeling states depend on the level and degree of recovery and on the person's supportive networks.

(B) REHABILITATIVE SERVICES.   These consist of actions directed toward assisting the person to regain the highest level of functioning possible and may include use of personal and/or environmental prostheses.

VII. (A) TERMINAL ZONE.   Eventually the person will exhaust all capacity for life functioning, and the ability of helpers to sustain life artificially will also be exhausted. The period of time between these conditions is the terminal phase of life. Feeling states may vary from existential resignation and contentment to raging anger and depression.

(B) PALLIATIVE ACTIONS.   Activities at this level recognize the terminal nature of the person's condition and seek to reduce pain and to promote personal fulfillment through communication with family and friends as far as possible.

For example, a married couple may find themselves arguing frequently and with great intensity, to the point where each partner is thinking about options to this situation. Crisis in the (a) sense would represent a Level III event (being at risk for predictable problems consequent to divorce). The appropriate form of professional help would be a marriage counselor who would provide problem-solving skills to deal adequately with current problems (i.e., treatment) as well as with future difficulties (i.e., prevention). Crisis in the (b) sense would represent a Level V event (being in the process of seeking a divorce). The appropriate form of professional help might be a divorce counselor who, after establishing that the couple were determined to get a divorce, would work to minimize the negative fallout from such an event, particularly with respect to the children. Obviously, presenting problems may not be the actual problems, and any form of counseling should be capable of shifting to whatever the level of client functioning. Thus whether crisis intervention is a preventive or a treatment activity depends on the context.

PREVENTION STRATEGIES

Figure 9-1 extends this conceptual discussion to a perspective on helping strategies. What may be a Level III problem for one partner may appear as a Level V problem for the other, a fact that may facilitate a clearer problem definition and possible resolution. Note that the forms of helping appear in stepwise fashion, indicating that earlier forms of helping may be used during the occasions when a later form of helping is at focus. For example, when a Level V crisis or acute problem exists, it is also theoretically possible to promote some aspects of the client's functioning that is at a Level I or II (as indicated in the Klein et al., 1977, study).

Indeed, it may be encouraging to the client to deal with some positives, as well as the crisis. It also gives the practitioner an opportunity to support client strengths as well as to confront weaknesses. This is not a trival comment as one of the distinguishing characteristics of primary prevention is its dual focus on strengths (to be promoted) and limitations (problems to be prevented or treated). With persons who are personally or socioculturally oppressed, this emphasis on

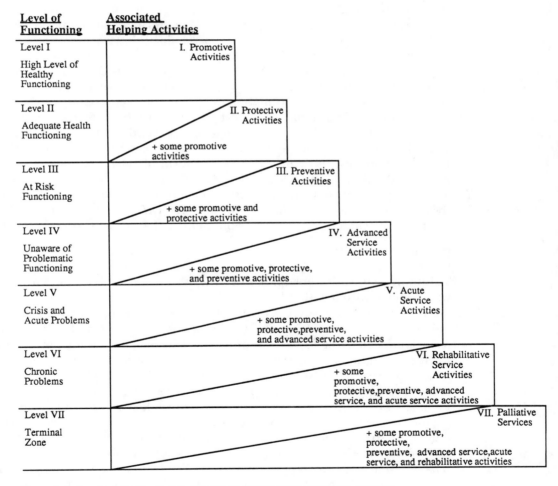

Figure 9-1 Levels of Healthy Functioning and Associated Forms of Helping Activities

strengths may be one of the few avenues of approach to the establishment of a workable relationship (Bloom, 1983). Thus primary prevention involves a configuration of problem definitions and a corresponding configuration of approaches for resolution.

Chapters to follow will examine a number of topics from the perspective of primary prevention, such as teenage pregnancy, suicide, child abuse, and AIDS. It may be useful to illustrate the health functioning continuum with reference to these topics.

Teenage Pregnancy

Teenage pregnancy may be viewed as something to be promoted under the special and minimal conditions that the couple is maturely bonded, with sufficient education to be the basis of an occupation that will provide adequately for their needs over a lifetime and when the infant is planned and wanted. The same phenomenon may be seen as the target of preventive activities in the situation where sexually active youths are neither ready nor able psychologically, socially, or economically to provide for an infant. Should that couple have an unwanted conception, pregnancy-testing kits would supply technological information before the pregnant woman would herself be aware of it. Amniocentesis is another technical procedure that provides information on genetic problems before birth and thus permits preventive alternatives. Abortion can be viewed either as a crisis intervention for an acknowledged problem or as a preventive action regarding an unwanted birth that lacks the genetic or psychosocial requirements for a fully human life. Postabortion counseling services is a form of rehabilitation, trying to reestablish the woman and her partner at a preconception level as far as possible. The fetus is terminated; this is the death of living tissue, albeit not independently living tissue. Humane considerations, not merely for the fetus but also for the mother, are required regardless of the politics that has enshrouded this issue.

Suicide

This topic requires an enlarging of the health functioning continuum. What we would seek to promote is a life worth living, using the potentials that lie within the person and the resources of the social environment to the benefit of both individual and society. We protect existing states of living, and we identify risk factors for people who experience problems in living. The literature on adolescent suicide prevention is blessed with a bountiful array of risk factors that are so clear and simple that fellow students in the junior and senior high schools can act as early warning systems for their friends. However, when a suicide attempt fails, we have to treat this situation as an existing problem and provide help for the person involved as needed. Then we begin the rehabilitation process, trying to reduce the stresses that led to the original action while increasing the sources of support that are inhibitory to them. Should a suicide attempt succeed, we have rehabilitation work to do not only with the family but also with the peer group and quite possibly the whole school body, which might react in a contagious way to this untimely and disordered death (Shulman, 1990).

Child Abuse

Again, the health functioning continuum commends to us that we promote the growth and development of our children to the fullest of their potential in a supportive environment. Children do not necessarily flourish by benign neglect, just because they are not physically beaten. Promotive actions require positive programming, in a way parallel to the concrete plans of treatment or rehabilitation. We take many steps to protect children's health and mental health and the continuity of their growth and development. Some of these steps are collective, such as school lunch programs to protect existing health nutrition (or to prevent problems for students who might lack adequate meals). Others are individual steps, such as the parent who happily buttons the top button of a child's coat against the winter winds, not necessarily to the pleasure of the child.

The prevention of child abuse, in contrast to promotion and protection of child welfare, involves a configuration of events since pressures to abuse may stem from the adult's own personal limitations, history, current stressful circumstances, or whatever. While we speak of promotion with regard to the child, we tend to think about the changes to the person and the circumstances of the abusing adult as related to child abuse. This change of focus is more apparent than real, for many levels of social systems are involved in any human enterprise. Should abuse occur, there is a need both to treat the hurt child and to work with the abuser appropriately (See Gondolf, 1987, for a sensitive proposal to match the interventions aimed at "men who batter" with a developmental model [Kohlberg] indicating what form of intervention these men might most profit from at a given stage in their development.) After the abuser is reoriented (controlled, educated, reformed), there is a need to rehabilitate the victim and others in the situation who were passive in the face of violence. There is much reorienting of all concerned. And should an abused child die, there is the work of mourning and restitution.

AIDS

It is interesting to compare the health functioning continuum of AIDS with that of teen pregnancy because in the case of a sexually transmitted virus, the recommendations are quite similar, whether or not homosexual relations are in question. We would seek to promote mature intimacy between individuals who are ready and able to assume the psychosocial responsibilities of the physical act of sex. That gays have had to organize their sexual activities in secrecy represents a socially caused problem in which homophobia is essentially an act of blaming the victim. There are irresponsible actors among gays as among nongay people. In terms of prevention, simple contraceptive barriers and basic hygiene will go a considerable way toward preventing AIDS, provided that the psychological and social supports are present to engage in these activities.

However, drug-related AIDS is a quite different matter, and its prevention initially involves the use of uncontaminated tools when abstinence is not possible. In the larger sense, prevention involves the entire community of users and the society within which this subculture survives. The entire "war on drugs" is an extension of prevention of drug-related AIDS, even though it is only a minor consideration in its overall strategy. AIDS currently admits of no treatment, only a slowing of the opportunistic diseases that attack AIDS victims. Treatment is essentially a mix of some rehabilitation and eventually palliative services.

These examples indicate how the health functioning continuum may be used to explore extended ranges of services, from promotion to treatment to palliative assistance at the end of life.

The public health model (of host, agent, and environment) offers one way to sort out types of helping strategies with the configural approach (Siefert, 1983). Let me preface this by noting that public health actions, from the sanitation movement in the nineteenth century to the mass inoculations of the twentieth, have led to the most spectacular health achievements in recorded history (see Bloom, 1965; Bloom, 1981). More people have been spared the misery and premature mortality of disease than by any other helping method, even though clinical medicine with its elaborate and expensive technology has received the lion's share of public attention and support.

Essentially, the public health model suggests that one or more aspects of the following triad of events has to be considered in any health action: The noxious agent (such as a disease organism like cholera), the host (a human being who may be exposed to the agent), and the environmental context (like a break in the sewage system leaking into the water supply, as in the famous case of Dr. Snow's study of the London cholera epidemic of 1848) have to be considered jointly. Actions are to be taken against any or all, as circumstances dictate.

The agent of the disease or the problem (and the vector that carries that agent) has to be identified and addressed, if possible. Dr. Snow never identified the causal agent of the cholera epidemic, but he was able to prevent further occurrences of the disease by making changes in the environmental context (removing the pump handle to the contaminated public well). By contrast, in the case of AIDS, the agent is known, but how to deal with the agent is not. For perspective, it should be noted that the same was true of the organism causing tuberculosis; it took 80 years from the time of its identification to the time when medications were developed that could destroy it.

In other cases, the agent may be multiple, as in the theory of stress-related mental health concerns, where what is relevant is the cumulation of any kind of stress past some conceptual limit, after which the host is at high risk for some physical or mental reaction (see Holmes & Rahe, 1967). In such circumstances, it may be possible to deal with only some of the causal agents, and major attention must be directed to other parts of the triad.

The host may be aided to resist the infection by acting in certain ways to prevent contact with the noxious agent. Sometimes actions involve doing something for the host, as in inoculation, in which the resistance is individually built in. Putting substances in common food sources is yet another approach to mass prevention, such as fluoridating the water supply. These are passive strategies in the sense that the actor doesn't have to do anything to be aided to resist the problem (Robertson, 1975).

There are also active strategies of prevention, such as teaching knowledge and skills to the host, as in using condoms as a barrier between the receptive host and the noxious agent. This strategy requires that the person choose to use this knowledge or skill at appropriate times. Of the two strategies, the passive strategy has a better record of effectiveness, while the active strategy is usually better received by the users, at least initially. Again, value issues emerge in a pair of questions: Whose right is it to choose or not choose the preventive action? Whose obligation is it to pay or not pay for any resulting problems?

The environment can be changed in many ways as well, making the connection between host and noxious agent less likely or less harmful. For example, free condom distribution points have been established in accessible locations for high-risk populations. Public information posters, toll-free hotlines, and information sources have been set up. School health education programs have been modified to include new kinds of content in new settings (such as health clinics in the schools). Social support groups have enabled young people to learn about problems and learn how to say no. Natural helping networks have been supported in their ordinary roles of providing growth-oriented stimulation, as well as aid in times of trouble. In these and other ways, the physical and sociocultural environments have been modified to reduce the likelihood of a spectrum of problems reaching school-age children (see Schinke & Gilchrist, 1984; Gilchrist & Schinke, 1985; Lofquist, 1983).

THE FUTURE OF PRIMARY PREVENTION

With the mounting number of severe personal and social problems and the limited number of persons who can treat victims with expensive and not always effective methods (Albee, 1950, 1983), it seems inevitable that society will eventually have to consider primary prevention as its major tool for humane and effective service. However, there is no guarantee that we can in fact prevent problems from occurring; the knowledge base in primary prevention is still very thin in spite of heroic efforts (see the publications from the Vermont Conferences on the Primary Prevention of Psychopathology for the best current materials on conceptual, empirical, and programmatic efforts in primary prevention, such as Albee & Joffe, 1977; Bond & Joffe, 1982; Bond & Rosen, 1980). With the development of specialized journals—*Journal of Primary Prevention, Prevention in Human Services, Journal of Preventive Psychiatry, Community Mental Health Journal, American Journal of Community Psychology,* and the venerable *American Journal of Public Health*—there is a rapid expansion in scientific and professional exchanges. The tasks ahead for primary prevention are challenging to say the least. But consider the alternatives if vigorous primary prevention were not to exist at personal, social, environmental, and international levels. Therefore, study with care the scholarly and provocative chapters on primary prevention in this anthology. The ultimate meaning of primary prevention consists of the actions of the large numbers of practitioners and citizens who are involved in working together to prevent predictable problems and to promote a desired future.

REFERENCES

ALBEE, G. W. (1950). *Mental Health Manpower Trends.* New York: Basic Books.

ALBEE, G. W. (1983). "Psychopathology, Prevention, and the Just Society." *Journal of Primary Prevention, 4*(1), 5–40.

ALBEE, G. W., and J. M. JOFFE (Eds.). (1977). *Primary Prevention of Psychopathology. Volume 1: The Issues.* Hanover, N.H.: University Press of New England.

AMBROSINO, S. (1979). "Integrating Counseling, Family Life Education, and Family Advocacy." *Social Casework, 60,* 579–585.

BLOOM, B. L. (1965). "The 'Medical Model,' Miasma Theory, and Community Mental Health." *Community Mental Health Journal, 1,* 333–338.

BLOOM, M. (1981). *Primary Prevention: The Possible Science.* Englewood Cliffs, N.J.: Prentice-Hall.

BLOOM, M. (1986). "Hygeia at the Scales: Weighing the Costs and Effectiveness of Prevention/Promotion, with Special Reference to Mental Retardation." *Journal of Primary Prevention, 6*(5), 27–48.

BLOOM, M. (1987). "Prevention." In A. Minahan, et al. (Eds.), *Encyclopedia of Social Work* (18th ed.). Silver Springs, Md.: National Association of Social Workers.

BLOOM, M. (1990). *Introduction to the Drama of Social Work.* Itasca, Ill.: Peacock.

BOND, L. A., and J. M. JOFFE (Eds.). (1982). *Primary Prevention of Psychopathology, Volume 6: Facilitating Infant and Early Childhood Development.* Hanover, N.H.: University Press of New England.

BOND, L. A., and J. C. ROSEN (Eds.). (1980). *Primary Prevention of Psychopathology. Volume 4: Competence and Coping during Adulthood.* Hanover, N.H.: University Press of New England.

GERMAIN, C. B. (Ed.). (1979). *Social Work Practice, People and Environments: An Ecological Perspective.* New York: Columbia University Press.

GONDOLF, E. W. (1987). "Changing men who batter: A developmental model for integrated intervention." *Journal of Family Violence, 2*:4, 345–359.

GILCHRIST, L. D. and SCHINKE, S. P. (Eds.) (1985). *Preventions Social and Health Problems Through Life Skills Training.* Seattle: School of Social Work, University of Washington.

HOLMES, T. H., and R. H. RAHE (1967). "The Social Readjustment Rating Scale." *Journal of Psychosomatic Research, 11,* 213–218.

KLEIN, N., J. F. ALEXANDER, and B. V. PARSONS (1977). "Impact of Family System Intervention on Recidivism and Sibling Delinquency: A Model of Primary Prevention and Program Evaluation." *Journal of Consulting and Clinical Psychology, 45,* 469–474.

LOFQUIST, W. A. (1983). *Discovering the Meaning of Prevention: A Practical Approach to Positive Change.* Tucson, Arizona: AYD Publications.

MEDNICK, S. A., and A. E. BAERT (Eds.). (1981). *Prospective Longitudinal Research: An Empirical Basis for Primary Prevention of Psychological Disorders.* New York: Oxford University Press.

PRICE, R. H., and S. S. SMITH (1985). *A Guide to Evaluating Prevention Programs in Mental Health* (Publication No. ADM 85–1365). Washington, D.C.: U.S. Department of Health and Human Services.

Public Health Service, U.S. Department of Health, Education, and Welfare. (1979). *Healthy People: The Surgeon General's Report on Health Promotion and Disease Prevention* (Publication No. PHS 79-55071). Washington, D.C.: U.S. Government Printing Office.

ROBERTSON, L. S. (1975). "Behavioral Research and Strategies in Public Health: A Demur." *Social Science and Medicine, 9,* 165–170.

SCHINKE, S. P., and L. D. GILCHRIST. (1984). *Life Skills Counseling with Adolescents.* Baltimore: University Park Press.

SHULMAN, N. M. (1990). "Crisis Intervention in a High School: Lessons from the Concorde High School Experiences," in A. R. Roberts (Ed.), *Crisis Intervention Handbook: Assessment, Treatment, and Research,* Belmont, Cal.: Wadsworth Publishing Co., 63–77.

SIEFERT, K. (1983). "Using Concepts from Epidemiology to Teach Prevention." In J. BOWKER (Ed.), *Education for Primary Prevention in Social Work.* New York: Council on Social Work Education.

Strategies and Models in Child Abuse Prevention

Deborah Daro

10

INTRODUCTION

ANNOUNCER:	Children believe what their parents tell them.
MOTHER 1:	You're pathetic. You can't do anything right.
FATHER 1:	You disgust me. Just shut up.
MOTHER 2:	You can't be my kid.
FATHER 2:	You're worthless.
MOTHER 3:	Hey stupid, don't you know how to listen?
FATHER 3:	You're never going to amount to anything.
MOTHER 1:	Why don't you go find some other place to live?
ANNOUNCER:	Words hit as hard as a fist. Stop and listen to what you're saying. You might not believe your ears.
MOTHER 4:	I wish you were never born.
ANNOUNCER:	Take time out. Don't take it out on your kid.

The initial step in preventing any type of harmful behavior is often rais-ing awareness of its detrimental impacts. Once awareness is raised, prevention efforts can then focus on substituting these behaviors with more positive alterna-tives. This prevention sequence has been particularly true in the case of child abuse. Parental mistreatment most frequently stems from an initial lack of awareness regarding the negative consequences of certain actions or inactions and a lack of knowledge or awareness of alternatives. The example just quoted, developed by the Advertising Council for the National Committee for Prevention of Child Abuse, focuses on raising public awareness with respect to the devastating impacts of verbal abuse. The parental comments are directed to a young girl whose eyes fill with tears as she repeatedly hears the message that she is worthless. The conclusion from this visual image is inescapable: the continuous belittling of a child destroys the child's sense of self and impedes positive emotional development.

For some parents, raising awareness may be sufficient to stop unintentional abusive or neglectful behaviors. For many others, however, more directed interventions are warranted to assist in incorporating various prevention messages into their ongoing behaviors. This realization has fostered the development of numerous parenting education programs, volunteer home visitors, and crisis intervention services in virtually all communities across the country. Generally aimed at first-time or at-risk parents, these services offer concrete assistance in enhancing child development knowledge, stress management, and parenting skills. Recently, prevention services have also targeted potential victims of maltreatment in an effort to help children resist or disclose abusive situations. A recent survey in 29 randomly selected counties in the United States found that over 75 percent of the hospitals, school districts, and community-based agencies contacted identified themselves as offering these types of prevention services (Daro et al., 1988).

The purpose of this chapter is to summarize the extent of the child abuse problem nationwide and to highlight the critical need for prevention services. As this summary indicates, two major service avenues currently dominate the child abuse prevention field: direct services to new or at-risk parents and services to the potential victims of maltreatment. The chapter identifies program characteristics in both of these areas that hold the most promise for success and offers strategies for building on these service models to enhance future outcomes.

SCOPE AND PREVALENCE

The scope of child maltreatment in this country is subject to wide debate. Interviews with random samples of households or individuals consistently project higher incidence and prevalence rates than formal reporting data indicate. One of the earliest and most rigorous studies on maltreatment estimated that in 1968 between 2.5 and 4 million families either failed to act or used physical force with the intent of hurting, injuring, or destroying their children (Gil, 1970). Subsequent household surveys on the level of intimate violence in America confirm that a minimum of a million children aged 3–17 residing in two-parent families are subject to serious physical abuse each year (Straus et al., 1980; Gelles & Straus, 1988).

These numbers, while dramatic in their own right, are even more disturbing when one considers that this research focused on only a portion of all maltreatment. They provide few, if any, insights into the number of children who experience chronic emotional maltreatment or fall victim to sexual abuse. Recent random and nonrandom surveys to determine the prevalence of sexual abuse suggest that pervasive sexual mistreatment of children continues in our society. A 1978 survey of 930 randomly selected women in San Francisco revealed that 28 percent of the respondents had experienced unwanted sexual touching and other forms of abuse before the age of 14 and that the percentage of victims in-

creased to 38 percent if one included all episodes occurring before the women turned 18 (Russell, 1984). Finkelhor (1984) reported that 6 percent of all males and 15 percent of all females in his random sample of 521 Boston parents had experienced sexual abuse before age 16 by a person at least five years older. In an earlier nonrandom study conducted by this same author, 9 percent of the males and 19 percent of the females experienced at least one unwanted sexual encounter before the age of 16, including intercourse, oral-genital contact, fondling, or an encounter with an exhibitionist.

These and similar studies have been used by child advocates to define the broad parameters of the maltreatment problem. Federal and local public officials, however, must rely on more formal estimates of the problem, estimates that suggest that the problem is by no means trivial. For example, the American Association for Protecting Children (AAPC, 1988) notes that over 2 million children were reported as suspected victims of maltreatment in 1986, a 200 percent increase over 1976 reporting levels. Of these reports, approximately 28 percent involved charges of physical abuse, 55 percent physical neglect, 16 percent sexual abuse, and 8 percent emotional maltreatment, percentages that reflect the fact that many children fall victim to multiple forms of maltreatment.

Most recently, reporting rates have begun to stabilize, rising only 2 percent between 1987 and 1986 (Daro & Mitchel, 1988). Explanations for this trend vary. On the one hand, this pattern may reflect the success of the reporting system in tapping into the maximum number of identifiable maltreatment cases. Professional education and public awareness efforts have been successful in alerting potential reporters to the signs of maltreatment and convincing them to report their suspicions accordingly. On the other hand, some authorities view this stabilization as the direct result of changes in child protective service policies. For example, in the state of Washington, almost one-third of all calls to protective services are screened out before any investigation is conducted. Other states, such as Vermont and Texas, have altered the definition of maltreatment, narrowing the range of behaviors that constitute reportable acts of abuse or neglect. Consequently, any reduction in the number of child abuse reports may be less a reflection of absolute incidence and more a reflection of the resources being expended on child abuse by public child protective service agencies.

Support for the continued existence, if not expansion, of the child abuse problem is found in the most recently completed federally funded National Incidence Study (Westat Associates, 1987). This study confirmed that over 1 million children, 16 out of every 1,000, were identified by child service professionals as being abused or neglected in 1985. This figure represents a 66 percent increase over the number identified during a similar study conducted in 1980 (Westat Associates, 1981). The largest increases were noted in cases involving moderate physical abuse and all forms of child sexual abuse. Though not significant, increases were also noted in the rates of fatal and serious physical abuse, all forms of emotional abuse, abandonment and refusal to provide necessary health care, educational neglect, and most forms of emotional neglect.

Further, despite extensive efforts to train professionals in their reporting responsibilities, the 1985 study determined that little change had occurred in the percentage of cases known to professionals that were formally reported. Fewer than one-third of the child abuse cases identified by law enforcement officials, medical personnel, educators, and social service providers are reported to child protective service agencies and substantiated (Westat Associates, 1987). This percentage ranges from a low of 16 percent for day care providers and 24 percent for teachers to a high of 61 percent for local police and 66 percent for hospital personnel.

Critics argue that relying solely on official reports of maltreatment or the National Incidence Study for accurate assessments of the level of child maltreatment is faulty because the actual incidence levels most likely exceed either of these projections. Despite this criticism, both of these estimates offer at least a base on which to begin discussing the scope of the problem and the relative frequency of different types of maltreatment. Though neither is able to provide a definitive ceiling for the problem, few experts will deny that these estimates are fairly accurate projections of the minimum scope of the problem. Taken as a minimum level, these numbers make a powerful case for prevention.

OVERVIEW OF PREVENTION

The need for a comprehensive prevention strategy for child abuse and neglect is justified for at least three reasons: the vast majority of treatment programs leave a sizable number of children at risk for future maltreatment; child maltreatment has serious and often fatal consequences for children, consequences from which they should be protected; and providing services only after a child is abused represents an enormous waste of scarce public resources.

Evaluations of child abuse treatment programs over the past decade have consistently underscored their limitations (Cohn & Daro, 1988; Daro, 1988). Frankly, treatment programs have not been especially successful in protecting children from continued abuse. Among protective service caseloads, reincidence rates of 30 to 40 percent are common (Herrenkohl et al., 1979; Laughlin & Weiss, 1981). Federal- and state-funded evaluations of sophisticated clinical demonstration projects, often consisting of weekly contact for 12 to 18 months, report reincidence among one-third to one-half of all clients (Cohn & Daro, 1988). Further, at termination, more than half of the clients served by these programs are considered by their service providers to remain at risk of abusing their children in the future. Program evaluations that have documented success in reducing the risk for future maltreatment through a combination of therapeutic, educational, and supportive services need to be kept in perspective. Very few follow-up studies have been conducted on these samples, and for many of these children, protection from future abuse requires permanent separation from their families.

Prevention services are also necessary to protect children from the extensive emotional and physical damage they suffer as the result of abuse. The documented consequences of abuse include chronic health problems; cognitive and language disorders as reflected in poor performances on virtually every standard measure used; socioemotional problems such as low self-esteem, lack of trust, low frustration tolerance, and poor relationships with adults and peers; difficulties in school, including poor attendance, misconduct, and learning disorders serious enough to warrant special education classes; and self-mutilative or other self-destructive behaviors (Bolton & Bolton, 1987; Daro, 1988). One evaluation of abused children who received therapeutic services from federally funded treatment programs reported that 14 percent of the victims under 12 years of age and 40 percent of the adolescent victims had attempted suicide or self-injury (Daro, 1988).

Of course, the ultimate damage from abuse is death. Annual telephone surveys of all 50 states conducted by the National Committee for Prevention of Child Abuse (NCPCA) found in 1986 and 1987 that an average of three children a day were reported as fatal victims of maltreatment. Perhaps more alarming is the fact that between 25 and 50 percent of these children were currently on child protective service caseloads or known to local protective service workers at the time of their death (Daro & Mitchel, 1988). Investigations of these deaths suggest that some percentage might have been prevented through more careful monitoring or assessments of family members and earlier, more comprehensive interventions.

Developing prevention services is not only good program planning, it is also good economic planning. Quite simply, the costs associated with remediating the consequences of maltreatment are staggering, as reported in a detailed benefit-cost analysis developed by Daro (1988). Initially, serious physical abuse cases, a category that represents only 3 percent of all reports, costs society annually at least $20 million in hospitalization costs and $7 million in rehabilitation costs to address the victims' immediate physical injuries and development problems. Further, in 1983, reported cases of child abuse cost society a minimum of $460 million in administrative and foster care placement costs. The types of intensive treatment services offered by federal demonstration programs suggest that thoughtful interventions with families reported for maltreatment can run between $2,860 per family per year for lay therapy and supportive services to over $28,000 per family per year for comprehensive therapeutic services, including remedial services for children. If only the severely abused children reported in 1983 received these intensive therapeutic services for one year, the costs would have exceeded $662 million.

In addition to these initial costs, the costs of maltreatment extend over time. Again, using Daro's conservative cost estimates, the long-term costs of abuse include $14.8 million in juvenile court and detention costs and $664 million in long-term foster care costs. Most disturbing is the limitations that serious physical abuse places on our nation's ability to be economically competitive. The 1,200 child abuse fatalities reported in 1986 cost society $645 million in potential future earnings. In 1987, another $608 million in potential earnings was eliminated from our economic future as a result of fatal child maltreatment. Can a society that hopes to compete in the world economy afford to suffer this continuous drain on its future labor pool? Further, the domestic need for a more productive labor force is also growing. Whereas today each 100 workers support 19 aged, these same 100 workers will have to support 38 aged by the end of this century (Ozawa, 1985). Every case of child abuse undercuts our nation's ability to achieve these productivity levels.

The efficient and effective use of public monies to prevent child abuse is a worthwhile goal. However, generating support for intervention into the private family prior to an overt failure on the part of parents to care adequately for or discipline their children is a complex issue. To date, the majority of prevention programs have targeted at-risk populations as defined by various causal theories of maltreatment. As we shall discuss, a wide range of educational and support services have been developed for new parents, teen parents, low-income families, families of children with special needs, and parents exhibiting various behavioral or emotional problems. Future prevention efforts, however, need to move beyond such targeted efforts and incorporate strategies that alter the normative standards of discipline and enhance a sense of community-wide responsibility for a child's well-being.

PREVENTION SERVICES

Similar to the history of child abuse treatment, the early conceptualization of child abuse prevention also drew heavily on standard medical practice. Prevention, in the context of health planning, can occur at three levels: primary prevention—targeting services to the general population with the objective of stopping any new reports of a given disease or condition; secondary prevention—targeting services to specific high-risk groups in order to avoid the continued spread of the disease or condition; and tertiary prevention—targeting services to victims of the disease or condition with the intent of minimizing its impact or negative consequences (Blum, 1974).

Although it has been argued that the lack of definitional clarity surrounding child abuse has made it difficult to define precisely what constitutes primary, secondary, and tertiary prevention, the field has successfully identified different programs for each of these intervention levels. In applying the medical model of prevention to child maltreatment, primary prevention has been limited to services or social policies aimed at individuals (primarily infants) or at a socially defined subset of individuals for the purpose of ensuring that the abuse never occurs; secondary prevention to services targeted to an individual or group of individuals identified as at high risk for purposes of ensuring that their offspring are not abused; and tertiary prevention to services initiated after maltreatment has occurred to prevent reincidence of abuse or neglect (Helfer, 1982).

Today the clinical and political climate for prevention is quite positive. Although disappointment in the overall effectiveness of treatment services has contributed to the increased interest in prevention among practitioners, the availability of funding for prevention efforts has certainly influenced the rapid development and dissemination of these strategies. In the past several years, most states have passed legislation to support prevention programs in general or to ensure the universal provision of a specific intervention.

One of the most innovative and widely disseminated sources for child abuse prevention funding is the Children's Trust Fund, a concept conceived in the late 1970s by Dr. Ray Helfer of the Michigan State University School of Medicine. A pioneer in the area of child abuse identification and treatment. Helfer designed the fund as a way of securing support for prevention efforts in an era of diminishing governmental budgets and increasing scrutiny of public responsibilities. Since 1980, advocates for child abuse prevention have established trust and prevention funds in 49 states; 29 states enacted these funds between 1985 and 1989.

The majority of children's trust and prevention funds incorporate innovative funding models using a variety of public and private sources. The most common public sources are appropriations; state income tax checkoffs; increased fees on marriage licenses, divorce petitions, birth certificates, and death certificates; and the sale of "family heirloom" birth certificates. In addition to these mechanisms, over one-third of the funds receive direct donations from private sources (Scott & Birch, 1986).

The governing boards of the trust and prevention funds are intended to create public-private partnerships within the states they serve. Board members generally include representatives from governmental agencies working to prevent child abuse and neglect, such as education, social services, mental health, law enforcement, and criminal justice. In addition, private citizens are appointed by the governor and the legislative leadership of the state. The responsibilities of the boards vary from state to state; they can be advisory or administrative, or both.

Eighteen of the 47 funds provide for placing one-half of the monies raised into a trust account; interest earned from the account is used to secure a permanent funding source for programs. In addition, the Child Abuse Prevention Federal Challenge Grant has been in effect since 1984, providing up to a 25 percent match in the prevention monies collected by the states. Currently, the federal challenge grant has an annual appropriation of $5 million.

A survey of the children's trust and prevention funds conducted by the National Committee for Prevention of Child Abuse in 1988 noted that over $27 million had been raised by these funds in 1987. This figure represents a 17 percent increase over the documented 1986 revenue levels, an increase significantly larger than the 2 percent increase in reports of child abuse noted during the same period. Almost 45 percent of these dollars are generated through direct applications from state legislatures, 20 percent of the money is generated by surcharges on documentary fees, and 15 percent comes from income tax checkoff systems. The balance of funding (20 percent) is obtained through other sources such as private donations or interest income.

A total of 39 trust fund administrators provided detailed expenditure data. Based on these data, over $21 million was allocated in 1987 to support more than 1,200 programs, over 20 percent more programs than were funded the year before. The distribution of these programs by prevention service category is as follows:

28 percent are parenting education programs, over 40 percent of which directly target teens.

21 percent are life skills training for children and young adults, three-quarters of which provide child assault prevention instructions to children and one-quarter of which provide interpersonal skills training or prepenting training for teens.

12 percent are support programs for new parents.

8 percent are public information and educational programs.

8 percent are services for abused and neglected children.

7 percent are self-help groups and other neighborhood support programs.

4 percent are crisis intervention services including telephone hotlines, respite care programs, and crisis counseling.

4 percent are public awareness campaigns, including the development of public service announcements.

8 percent are other types of prevention services, including day care, program evaluation, and community development efforts.

Child abuse prevention represents a major challenge for our society. Effective prevention systems need to include a variety of therapeutic, educational, and support services targeted to potential victims, potential perpetrators, and aspects of the social fabric that nurture abusive behaviors. On balance, two major prevention avenues have generated the most interest in terms of the number of providers and researchers attracted. The first group, the parenting enhancement models, includes efforts aimed at parents perceived to be at higher than average risk of being physically abusive or neglectful. Evaluations of these programs have produced encouraging findings with respect to improving parenting skills and child development knowledge, particularly with teenage mothers. This body of research also include the best empirical evidence of a reduction in actual child abuse rates resulting from such early interventions. The second group, the child empowerment service models, is a more homogenous cluster of strategies that target their efforts to the potential victims of abuse, enabling them to resist threats of maltreatment, particularly sexual assault. In contrast to the gradual development of parenting enhancement services, the proliferation of child assault prevention curricula and related materials has outpaced research findings. The remainder of this chapter reviews the empirical evidence on these two prevention strategies and the implications of this research for future practice and policy.

PARENTING ENHANCEMENT SERVICES

The richest body of empirical evidence regarding the effectiveness of prevention services is found among programs that offer specific services to high-risk parents. The content and structure of these programs vary, but they share certain critical service goals:

> Increasing the parent's knowledge of child development and the demands of parenting
>
> Enhancing the parent's skill in coping with the stresses of infant and child care

Enhancing parent-child bonding, emotional ties, and communication
Increasing the parent's skill in coping with the stress of caring for children with special needs
Increasing the parent's knowledge about home and child management
Reducing the burden of child care
Increasing access to social and health services for all family members

Both home-based programs and center-based programs incorporating these goals have demonstrated a wide range of positive client outcomes. Specific gains have included improved mother-infant bonding and maternal capacity to respond to the child's emotional needs (Affholter et al., 1983; Dickie & Gerber 1980; Field et al., 1980; O'Connor et al., 1980); a demonstrated ability to care for the child's physical and developmental needs (Field et al., 1980; Gabinet, 1979; Gray, 1983; Gutelius et al., 1977; Larson, 1980; Love et al., 1976; Olds et al., 1986; Travers et al., 1982); fewer subsequent pregnancies (Badger, 1981; Olds et al., 1986; McAnarney et al., 1978); more consistent use of health care services and job training opportunities (Powell, 1986); and lower welfare use, higher school completion rates, and higher employment rates (Badger, 1981; Gutelius et al., 1977; Seitz et al., 1985; Powell, 1986; Polit, 1987). In identifying the types of parents most likely to benefit from these educational and supportive services, several have noted particular success with young, relatively poor mothers (Badger, 1981; Gabinet, 1979; Olds et al., 1986) and with mothers who felt confident in their lives prior to enrolling in the program (Powell, 1986).

At least two longitudinal studies suggest that comprehensive parenting services not only produce initial gains but also that these gains are strengthened over time. Seitz and her colleagues (1985) successfully tracked, ten years later, 15 of 17 matched sets of families, half of whom had received a coordinated set of medical and social servies, including day care for their children. Following the birth of the baby, the team pediatricians saw the mother and the baby daily in the hospital and scheduled an initial home visit following discharge. Each family received 13 to 17 well-baby visits; an average of 28 home visits by a social worker, psychologist, or nurse; and 2 to 28 months of day care services over the entire treatment period. Families were enrolled from pregnancy through 20 months postpartum.

Although the sample is small and was limited to first-time mothers, repeated follow-up studies on the treatment families noted a steady improvement from termination to five years later and then to the ten-year posttermination study. Specific differences included the mother's level of education, the family's financial independence, and the child's school performance. For example, average educational achievement for treatment mothers was 13.0 years, whereas the control sample had an average of only 11.7. Further, over 85 percent of the treatment families had at least one full-time wage earner or equivalent, a situation that was true for only 53 percent of the control families. Significant differences were also noted between the two groups of children in terms of school performance. Independent ratings by the children's elementary school teachers indicated positive adjustment for almost two-thirds of the 16 treatment children, a rating given to only 26 percent of the 15 control children.

Similar gains were noted in a five-year follow-up of 32 multirisk families who received intensive, comprehensive services through the Clinical Infant Development Program (CIDP) of the National Institute of Mental Health (Wieder et al., 1988). Unlike the previous study, all of the women in this sample had at least one other child prior to project enrollment. The three components of this multiyear program were organizing basic services for adequate food, housing, medical care, and educational opportunities; providing a constant emotional relationship with the family in order to establish trust; and providing specialized services to the infant and parents geared to meet the challenges at each stage of development.

Significant gains were noted on all of the dimensions tested. Although many of the families continued to exhibit some functional problems, economic and personal improvements were significant. Over 60 percent of the adult mothers and almost three-quarters of the women initially seen as teen parents were employed at follow-up, a factor that accounted for a significant drop in the percentage of clients receiving welfare. Further, only 5 percent of the adult program participants were reported for child abuse during the five-year period, and none of these reports involved the child who had received services as part of this program.

The work of David Olds and his colleagues (1986) has provided some of the best empirical evidence to date that the provision of a specific service model does indeed reduce the incidence of child abuse and neglect. The 400 participants in this study, all of whom were first-time mothers, were randomly assigned to one of four conditions in which the most intensive level of services involved regular prenatal and postnatal home visits by a nurse practitioner. The nurse home visitors carried out three major activities: parent education regarding fetal and infant development, the involvement of family members and friends in child care and support of the mother, and the linkage of family members with other health and human services.

Those who received the most intensive intervention had a significantly lower incidence of reported child abuse over the two-year postbirth study period. Whereas 19 percent of the comparison group at greatest risk for maltreatment (i.e., poor, unmarried teens) were reported for abuse or neglect, only 4 percent of their nurse-visited counterparts were reported. Of these cases, 50 percent involved reports of neglect only and 50 percent involved reports of neglect and physical abuse. Although these results were not true for older program participants, the dramatic gains realized with first-time teen mothers suggest that this group may benefit particularly from prevention services. In addition to having a lower reported rate of child abuse, infants whose mothers received nurse home visits had fewer accidents and were less likely to require emergency room care. The mothers also reported a less frequent need to punish or restrict their children.

The use of home visitors has been identified by others as achieving notable gains in parent-child interactions and in improving children's developmental progress. For example, Project 12-Ways, a multifaceted home-based service program in central Illinois, provides intensive services to families who have been reported to the state Department of Children and Family Services (DCFS) for abuse, neglect, or being at risk of abuse or neglect. Educational and support services are provided to program participants in their homes by advanced graduate students in the Behavior Analysis and Therapy Program at Southern Illinois University. The specific topics covered during these home visits include parenting skills, stress management, self-control, assertiveness training, health maintenance, job placement, and marital counseling. Repeated evaluations of the program (Lutzker & Rice, 1984, 1987) have documented significantly fewer repeated abuse and neglect incidents among program participants than among DCFS clients not receiving this intervention. While enrolled in the program, only 2 percent of a randomly selected number of Project 12-Ways' clients were reported for maltreatment, compared to 11 percent of the control group. In the year following termination of services, 10 percent of the treatment families and 21 percent of the nontreatment families were reported for maltreatment.

Larson (1980) noted similar gains in an assessment of the Prenatal Intervention Project in Montreal, but only in cases in which such visits began prior to the child's birth. In this case, the home visitors were women with undergraduate degrees in child psychology who had received special training in preventive child health care. The home visits were designed to provide information about general caretaking topics, such as feeding, sleep schedules, clothing, accident prevention, and the need for regular well-child care. The visitors also encouraged the mothers to talk to their infants during caregiving and to respond to their vocalizations. Child development counseling involved reviewing with the mother her child's developmental competence and suggesting activities that she could engage in to promote the child's capabilities.

The subjects, all of whom were working-class mothers, were randomly assigned to one of three conditions: early visiting, which involved approximately 11 visits between the seventh month of pregnancy and one year postpartum; late visiting, which involved approximately 11 visits between six weeks and one year postpartum; and a control condition in which no visits were made. The early-visited group showed a significant advantage over both of the other groups in several areas. The children in the early-visited group had a lower accident rate and exhibited fewer feeding problems, and the mothers scored higher on assessments of maternal behavior and in providing appropriate and stimulating home environments. Also, more fathers participated in the early-visited group.

Recently, positive findings have been noted among programs providing services for a relatively short period of time. For example, Taylor and Beauchamp (1988) reported notable differences in parenting knowledge, skills, and attitudes among participants receiving four visits by a student nurse volunteer compared to a no-service control group. Program participants received one visit while in the hospital and three subsequent home visits one, two and three months postpartum. Each visit lasted approximately 90 minutes and covered the issues of stress management, family adjustment following birth, parenting patterns, utilization of resources, child development, and child management. Participants in both the treatment group and the control group were assessed one month and three months postpartum by interviewers unaware of the participants' group membership. Assessment instruments included pen-and-pencil tests regarding child development knowledge and parenting attitudes, an observational videotape of the mother preparing the infant for bed, and an open-ended interview to assess parent competence. Those who received the visits scored significantly higher on tests of child development, expressed more democratic ideas regarding child rearing, had more positive parent-infant interactions, and demonstrated greater problem-solving abilities.

A number of parenting enhancement models using a center-based service delivery method have also produced positive gains in overall parenting skills and in the use of community resources (Levine, 1988). For example, Avancé Educational Programs for Parents and Teens serves a predominantly low-income Mexican-American community in San Antonio through the provision of comprehensive parenting education. The nine-month service period includes center-based weekly bilingual discussions on child growth and development, toy-making classes, day care practicum, field trips, library use, transportation, information and referral, and communal holiday celebrations. Evaluations of these efforts have found participants to be more hopeful about the future, to be more willing to assume the role of educator with their children, to hold less severe conceptions of punishment, and to be more willing to utilize social supports to gain help (Rodriguez & Cortz, 1988).

One of the most widely disseminated group-based models is the Minnesota Early Learning Demonstration (MELD), an intensive two-year parenting education and support program. Since its inception in 1975, six specific programs have been developed: MELD for New Parents, MELD for Young Moms, MELD Plus for growing families, La Familia/MELD for Hispanic families, MELD Special for parents of children with specific needs, and HIPP/MELD for hearing-impaired parents. Each program's purpose is to provide the most useful information available in the most supportive environment that can be created. MELD's mission is to get families off to a good start and to eliminate the potential for maltreatment by never letting abusive or neglectful patterns begin. MELD staffers believe that there is no one right way to parent and encourage participants to make the child-rearing choices that are appropriate for them and their children. The program demonstrates that if participants are supported in their efforts to be good parents and if they are exposed to good information and alternative ways of addressing child-rearing issues, they will be able to make the choices that enhance their children's well-being as well as their own.

Although the program has never been evaluated in terms of child abuse prevention, the immediate outcomes demonstrated by program participants are encouraging (Ellwood, 1988; Miller, 1988). A recent evaluation of the MELD Young Moms program conducted by the Child Welfare League of America noted that 80 percent of the participants had finished or were completing high school, compared to an overall school completion rate of only 20 percent for the general adolescent parent population. Also, while 25 percent of all teenage mothers experience a repeat pregnancy within a year of their first birth, MELD Young Mom participants have a repeat pregnancy rate of only 10 to 15 percent. Changes were also noted in the parents'use of discipline, where the percentage of parents who spanked their children decreased from 56 percent at the start of the program to only 12 percent at the conclusion of services.

The collective results just outlined underscore the difficulty in addressing the myriad of issues associated with an increased risk for maltreatment under the rubric of a single service framework. Offering services in a client's home has a number of distinct advantages, particularly when the objective is to reduce the likelihood of maltreatment. Such services offer the provider an excellent opportunity to assess the safety of the child's living environment and to work with the mother in very concrete ways to improve parent-child interactions. The method also affords the client a degree of privacy and the practitioner a degree of flexibility difficult to achieve in center-based programs.

The method, however, is not without drawbacks. The costs of these programs can be quite substantial, particularly if, as in the case of the Olds (1986) study, the home visitors are nurse practitioners or clinical social workers. Even if trained paraprofessionals or volunteers are used, the strategy is labor-intensive and involves considerable transportation costs. Also, the one-to-one service model places a tremendous burden on the individual provider. Musiak and colleagues (1987) found that staff members' expectations of themselves and of their clients play a significant role in the extent to which material is accurately presented and the extent to which clients respond in a positive manner. Further, the home setting makes it potentially more difficult to focus on parent-child relationships or on a given set of parenting skills. Often clients are not prepared for the worker's visit although these appointments may be longstanding (Baskin et al., 1987). A clinician may need to spend considerable time focusing the mother on the issues or tasks to be addressed during the visit and away from the normal, daily distractions found in home settings.

In contrast, parenting services offered through a community-based family service center or health care facility provide participants with an opportunity to share child-rearing and personal problems with other parents in similar situations. Strategies such as the MELD program establish an ongoing support group for parents to draw on both during and outside the actual service delivery process, further reducing the level of isolation. Often the place where group meetings are held becomes identified as a general support center for all parents to use in addressing a wide range of issues. In this sense, the strategy serves as a foundation for a more universal child abuse prevention effort in which parents seeking assistance need not first be identified as requiring "special" services.

The major difficulty that these programs face is the organizational demands they place on group participants. Regular attendance at weekly group meetings requires a good deal of motivation and structure on the part of a young mother. Evaluations of these efforts suggest that only a fraction of participants are able to demonstrate this level of control. Dropout rates of as high as 40 to 50 percent have been noted by several program reviewers (Johnson & Breckenridge

1982; Lochman & Brown, 1980). Unlike the home-based models, continued participation in a center-based program is contingent on a parent's willingness to cope with the transportation and child care demands inherent in attending any event outside of one's home.

Reaching the full spectrum of the at-risk population requires some combination of both methods as well as the provision of crisis intervention services and respite care. Center-based services, particularly if they are associated with local junior and senior high school programs for adolescent parents, offer excellent opportunities for a highly motivated teenage mother not only to improve her parenting skills but also to continue her education and to establish a stable life for herself and her infant. Home-based programs, with their more individualized and flexible service delivery system, are particularly useful with a more isolated population and with mothers who lack the interest or the motivation to participate in a group program. Crisis intervention and respite services must be added to both of these strategies to provide a safety valve for new parents.

CHILD EMPOWERMENT SERVICE MODELS

As discussed so far, the prevention of physical abuse and neglect has focused primarily on altering parental behavior or on providing parents under stress an opportunity to seek help before they strike out at their child. In contrast, the prevention of child sexual abuse has centered on the provision of child assault prevention instructions in the schools, a strategy aimed at altering the behavior of children. This intervention provides classroom-based instruction for children of all ages on how to protect themselves from sexual assault and what to do if they experience actual or potential abuse. A survey of over 250 school districts nationwide found that virtually all schools offer this instruction to both their elementary and high school students (Daro et al., 1988).

Methods for providing this instruction vary along a number of key dimensions, including the characteristics and background of the instructor, the frequency of the presentations, and the specific content of the message. All of the programs, however, share a number of common goals and objectives:

> Direct instruction to the child on the distinction between good, bad, and questionable touching
>
> The concept of body ownership or the rights of children to control who touches their bodies and where they are touched
>
> The concept of keeping secrets and the importance of the child to tell if someone touches him or her even if that person tells the child not to reveal the incident
>
> The ability to act on one's intuition regarding when a touch or an action makes a child feel uncomfortable even if the child does not know why he or she is uncomfortable
>
> Assertiveness skills, ranging from repeatedly saying no to someone who wants to do something that makes a child feel uncomfortable to the use of various self-defense techniques (e.g., yelling, kicking, fighting back)
>
> The existence of support systems to help the child who experiences any form of maltreatment

In addition, all of the programs include some type of orientation or instruction for both parents and school personnel. These sessions cover a number of topics, including a review of the materials to be presented to the children, a summary of the local child abuse reporting system, a discussion of what to do if someone suspects that a child has been mistreated, and a review of local services available to victims and their families.

Evaluations of these programs have increased dramatically in recent years and have documented several notable gains, especially with elementary school–aged children. A recent review of 25 such studies indicate that these evaluations consistently report that significant learning follows the presentations (Finkelhor & Strapka, in press). Participants who have received these instructions demonstrate an increase in knowledge about safety rules and are more aware of what to do and whom to turn to if they have been or are being abused. However, children have greater difficulty in accepting the idea that abuse can occur at the hands of someone they know. Further, the programs create an environment in which children can more easily disclose prior or ongoing maltreatment. In other words, independent of the impact these programs may have on future behavior, they do offer an opportunity for present victims to reach out for help, thereby preventing continued abuse.

As for future impacts, relatively little is known about whether these efforts actually reduce the likelihood for sexual abuse. Although at least one study has documented a change in a child's behavior toward strangers following receipt of this intervention, these gains were most notable among children who displayed a strong sense of self-image prior to the intervention (Fryer et al., 1987). Additional questions have been raised regarding the appropriateness of this intervention for preschool children (Gilbert, 1988). Some knowledge acquisition has been found among 4- and 5-year-olds, but these gains are generally less than those noted for older children. Further, since young children are dependent on adults for their care, it may be inappropriate as well as unrealistic to expect preschool programs to decrease the likelihood for abuse significantly.

Recognition of these shortcomings has led to the development of more skill-oriented training among a number of providers. For example, the Seattle-based Committee for Children revised its preschool materials to deemphasize a child's need to rely on his or her own feelings. Instead, the most recent version of *Talking about Touching: Personal Safety for Preschoolers and Kindergartners* (Committee for Children, 1988) establishes specific rules for children to apply to various situations. A long-term comprehensive program involving 27 lessons presented over a 12-month period, the curriculum extends to areas of personal safety the types of rule-oriented guidelines children are given regarding fire and traffic safety (do not play with matches, look both ways before crossing a street, etc.). Children learn to determine "safe" and "unsafe" touching on the basis of simple, straightforward guidelines such as "No one should touch your private parts, and if someone does, you should tell an adult." In this way, the burden of determining appropriateness is placed on adults rather than on the child.

Similarly, the Children Need to Know Personal Safety Program, developed by Sherryll Kerns Kraizer, relies on roleplaying to teach children the following concepts:

> Your body belongs to you.
>
> You have a right to speak up anytime someone touches you in a way that you don't like, that makes you feel uncomfortable, or that you think is wrong.
>
> Speaking up effectively includes using your words, body language, and eye contact.
>
> If a person doesn't stop after your first request, say, "I'm going to tell if you don't stop."
>
> Tell and keep telling until someone listens and helps you.
>
> Touch should never have to be a secret.

Critical to this ten-session program is the repeated application of various role-plays in which children are given an opportunity to respond to the range of ploys frequently used by molesters to engage their victims, such as bribery, emotional coercion, indifference, intimidation, and threats.

Evaluations of this approach have found it to be effective in strengthening a child's ability to resist abusive situations. In an experimental study involving 66 children in kindergarten through grade 2 randomly assigned to experimental treatment and control conditions, significant differences between the two groups were noted following program implementation. Most notable were an increased likelihood for members in the experimental group to declare that they would tell a responsible adult of an incident both when coerced and when asked to keep the encounter a secret (Kraizer & Fryer, 1987).

The widespread provision of child assault prevention instruction represents the first attempts at confronting the child abuse problem by strengthening potential victims to resist or at least not quietly accept mistreatment. To say this, however, does not minimize the need for further research and reform. Underscoring all of these efforts must be a commitment to evaluate program effectiveness with children of all ages, to monitor the relationship of these programs to later learning, and to study how young children today are coping with the increasing references to sexual abuse and child abductions in all aspects of their lives. Model curricula need to be developed, implemented, and evaluated that place greater emphasis on the role of parents and day care providers in conveying safety concepts to children as well as creating safer environments for children.

Further, child assault prevention programs need to expand their explicit outcomes. Knowledge regarding child sexual abuse, the need for a child to tell an adult if he or she is threatened or abused, and the need for a child to avoid risky situations are all important messages. Equally important, however, is the need to continue to develop accurate measures of the ability of these programs to enhance positive self-awareness and solid decision-making skills. Research on young adults involved in various problem behaviors such as teen pregnancy, drug use, and delinquency suggest that these individuals frequently share an inability to cope with the demands of modern living. Educators have identified a common set of skills as essential for rejecting these behaviors in favor of more appropriate, healthy, and productive life choices. These attributes include communication skills, problem-solving and planning skills, assertiveness skills, negotiated conflict resolution, friendship skills, peer resistance skills, low-risk choice-making skills, stress reduction skills, self-improvement skills, consumer awareness skills, self-awareness skills, critical thinking skills, and basic academic skills (Benard, 1989). To the extent that child assault prevention programs mature into curricula that offer explicit opportunities for this type of skill building to occur, such programs enhance their ability to prevent not only child abuse but also a host of other dilemmas children face.

SUMMARY AND FUTURE DIRECTIONS

Intuitively, the notion of preventing child abuse is attractive from both a humanitarian and child advocacy perspective and a social cost perspective. Children have a right not to be mistreated, and society as a whole has a responsibility to protect the future generation from such harm at the hands of its parents or caretakers. Although intervention to remediate the negative consequences of maltreatment can be considered society's minimal responsibility, policies aimed at avoiding the initial abuse are particularly attractive in that the child does not have to experience harm before services are made available and society is able to avoid the significant costs of long-term therapeutic interventions.

The National Committee for Prevention of Child Abuse has outlined a comprehensive approach to reduce child abuse and neglect rates that includes the following elements (Cohn, 1983):

> Educational and support services for all new parents around the time their children are born
>
> Continued opportunities for parenting education to help parents adjust to the ever-changing demands of their children
>
> Early and regular child and family screening and treatment to ensure prompt attention to any health or developmental problems
>
> Adequate child care opportunities to furnish parents with quality regular and occasional out-of-home care for their children
>
> Programs for abused and neglected children to remediate the immediate consequences of maltreatment and to minimize the risk of additional functioning problems as the child matures
>
> Life skills training for children and young adults to equip them with the interpersonal skills and knowledge they will need in their future adult roles and in protecting themselves from being abused
>
> Self-help groups and other neighborhood supports to foster a sense of community responsibility and care for the well-being of parents and children

Realizing these service and policy elements is a formidable task. At a minimum, energies must focus on three areas:

> Institutionalizing child abuse prevention services within agencies that have ongoing contact with families and children
>
> Encouraging all individuals to serve as a resource for parents under stress

Eliminating cultural norms and values that promote the use of violence toward children (and others)

Expansion of Services and Supports for Parents

As things stand now, it remains important for all parents to receive quality assistance throughout their child-rearing years. To accomplish this task, prevention services must be more fully integrated into institutions that interact with parents. For example, all local hospitals with maternity wards need to develop education and support services for all women delivering at their facilities. Initially these services might be limited to first-time parents, gradually expanding to include all new mothers and fathers. Further, all local junior and senior high school administrators need to integrate parenting and life skills education into the standard curriculum. In addition, all high school districts should develop and implement a comprehensive educational and support program for pregnant and parenting teens. Key services to include in such a program would be day care, vocational training, support groups, and financial planning.

The provision of parenting classes through local school districts is already under way in Missouri and Minnesota, although in both cases funding for these programs is woefully inadequate. The Early Childhood Family Education Program establishes weekly in-class discussions for all adults who are pregnant or have children under the age of 5. Each session includes a 15- to 45-minute parent-child interaction period. While available for all parents, only 6 percent of the target population was served in 1987. Similarly, the Missouri Parents as Teachers program provides funding to serve only 30 percent of the parents of children under the age of 3, although all parents are technically eligible.

Prevention advocates also need to integrate parent enhancement services into the broad range of organizations with which parents interact. Both home visitor programs and center-based education and support groups must be established, thereby providing a network of services for parents with different personal skills and needs. Local churches, recreational centers, housing associations, day care collectives, and civic organizations must all be engaged in supporting parents in their local community, either directly, through the development and implementation of a new parent program, or indirectly, by contributing volunteers or funding to existing efforts.

Equal to the expansion of services to parents must be an expansion of direct services to children. Child assault prevention programs need to be well integrated into broader curricula emphasizing solid decision-making skills and social competence. Further, teachers and child care professionals need expanded training on how best to support children in crisis, recognizing the signs of child abuse or neglect. Rather than relying on such instruction to exist independent of the educational system, such instruction must be considered as essential to the educational development of a student as the enhancement of cognitive skills.

Not all victims of maltreatment repeat the cycle of violence or neglect they experienced in raising their children. However, research has found that victims of maltreatment are six times more likely than nonabused children to mistreat their own children (Kaufman & Ziegler, 1989). Such a correlation underscores the need to include the provision of therapeutic services to victims of maltreatment in any comprehensive prevention strategy. Unfortunately, local child protective service administrators report that they are able to provide remedial or therapeutic services to fewer than one-third of the victims they identify (Daro & Mitchel, 1988). The expansion of such services as therapeutic preschool, play therapy, and group and individual counseling must rely on both the better intergration of existing service systems and an increase in the total pool of services.

Central to expanding service levels is generating additional revenues in both the public and private sectors. The continued growth of the children's trust and prevention funds in the majority of states is one indicator of expanded public support for prevention. In addition, individual counties are drafting local tax schemes to increase the resources available for children's programs. In Florida, for example, over a dozen counties have passed or initiated referendums to assess homeowners an additional $25 per year to support a juvenile welfare board. The purpose of these boards are to assess the service needs for local children, coordinate efforts presently underway to meet these needs, and support new service initiatives when parent efforts prove inadequate (Volsky, 1988).

Encouraging Individuals to Become Involved

Preventing child abuse requires not only an expansion of formal service systems but also increased capacity among informal sources of support. Simply put, individuals need to become more directly concerned and involved in the prevention process throughout all aspects of their lives. Public opinion polls conducted for NCPCA in recent years have noted that two-thirds of the American public feel that they can do a lot to prevent child abuse, and one-quarter report actually having taken steps to prevent child abuse in the past year. The main personal activities respondents listed were reporting someone for abuse (21 percent), not abusing or hitting their own children (16 percent), working as a volunteer or counselor (17 percent), speaking to a friend or relative about abuse (13 percent), educating adults on how not to be abusive of children or how not to be victimized (12 percent), stopping someone from hitting a child (5 percent), and serving as foster parents (3 percent).

For many individuals, the hardest thing to do is to interfere in the rearing of children. Many find it difficult to talk with close friends or relatives about their parenting, not to mention approaching a stranger. However, until individuals demonstrate such concern, family violence will continue. To assist individuals in overcoming their fears of reaching out and offering assistance to parents in stress, the Franklin County Children's Task Force in Farmington, Maine, published the following supportive things to say to parents and children in abusive or near-abusive situations:

> "She seems to be trying your patience."
> "It looks like it's been a long day for both of you."
> "He has beautiful (eyes)"—to get the parent in a more positive mood.

"My child used to get upset like that."

"Children can wear you out, can't they? Is there anything I can do to help?"

Strike up a conversation with the adult. See if you can redirect his or her attention away from the child.

Sympathize with the parent, even if it's just a knowing glance or a smile.

Divert the child's attention (if the child is misbehaving) by talking to the child, engaging the child in conversation.

Praise the child and/or the parent at the first opportunity.

If the child is in danger, offer assistance. For example, if the child was left unattended in a grocery cart, stand by the child until the parent returns.

Offering such assistance to parents under stress might be viewed as an intrusion into their privacy. However, when such support is offered in the non-judgmental manner outlined here, it not only provides a break in a potentially escalating cycle of violence but also conveys the message that parents are not alone in rearing their children. To the extent that society wants to reap the benefits of a productive next generation, each member of society has the responsibility to protect children from behaviors that might limit their potential to achieve these objectives.

Ending Violence toward Children

Preventing physical abuse requires the elimination of all forms of violence toward children. Gelles and Straus (1988) have called for the development of a cultural ethic that hitting children is inappropriate, citing the ban on corporal punishment passed by the Swedish legislators in 1979. "After nearly two decades of research on the causes and consequences of family violence," they write, "we are convinced that our society must abandon its reliance on spanking children if we are to prevent intimate violence" (p. 197).

The widespread acceptance of physical punishment, as evidence by Gelles and Straus's own work, bode against achieving any type of legislative ban on spanking in the near future. However, several interim steps toward this long-term objective can be implemented. First, every state can ban the use of corporal punishment in its schools. As of 1988, 11 states and several local municipalities had passed such legislation, suggesting that political resources and public support can be successfully marshaled around this issue (Moelis, 1989).

Second, organizations and parent groups that are reluctant to support an outright ban on corporal punishment should find greater agreement among their memberships regarding a ban on the use of corporal punishment with infants. Although over 90 percent of parents with 3- or 4-year-olds report using physical punishment, only 21 percent of parents with infants report using this method of discipline (Wauchope & Straus, 1987). Certainly, members of any group concerned with the welfare of children would agree that the most vulnerable members of society, children under 1 year of age, should be afforded maximum protection from physical mistreatment regardless of the label used.

Finally, parenting education and support services must offer parents clear and workable alternatives to physical punishment. Haeuser (1988) suggests that unlike Swedish society, which for a variety of reasons can accept a law prohibiting all physical punishment, our society must depend on establishing a highly visible child-rearing norm that parents can adopt voluntarily. Greater care must be taken in documenting not only the negative consequences of repeated and often excessive physical punishment but also the positive results of alternative discipline methods. Behavioral modification techniques that rely on consistency, fairness, and negotiations not only move children away from negative behaviors but also instill the positive values and skills necessary for healthy personal development and social integration. To the extent that parents can be made to realize that they and their children have much to gain by avoiding corporal punishment, the more likely they are to withdraw voluntarily from this most damaging practice.

Some people argue that prevention is extremely problematic within any reasonable scope of fiscal effort and within the values of a free society that gives people the right to be left alone. Also, to promote new discipline standards that do not rely on the use of corporal punishment is to advocate behavior contrary to the parenting realities in the majority of American homes. Despite these difficulties, responding only after the fact ensures the continuous need for society to deal with the victims that dysfunctional families, individuals, and social policies will inevitably produce.

REFERENCES

AFFHOLTER, D., D. CONNELL, AND M. NAUTA. (1983). "Evaluation of the Child and Family Resource Program: Early Evidence of Parent-Child Interaction Effects. *Evaluation Review, 7,* 65–79.

American Association for Protecting Children. (1988). *Highlights of Official Child Neglect and Abuse Reporting.* Denver: American Humane Association.

BADGER, E. (1981). "Effects of a Parent Education Program on Teenage Mothers and Their Offspring." In K. G. Scott, T. Field, and E. Robertson (Eds.), *Teenage Parents and Their Offspring.* Orlando, Fla.: Grune & Stratton.

BASKIN, C., W. UMANSKY, AND W. SANDERS. (1987). "Influencing the Responsiveness of Adolescent Mothers to Their Infants." *Zero to Three, 8,*(2), 7–11.

BENARD, B. (1989). "*Life Skills for Children and Youth.*" Paper presented at the Children's Trust Fund Forum, January 27, Austin, Texas.

BLUM, H. (1974). *Planning for Health: Development and Application of Social Change Theory.* New York: Human Sciences Press.

BOLTON, F., AND S. BOLTON. (1987). *Working with Violent Families: A Guide for Clinical and Legal Practitioners.* Newbury Park, Calif.: Sage.

COHN, A. (1983). *An Approach to Preventing Child Abuse.* Chicago: National Committee for Prevention of Child Abuse.

COHN, A., AND D. DARO. (1988). "Is Treatment Too Late? What Ten Years of Evaluative Research Tell Us." *Child Abuse and Neglect, 11,* 433–442.

Committee for Children. (1988). *Talking about Touching: Personal Safety for Preschoolers and Kindergartners.* Seattle: Committee for Children.

DARO, D. (1988). *Confronting Child Abuse.* New York: Free Press.

DARO, D., N. ABRAHAMS, AND K. ROBSON. (1988). *Reducing Child Abuse 20% by 1990: 1985–1986 Baseline Data.* Chicago: National Committee for Prevention of Child Abuse.

DARO, D., AND L. MITCHEL. (1988). *Deaths Due to Maltreatment Soar: The Results of the Eight Semi-annual Fifty-State Survey.* Chicago: National Committee for Prevention of Child Abuse.

DICKIE, J., AND S. GERBER. (1980). "Training in Social Competence: The Effects on Mothers, Fathers, and Infants." *Child Development, 51,* 1248–1251.

ELLWOOD, A. (1988). "Prove to Me that MELD Makes a Difference." In H. Weiss and F. Jacobs (Eds.), *Evaluating Family Programs.* Hawthorne, N.Y.: Aldine.

FIELD, T., S. WIDMAYER, S. STRINGER, AND E. IGNATOFF. (1980). "Teenage, Lower-Class, Black Mothers and Their Pre-term Infants: An Intervention and Developmental Follow-up." *Child Development, 5,* 426–436.

FINKELHOR, D. (1984). *Child Sexual Abuse: New Theory and Research.* New York: Free Press.

FINKELHOR, D., AND N. STRAPKA. (1991). "Sexual Abuse Prevention Education: A Review of Evaluation Studies." In D. Willis, W. Holden, and M. Rosenberg (Eds.), *Child Abuse Prevention.* New York: Wiley.

FRYER, G., S, KRAIZER, AND T. MIYOSKI. (1987). "Measuring Actual Reduction of Risk to Child Abuse: A New Approach." *Child Abuse and Neglect, 11,* 173–179.

GABINET, L. (1979). "Prevention of Child Abuse and Neglect in an Inner-City Population: II. The Program and the Results." *Child Abuse and Neglect, 3,* 809–817.

GELLES, R., AND M. STRAUS. (1988). *Intimate Violence: The Causes and Consequences of Abuse in the American Family.* New York: Simon & Schuster.

GIL D. (1970). *Violence Against Children.* Cambridge, MA: Harvard University Press.

GILBERT, N. (Fall, 1988). "Teaching Children to Prevent Sexual Abuse." *Public Interest, 93,* 3–15.

GRAY, E. (1983). *Final Report: Collaborative Research of Community and Minority Group Action to Prevent Child Abuse and Neglect. Volume 1: Perinatal Interventions.* Chicago: National Committee for Prevention of Child Abuse.

GUTELIUS, M., A. KIRSCH, S. MACDONALD, M. BROOKS, AND T. MCERLEAN. (1977). "Controlled Study of Child Health Supervision: Behavior Results." *Pediatrics, 60,* 294–304.

HAEUSER, A. (1988). *"The Physical Punishment Neurosis: Can It Be Cured?"* Paper presented at the National Symposium on Child Victimization, April 27–30, Anaheim, Calif.

HELFER, R. (1982). "A Review of the Literature on the Prevention of Child Abuse and Nelgect." *Child Abuse and Neglect, 6,* 251–261.

HERRENKOHL, R., E. HERRENKOHL, B. EGOLF, AND M. SEECH. (1979). "The Repetition of Child Abuse: How Often Does It Occurs?" *Child Abuse and Neglect, 3,* 67–72.

JOHNSON, D., AND J. BRECKENRIDGE. (1982). "The Houston Parent-Child Development Center and the Primary Prevention of Behavior Problems in Young Children." *American Journal of Community Psychology, 10,* 305–316.

KAUFMAN, J., AND E. ZIEGLER. (1989). "The Intergenerational Transmission of Child Abuse." In D. Cicchetti and V. Carlson (Eds.), *Child Maltreatment: Theory and Research on the Causes and Consequences of Child Abuse and Neglect.* Cambridge: Cambridge University Press. (pp. 129–150).

KRAIZER, S., AND G. FRYER. (1987). *Preventing Child Sexual Abuse: Measuring Actual Behavioral Change Attributable to a School-based Curriculum.* Palisades, N.Y.: Coalition for Children and Health Education Systems.

LARSON, C. (1980). "Efficacy of Prenatal and Postpartum Home Visits on Child Health and Development." *Pediatrics, 66,* 191–197.

LAUGHLIN, J., AND M. WEISS. (1981). "An Outpatient Milieu Therapy Approach to Treatment of Child Abuse and Neglect Problems." *Social Casework, 62*(2), 106–109.

LEVINE, C. (Ed.). (1988). *Programs to Strengthen Families.* Chicago: Family Resource Coalition.

LOCHMAN, J., AND M. BROWN. (1980). "Evaluation of Dropout Clients and of Perceived Usefulness of a Parent Education Program." *Journal of Community Psychology, 8,* 132–139.

LOVE, J., M. NAUTA, C. COELEN, K. HEWETT, AND R. RUOPP. (1876). *National Home Start Evaluation: Final Report, Findings and Implications.* Ypsilanti, Mich.: High Scope Educational Research Foundation.

LUTZKER, J., AND J. RICE. (1984). "Project 12-Ways: Measuring Outcome of a Large In-Home Service for Treatment and Prevention of Child Abuse and Neglect." *Child Abuse and Neglect, 8,* 519–524.

LUTZKER, J., AND J. RICE. (1987). "Using Recidivism Data to Evaluate Project 12-Ways: An Ecobehavioral Approach to the Treatment and Prevention of Child Abuse and Neglect." *Journal of Family Violence, 2,* 283–290.

MCANARNEY, E., K. ROGHMAN, B. ADAMS, R. TATLEBAUM, C. KASH, M. COULTER, M. PLUME, AND E. CHARNEY. (1978). "Obstetric, Neonatal, and Psychosocial Outcome of Pregnant Adolescents." *Pediatrics, 61,* 199–205.

MILLER, S. (1988). "The Child Welfare League of America's Adolescent Parents Projects." In H. Weiss and F. Jacobs (Eds.), *Evaluating Family Programs.* Hawthorne, N.Y.: Aldine.

MOELIS, C. (1989). *Abolishing Corporal Punishment in the Schools: A Call for Action.* Chicago: National Committee for Prevention of Child Abuse.

MUSIAK, J., V. BERNSTEIN, C. PERCANSKY, AND F. STOTT. (1987). "A Chain of Enablement: Using Community-based Programs to Strengthen Relationships between Teen Parents and Their Infants." *Zero to Three, 8*(2), 1–6.

O'CONNOR, S., P. VIETZE, K. SHERROD, H. SANDLER, AND W. ALTEMEIER. (1980). "Reduced Incidence of Parenting Inadequacy Following Rooming-in." *Pediatrics, 66,* 176–182.

OLDS, D., R. CHAMBERLIN, AND R. TATLEBAUM. (1986). "Preventing Child Abuse and Neglect: A Randomized Trial of Nurse Home Visitation." *Pediatrics, 78,* 65–78.

OZAWA, M. (1985). *Public Interest in Children.* Paper presented at the Seabury Lecture, School of Social Welfare, University of California, Berkeley, April 29.

POLIT, D. (1987 January–February). "Routes to Self-sufficiency: Teenage Mothers and Employment." *Children Today,* pp. 6–11.

POWELL, D. (1986 March). "Parent Education and Support Programs." *Young Children,* pp. 47–53.

RODRIGUEZ, G., AND C. CORTEZ. (1988). "The Evaluation Experience of the Avance Parent-Child Education Program." In H. Weiss and F. Jacobs (Eds.),

Evaluating Family Programs. Hawthorne, N.Y.: Aldine.

RUSSELL, D. (1984). *Sexual Exploitation: Rape, Child Sexual Abuse, and Sexual Harassment.* Newbury Park, Calif.: Sage.

SCOTT, J., AND T. BIRCH. (1986). *Summary of Children's Trust Funds* (Working Paper No. 20). Chicago: National Committee for Prevention of Child Abuse.

SEITZ, V., L. ROSENBAUM, AND N. APFEL. (1985). "Effects of Family Support Intervention: A Ten-Year Follow-up." *Child Development, 56,* 376–391.

STRAUS, M., R. GELLES, AND S. STEINMETZ. (1980). *Behind Closed Doors: Violence in the American Family.* Garden City, N.Y.: Anchor/Doubleday.

TAYLOR, D., AND C. BEAUCHAMP. (1988). "Hospital-based Primary Prevention Strategy in Child Abuse: A Multi-level Needs Assessment." *Child Abuse and Neglect, 12,* 343–354.

TRAVERS, J., M. NAUTA, AND N. IRWIN. (1982). *The Effects of a Social Program: Final Report of the Child and Family Resource Program's Infant and Toddler Component.* Cambridge, MA: ABT Associates.

VOLSKY, G. (1988 September 4). "Florida County Will Vote on Child Welfare Plan." *New York Times,* p. 15.

WAUCHOPE, B., AND M. STRAUS. (1987). "*Age, Class, and Gender Difference in Physical Punishment and Physical Abuse of American Children.*" Paper presented at the Third National Conference on Family Violence Research, University of New Hampshire, Durham, July 6–9.

Westat Associates. (1981). *National Study of the Incidence and Severity of Child Abuse and Neglect.* Washington, D.C.: U.S. Government Printing Office.

Westat Associates. (1987). *Study of the National Incidence and Prevalence of Child Abuse and Neglect.* Washington, D.C.: U.S. Government Printing Office.

WIEDER, S., S. POISSON, R. LOURIE, AND S. GREENSPAN. (1988). "Enduring Gains: A Five-Year Follow-up Report on the Clinical Infant Development Program." *Zero to Three, 8*(4), 6–11.

The Crisis of AIDS for Adolescents
The Need for Preventive Interventions

Joanne E. Mantell and Steven P. Schinke | 11

INTRODUCTION

Characterized as the plague of the twentieth century, AIDS is a major crisis for individuals, institutions, communities and society at large, and will continue to be a major public health problem in the 1990s. Every state in the United States and 181 countries had reported cases of AIDS as of March 1, 1990 (U.S. Centers for Disease Control, 1990a; World Health Organization, 1990). More than 222,000 cases* have been cumulatively reported worldwide, and by the end of April 1990, 132,510 of them among Americans (U.S. Centers for Disease Control, 1990a). In 1990, between 52,000 and 57,000 cases are expected to be diagnosed and about another 1 million people are presumed to be infected in the United States (U.S. Centers for Disease Control, 1990b). By 1993, the number of new cases is expected to be between 61,000 and 98,000; between 151,000 and 225,000 people with AIDS will be alive during the year (U.S. Centers for Disease Control, 1990b). With increased survival of people with AIDS and about 80,000 new infections each year, HIV-related disease will continue to require increased health, social, and prevention services (U.S. Centers for Disease Control, 1990b).

AIDS is no longer confined to homosexual and bisexual men and intravenous (IV) drug users. Since mid-1987, AIDS cases due to intravenous drug use among heterosexuals, heterosexual sexual contact, and perinatal transmission have increased (U.S. Centers for Disease Control, 1990a). More than 2,116 children under 13 years of age had been reported with AIDS by February 1990 (U.S. Centers

*This number is believed to be grossly underreported (Hilts, 1989).

185

for Disease Control, 1990a); most of the "pediatric" cases are attributed to maternal-infant transmission during pregnancy, delivery, or shortly after birth. (Ziegler, 1985; Pahwa, 1986).

To date, HIV infection has not posed a serious threat to the majority of American youth as fewer than 1 percent of the cumulatively reported AIDS cases had occurred among 13–19 year-old youth (U.S. Centers for Disease Control, 1990a). This low percentage may be the primary reason for the lack of aggressive promotion of HIV prevention via health and social services for adolescents.

As the epidemic has unfolded, the potential for HIV infection among subsets of adolescents in the U.S. is becoming of paramount concern. All youth are not at equal risk for becoming infected with HIV. In the absence of population-based seroprevalence studies, there are no reliable estimates of the numbers of infected teens. HIV infection rates among defined groups such as military applicants, job corps applicants, runaways, college students, and sexually transmitted disease clinic patients have been the primary sources for estimating prevalence among adolescents. Recent seroprevalence studies show a 0.2 percent seroprevalence rate (30 seropositives) among the 16,861 college students tested (Bacon, 1989). Also, rates of sexually transmitted diseases (STDs) in the adolescent population are high, reflecting unprotected sexual intercourse. The seroprevalence among 1,141,164 military applicants less than 20 years of age was 0.34 per 1000 (393 applicants) between October 1985 and March 1989 (Burke et al., 1990), with higher rates among blacks (1.06 per 1000) and Hispanics (0.31 per 1000) compared to their white counterparts (0.18 per 1000). HIV infection was detected among adolescent recruits in 41 states and the District of Columbia, with the highest rates in California, New York, and Texas.

As supported by epidemiologic data, adolescents at highest risk are males who engage in same-sex sexual intercourse. Intravenous drug use is the other major risk behavior associated with HIV transmission among adolescents. Some health care providers have argued that adolescents are at high risk because of their experimentation with sex and drugs. Moreover, the prolonged latency period between infection and symptom onset masks the true incidence of the disease among adolescents (Hein, 1988). Twenty-one percent of all AIDS cases to date have occurred among people aged 20 to 29. Many were probably infected with the virus in their teens, as the average time between infection and development of AIDS is 10 years. Of the cumulatively reported AIDS cases among teens in the United States, about one-half are black (35 percent) or Hispanic (18.0 percent) and 45 percent are white; the remaining 2 percent are of Asian Pacific Islander or American Indian or Alaskan Native origin (U.S. Centers for Disease Control, 1990a).

This chapter addresses the impact of the AIDS epidemic on adolescents and the implementation of systematic approaches to prevent acquisition and transmission of HIV infection. First, adolescents' risk behaviors associated with HIV infection and their impact are described, followed by a discussion of the multifaceted crises of the disease. Frameworks for AIDS preventive interventions that aim to modify high-risk behaviors and concomitant barriers are then out-lined. The chapter concludes with a discussion of a set of recommendations about AIDS prevention strategies and methods of dissemination.

HIV-RISK BEHAVIORS AMONG ADOLESCENTS

With the normal developmental and transitional life crises of adolescence, risk-taking behaviors may elevate adolescents' chances of contracting HIV infection. Drugs, along with emotional instability, may cloud adolescents' decision making and lead to poor judgment with respect to precautionary sexual behaviors. Failure to use condoms with potentially high-risk partners can increase the risk of HIV exposure. In this section, trends in adolescent drug use, sexual activity, and sexually transmitted diseases are described. Also, there is discussion about subsets of the adolescent population at highest risk for HIV infection.

Drug Use and Sexual Behavior

Despite a decline in illicit drug use from 1979 to 1986, the proportion of high school students who are frequent substance users has increased significantly since 1983 (Johnston et al., 1986; Kerr, 1987). In 1985, three-fifths of all high school seniors in the United States reported experimenting with drugs (Bennett, 1986). Cocaine has accounted for 16.5 percent of all drug-related deaths among adolescents between the ages of 10 and 19 years (Drug Abuse Warning Network, 1984), and in a 1986 study, 1.1 percent of all high school students reported that they had used heroin (Bachman et al., 1987). In 1987, data from the National Adolescent Student Health Survey (National Center for Health Statistics, 1989) revealed that 77 percent of the eighth graders and 89 percent of the tenth graders reported using alcohol, 15 percent and 35 percent, respectively, reported marijuana use, and 4 percent and 8 percent, respectively, reported using cocaine.

There is some evidence that teens who use one type of drug are more likely to use another drug, and that use of drugs is associated with sexual activity. In 1980, about 3.5 million teens had problems with alcohol (Hawkins, 1982); alcohol abuse can put adolescents at risk for addiction to other drugs and, as a result of disinhibition, may lead to sexual activities that involve the exchange of semen or blood. Marijuana use is related to polydrug use as well as delinquency, un-protected sexual activity, and cigarette smoking (Newcomb & Bentler; 1986; Jessor et al., 1986). Peer support for drug use may reinforce drug use among adolescent drug users. One study found that pregnant drug-using inner-city adolescents were more likely to have drug-using partners than those who did not use drugs; drug use was also associated with negative life events and exposure to emotional or physical abuse during pregnancy (Amaro et al., 1990). Moreover, a recent study found that recency and intensity of drug use were predictive of persistent use in young adulthood; this underscores the importance of early preventive intervention (Raveis & Kandel, 1987).

About half of the adolescent population in the United States have engaged in intercourse by the age of 19 (Guttmacher Institute, 1981). One in four female teenagers has been pregnant, and each year, 470,000 of them give birth. From 1974 to 1980, the pregnancy rate for all females aged 15 to 19 increased by about 7 percent, from 81.8 pregnancies per 1,000 females to 88.5 (Spitz et al., 1987). Reported rates of sexually transmitted diseases other than AIDS are high, occurring in about one teen in seven (Lumiere & Cook, 1983); in 1987, about 2.5 million teenagers had an STD (National Center for Health Statistics, 1987). STDs such as chlamydia have been associated with having more than one sexual partner, more years of sexual activity, more frequent sexual activity, and early initiation of sexual intercourse (Blythe et al., 1988). These data suggest that many teens do not practice safer sex. When rates of gonorrhea, syphilis, and chlamydia of adolescents aged 10 to 14 and 15 to 19 years, as measured by the number of cases per 100,000 sexually experienced females in the age group, are compared to those among young adults, adolescents have higher rates of STDs (Hein, 1987, 1988).

Perhaps most important in terms of the potential for HIV infection is the increased use of crack cocaine among inner-city adolescents. With crack now becoming the drug of choice, the link between sex and drugs is more pronounced. Crack use is associated with increased sexual arousal, and thus leads to frequent sexual activity; in addition, trading sex for crack may put female crack users at risk for HIV infection (Williams et al., 1988). Crack use has been associated with an increased incidence of syphilis and gonorrhea among inner-city teens and adults (U.S. Centers for Disease Control, 1989). Among a sample of 222 black crack-using adolescents in the San Francisco/Bay area, about half reported that they had sex while on crack (Fullilove et al., 1990). Those who combined crack with sex were more likely to report at least one STD than those who did not combine crack with sex (51 percent vs 34 percent). In addition to crack, the majority of these youth reported marijuana and alcohol use, and 9 percent reported heroin use and 6 percent cocaine use (Fullilove & Fullilove, 1989).

Adolescents' perceptions of invincibility, invulnerability to disease, and immortality perpetuate risk-taking behaviors and make it difficult for them to "accept" AIDS prevention messages. Adolescents may minimize the risk of contracting AIDS because they do not personalize risk. Some adolescents are unwilling to accept themselves as sexual beings. For others, the immediate consequences of their behaviors is what matters; the risk of sexual transmission of HIV is perceived to be low because it is not seen as imminent (Goleman, 1987). Also, because adolescents tend to perceive themselves at the center of the universe or are uncomfortable with their budding sexuality, they may be unwilling to take preventive measures, such as buying condoms, out of fear that everyone will know that they are sexually active. Moreover, since few adolescents have contracted AIDS, youth lack peer role models who have AIDS and therefore have difficulty in recognizing the dangers of the disease (Worthington, 1986). Finally, the exploration of sexuality, struggle with sexual identity, and peer norm pressures may increase adolescents' risk-taking behaviors.

Homosexual Behavior among Youth

Homosexually-oriented male adolescents are likely to be at increased risk of exposure to HIV infection. Because of the compelling need to be deceptive and hide "in the closet," many gay youth feel emotionally restricted and socially isolated (Hunter & Schaecher, 1987; Martin, 1982). The inability to express their sense of difference and to conform to the expected gender role and the social stigma attached to homosexuality often lead gay adolescent males to have casual sexual encounters in public places (Remafedi, 1987). This stigma and concomitant sense of isolation and social ostracism by peers frequently results in their socializing with older men—men who are more likely to be HIV-infected (Makulowich, 1988).

Sexual behavior should not be equated with social or sexual identity, since there may be a discrepancy between the two. In the struggle with and confusion about their sexuality, some adolescents will have sex with same-sex partners as part of normal sexual experimentation and not consider themselves to be homosexual.

As a method of birth control, heterosexual females may engage in receptive anal intercourse—a behavior associated with homosexuality—with heterosexual male partners. In a 1987 survey of primarily black and Latin sexually active adolescents, one-quarter (28) of those surveyed reported that they had engaged in anal and vaginal intercourse (Jaffee et al., 1988). About three-quarters reported that they never used condoms during anal intercourse. The practice of anal intercourse was positively associated with age, but was unrelated to race or ethnicity. Similarly, in a survey of inner-city women of childbearing age attending women's health clinics, 12.6 percent reported having had anal intercourse to prevent pregnancy (Di Vittis et al., 1990). A study of 968 black college students revealed that 17 percent reported that they had engaged in anal intercourse; 10.43 percent of this behavior was accounted for by women (Thomas et al., 1989). Thus in assessing adolescents' level of HIV risk, service providers should not be deceived by the self-labeling process. If a heterosexually-identified female engages in unprotected anal intercourse, especially with multiple partners, she is not at any less risk than a homosexually-identified male adolescent (Savin-Williams & Lenhart, in press).

Ethnic Minority Youth

Minority adolescents may be at greater risk for becoming infected with HIV compared to whites because of their reported lower levels of AIDS knowledge, greater misconceptions about modes of HIV transmission (Di Clemente et al., 1988), and greater likelihood of having sexual intercourse without a condom (Kegeles et al., 1988). Black adolescents may be at greater risk for HIV infection than their white counterparts because a greater proportion engage in sexual intercourse rather than precoital behaviors (Smith & Udry, 1985). One survey of sexual behavior patterns indicated that 80 percent of black urban females had intercourse by age 19, compared to 60 percent of white urban females (Zelnick & Kantner, 1979). Hispanic adolescents have about the same rate of unintended pregnancies as their white counterparts, but higher rates of sexually transmitted diseases and drug use (Torres & Singh, 1986).

This constellation of risk behaviors—early onset of sexual activity, sexual and drug experimentation, and inconsistent use of condoms—increases the likelihood of adolescents' exposure to HIV and other infections. In addition, the role of socioenvironmental factors cannot be discounted. Drug activity is common in economically disadvantaged, inner-city neighborhoods inhabited by ethnic minorities and may be a temptation to youth who aspire to have money and material things.

Street Youth

Adolescents on the streets represent a broad spectrum of youth and include runaways, children of homeless families, the hardcore unemployed, multiple substance users involved in hustling, and people involved in the drug trade. About 187,500 teens are believed to be involved in drug use, drug trafficking, prostitution, and solicitation. Crack cocaine, in particular, may be responsible for increased "survival sex" among homeless youth (King, 1989). High rates of sexually transmitted diseases reflect these adolescents' low use of condoms. Data on youth admitted to a New York City juvenile detention facility between 1983 and 1984 indicated a 3 percent prevalence rate for gonorrhea among boys and an 18.3 percent rate among girls; the prevalence of syphilis was 0.63 percent for boys and 2.5 percent for girls (Alexander-Rodriguez and Vermund, 1987).

Each year, there are an estimated 1 million teen runaways, of which a quarter may be homeless street youth (U.S. Department of Health and Human Services, 1983, 1986). In San Francisco, an estimated 1,500 to 2,000 teenage runaways roam the streets (Axthelm, 1988). The National Runaway Switchboard reported more than 150,000 callers in 1984 (METRO-HELP, 1984).

Runaway youth, frequently referred to as "throwaways," are susceptible to HIV infection because of high-risk situations in their lifestyle. Sexual abuse, physical victimization and drug-related prostitution must be factored into the risk equation. For example, at two Los Angeles clinics, it was found that runaways were more likely to suffer from pelvic inflammatory disease, abuse drugs, engage in street prostitution, and be depressed than nonrunaway youth (Yates et al., 1988). Their health care is likely to suffer, and in seeking treatment for HIV-related disease, medical paternalism often overshadows their right to informed consent (Wolf, 1990).

A recent study conducted by New York City's Covenant House found that 6.5 percent of their adolescent shelter clients aged 16–20 were HIV-seropositive (Daley, 1988). Covenent House has stepped up its AIDS outreach activities and is setting up storefronts and mobile vans in New Jersey for HIV counseling, testing, and case management services (*New York Daily News*, 1989). In Southern Florida, crack addiction and prostitution are believed to be rampant among the estimated 7,000 to 10,000 runaways (Petchel, 1989). In Texas, of the 213 runaway youth at an alternative school center, only 13 percent reported always using condoms, and 7 percent reported having injected drugs (Hudson et al., 1989).

PATHWAYS TO PREVENTION

Gaps in AIDS Knowledge

Unfortunately, there is a relative dearth of empirical data on how AIDS has affected both straight- or gay-identified adolescents. Extant data, however, reveal that adolescents are misinformed about AIDS. A study of 1,326 students in family life education classes in ten San Francisco high schools suggests that knowledge of AIDS is uneven (Di Clemente et al., 1986). Two-fifths were unaware that condom use could lower the risk of exposure.

A survey (Davis et al., 1986) of 363 eighth, ninth and eleventh graders in selected secondary schools in Bridgeport, Connecticut, indicated that while the majority knew that intimate sexual contact with an infected person was a mode of transmission, 37 percent believed that giving blood and 17 percent that snorting drugs could cause the spread of HIV; 16 percent believed that mosquitos could transmit HIV. A significant proportion were unsure whether giving blood (34 percent) or getting bitten by a mosquito (25 percent) were means of transmission. Confusion about the role of donating blood in HIV infection still existed in 1987 as 47 percent of the respondents in the National Adolescent Student Health Survey believed that giving blood increases the likelihood of becoming infected (World Health Organization, 1989). Moreover, 51 percent believed that living in a household with a person with AIDS would increase their risk for developing the disease. These misperceptions about the risk of HIV infection associated with casual means of transmission have also been reported in surveys of American adults.

Although a Gallup survey indicated that teenagers' awareness of how AIDS is transmitted increased over the one-year period between 1985 and 1986, 37 percent of the 248 teenagers surveyed nationwide and 42 percent of the 100 of them in New York City were unable to name specific measures to prevent AIDS (Gallup, 1987). This lack of knowledge about HIV transmission modes and prevention is further confirmed by results of a random-digit telephone survey of 860 adolescents aged 16–19 years which indicated that 22 percent were unaware that AIDS is transmitted by semen and 29 percent that vaginal fluids were a source of transmission (Strunin & Hingson, 1978).

The San Francisco high school survey also revealed that AIDS anxiety was high, with three out of four students reporting being "worried about contracting the disease" and four out of five, being "afraid of AIDS." In contrast, the Massachusetts survey found that 54 percent of the adolescents did not worry at all about getting AIDS (Strunin & Hingson, 1987). With respect to teenagers' emotional responses to AIDS, fear and anxiety could be enabling factors or barriers to health-protective behaviors. The key is to teach teens how to channel their anxieties so as to preclude adoption of unsafe sexual and drug practices.

The knowledge gap is even greater for black and Latino youth than their white counterparts, particularly with respect to modes of transmission, their beliefs about the effectiveness of condoms in preventing HIV infection and personal susceptibility to AIDS (Di Clemente et al., 1986, 1988). One study found that less than 30 percent of an undergraduate college population at an East Coast university knew that HIV was not transmitted by insects (Thomas et al., 1989). Another study reported that perceptions were lowest among black and Latino male high school students and did not reflect their true HIV-related risks (Dolcini et al., 1988).

Condom Use

Condoms are advocated as a viable method for preventing HIV transmission among sexually active adolescents. Unfortunately, they are not uniformly used (Strunin & Hingson, 1987; Di Clemente et al., 1986). In one national poll, only 39 percent of the high school students surveyed indicated that they used contraceptives whenever they had sex (Van Biema, 1987). A survey of 99 adolescent females attending a comprehensive adolescent health clinic indicated that even though AIDS had influenced their sexual behavior, only 10 percent reported they had used condoms and the pill to prevent HIV and pregnancy (Rickert et al., 1989).

Taken together with the fact that teens are often unable to connect sexual behaviors with their consequences, these data suggest that teenagers are likely to engage in unprotected sexual activity. Thus the need for youth to be a primary target audience for AIDS prevention education is underscored. In particular, education should be directed toward helping adolescents acknowledge their personal risk for HIV and teaching condom use as a method of prevention.

Education of adolescents is seen as the front line of defense in stemming the tide of the AIDS epidemic. The former surgeon general of the United States, Dr. Everett Koop, made landmark history as being the first Federal official to recommend comprehensive AIDS sex education. In his dramatic preface statement on AIDS on October 22, 1986, Koop urged targeting sex education to children and adolescents to prevent the spread of AIDS:

> Many people . . . especially our youth . . . are not receiving information that is vital to their future health and well-being because of our reticence in dealing with the subjects of sex, sexual practices, and homosexuality. This silence must end. We can no longer afford to sidestep frank, open discussions about sexual practices . . . homosexual and heterosexual. Education about AIDS should start at an early age so that children can grow up knowing the behaviors to avoid to protect themselves from exposure to the AIDS virus. (p. 3)

The need to educate young people was further buttressed by the report from the Institute of Medicine of the National Academy of Sciences (1986) which stressed the use of vernacular language to describe the relative safety of specific sexual practices:

> Sex education in schools is no longer only advice about reproductive choice, but has now become advice about a life-or-death matter. Schools have an obligation to provide sex and health education, including facts about AIDS, in terms that teenagers can understand (p. 11)

In addition, a hearing on AIDS and teenagers before the House Select Committee on Children, Youth and Families, chaired by representative George Miller of California, reinforced the threat of AIDS to youth (*The New York Times*, 1987).

The lethal nature of AIDS has forced our country, including parents, the clergy, school officials, and youth service providers, to confront sexuality and talk more openly about it. Volatile debates have surfaced about educating adolescents in the schools and whether AIDS prevention and adolescent sexuality education should be mainstreamed into the broader context of adolescent life (Broznan, 1987).

Unfortunately, youth-serving agencies often lack the training and skills to deal with HIV-related problems, and those providing HIV services may lack experience and expertise in dealing with adolescents.

AIDS AS A CRISIS

The public's perception of AIDS has led to an epidemic of fear that contributes to the crisis situation of AIDS. Despite empirical research indicating that AIDS cannot be transmitted through casual means (Friedland et al., 1986), public opinion polls have showed that fear of contagion is widespread. Moreover, with the disease spreading increasingly beyond homosexual/bisexual men and IV drug users, many people are beginning to feel vulnerable to being exposed to the AIDS virus. Sexually active people who have unprotected sex with people they do not know well are often unaware of the sexual and drug histories of these sexual partners.

The threat of AIDS is further exacerbated by its high fatality rate. About 54 percent of all AIDS patients in the United States have died from the disease. The average life expectancy from diagnosis to death is about 18 to 24 months, depending on type of opportunistic infection; among IV users, it is only 6 to 10 months (Rothenberg et al., 1987). By the end of 1991, there will have been cumulatively more than 179,000 AIDS-related deaths in the United States, with 54,000 occurring in 1991 alone (Institute of Medicine, 1986). Among heterosexuals, the risk of AIDS is generally believed to be greatest among the inner-city urban poor because of sexual and IV drug transmission as a result of contact with addicts and drug dealers in their neighborhoods. Ethnic minorities, who are disproportionately represented among the poor, are therefore at increased risk as well because of IV drug use or being the sex partner of an IV drug user.

The array of psychological, social, behavioral, economic, and legal crises that emerge as a consequence of AIDS require aggressive intervention. Lopez and Getzel (1984) have argued that AIDS does not lend itself to a "pure crisis intervention model" of psychosocial treatment because persons with AIDS face continual health crises and are therefore unable to achieve reintegration following a crisis state. We agree with the Lopez and Getzel argument. Accordingly, in the remainder of this chapter, traditional definitions of crisis intervention as formulated by Parad (1965), Lindemann (1944), Rapoport (1962), Caplan (1964), and Golan (1978), are not used.

"Treatment" Strategies

The way to mitigate the impact of the crises of HIV-spectrum disorders is through education. Being at risk for HIV infection or being seropositive is a crisis for many people. Crisis theory is used as a frame of reference for the chapter. We employ a generic approach to "treatment" that emphasizes preventive intervention with a population at risk rather than crisis intervention with individuals who have experienced the trauma of disease. Primary prevention strategies are viewed as requisite crisis measures for the launching of a responsible public response to cope with the AIDS epidemic.

For most adolescents, AIDS is a disease that could theoretically affect them and therefore requires sexual behaviors that include condom use. For the subsets of adolescents who practice high-risk behaviors, AIDS represents another quagmire in their normal developmental crises. In the era of AIDS, sex, drugs, and hedonism may bring about death rather than merely pregnancy. Crises stemming from restrictions on sexual activity and the threat of premature death add fuel to the crisis of adolescent sexuality. These crises are compounded by the threat of AIDS, which compels adolescents to grow up and assume adult health-protective role behaviors prematurely.

Thus education and prevention are viable strategies for heading off the crises of AIDS. As with treatment-oriented crisis intervention, AIDS risk-reduction preventive interventions can lead to problem resolution and cognitive and behavioral reintegration. For example, once safer sex practices are learned and incorporated into everyday life, an individual can resume sexual activity and maintain equilibrium with this new repertoire of tools and skills. Behavioral and psychosocial approaches to preventing the crises of AIDS entail concrete actions that not only limit exposure to the disease but reduce stress and anxiety. These preventive interventions include social support influence and life and social skills approaches, both of which are common crisis intervention techniques to promote adaptive behaviors.

PROMOTING BEHAVIOR CHANGE: PRACTICE FRAMEWORKS FOR AIDS PREVENTION

Preventive intervention is believed to be an important means for reducing HIV transmission. Preventive intervention programs aim to educate people to curtail drug use and high-risk sexual practices, thus limiting potential exposure to HIV. Major objectives are to increase individuals' awareness of how to protect themselves and to develop social supports for maintaining low-risk practices. For vulnerable adolescents whose lifestyle and individual behavior practices elevate their risk, explicit sex education and support services are essential.

Conceptual Framework

The PRECEDE framework (the acronym stands for predisposing, reinforcing, and enabling cause in educational diagnosis and evaluation) provides a useful model for understanding determinants of AIDS prevention behavioral outcomes (Green et al., 1980). Applied to AIDS, the model can shape the focus of risk-reduction interventions by identifying critical factors that lead to reduced negative health behaviors, such as unprotected sexual intercourse. Predisposing factors, which include social demographics and knowledge, attitudes, and values about AIDS and sexuality, are antecedent to a specific behavior and provide a rationale for that behavior. Enabling factors also precede behavior and include availability of and accessibility to psychosocial and concrete resources and personal skills that facilitate or inhibit adoption of the practice. Reinforcing factors, such as peer, parental, and health professionals' attitudes toward sex and condom use provide an incentive or deterrent to the action and contribute to the existence or extinction of the target behavior.

With respect to AIDS, a number of predisposing factors might deter the practice of safer sex. First, adolescents may be ill-informed about reproductive and sexual matters and not use condoms (Nadelson et al., 1980; Rogel et al., 1980; Zabin & Clark, 1981; Morrison, 1985). Second, beliefs about personal invulnerability to HIV exposure, lack of expectations about having sex, and lack of belief in the efficacy of condoms may account for unsafe sexual behavior. Third, as is apparent with smoking (McCaul & Glasgow, 1985) and suicide, difficulty in seeing the long-term consequences of a behavior and failure to make a connection between a behavior and its health outcome may contribute to teenagers' taking the risk of unprotected sex. Fifth, low self-esteem may weaken an adolescent's convictions about the need for safer sex. For such individuals, negotiations with a partner may lead to unsafe activities when the importance of peer acceptance becomes overriding. Alternatively, the potential adverse outcome associated with having unprotected sex—AIDS and eventually death—may motivate some adolescents to use condoms at all times. Finally, adolescents' feelings about loss of spontaneity, premeditated sexual activity, and inhibition of sexual pleasure associated with condom use are other barriers to safer sex practices (Anderson et al., 1978).

Enabling factors for positive AIDS health behaviors include self-efficacy of using condoms, social and personal competence skills, communication skills to negotiate with a partner, access to condoms and school-based sex education. Reinforcement for protected sex might be provided by peer group members, parents, and teachers who not only support the adolescents' use of condoms but also personally subscribe to safer sex behaviors. All of these factors are important to understanding health actions and the positive and negative influences that impinge upon them.

School-based Education and the Controversy Surrounding It

As a major socializing agency and force in modeling adolescents' behaviors, schools are natural sites for AIDS prevention programming, AIDS-related sex education can be easily incorporated into family life classes. Support for AIDS education in the schools has mounted, despite vigorous debate about the nature of the information to be offered. The United States Centers for Disease Control has provided funding to states for the development of AIDS prevention education in the schools. A 1987 survey sponsored by the United States Conference of Mayors of 73 of the nation's largest school districts and 25 state school agencies found that 54 percent endorsed teaching about AIDS, mainly to students in grades seven through twelve.

The Reagan administration issued an AIDS education plan for youth that included information about condoms but left the decision to local communities for determining specific school curricula (*The New York Times,* 1987a). The struggle between the federal government and local communities for control of the comprehensive AIDS prevention education (CAPE) programs still exists. In San Francisco, only 20 parents out of 22,000 were reported to prohibit their children from attending AIDS education classes (McAuliffe, 1987). In Tennessee, a survey of 1195 adults indicated that 87.5 percent supported AIDS education in the schools (U.S. Centers for Disease Control, 1990d). Two-thirds of the nation's public school districts reported that they included AIDS education information in their curricula in 1988–1989 (U.S. General Accounting Office, 1990a).

Despite parental and school district support for AIDS education, education is not provided at every grade level. Only 5 percent of the public school districts in the United States provided AIDS education at every grade level (U.S. General Accounting Office, 1990a). The New York State Board of Regents mandated AIDS instruction for children from kindergarten through the twelfth grade; seven other states had such a plan in effect in 1987 (*The New York Times,* 1987a).

Part of the controversy relates to whether specific HIV-related topics, for example, homosexuality, anal intercourse, safer sex practices or proper condom use, should be covered in the school setting. There is no consensus on the age at which AIDS and sex education should begin or how explicit teaching materials should be (New York State Senate Majority Task Force on AIDS, 1987). Local communities can decide whether CAPE programs should be mandated for adolescents. Consequently, these flexible standards have resulted in the provision of uneven AIDS education in the United States (Di Clemente, 1988). AIDS has also fueled a related controversy over the provision of birth control devices in school-based health clinics.

From a community perspective, the threat of AIDS has compelled religious and political groups grounded in conservatism, fundamentalism, and Catholicism to take a strong stance against sex education in schools and through television promotion. Teaching about homosexuality and anal intercourse is dissonant with religious systems that perceive homosexuality as deviant behavior and an unacceptable alternative lifestyle. Opponents of school-based sex education argue that abstinence is the only way to prevent the spread of AIDS. The United States Catholic Conference assailed the advertising of condoms on television because it represented "a gross violation of the rights of parents to guide the moral and social development of their children" (Collins, 1987). This stance was confirmed more recently by a committee of Catholic bishops, who advocated chastity for adolescents (*The New York Times,* 1989a; Steinfels, 1989). Promoting condom use among teenagers is viewed as implicitly condoning premarital sex and contraception, encouraging promiscuity, and increasing premature sexual activity. Moreover, opponents believe that this prevention message is counter to values of sexual self-discipline and restraint and erodes the underlying fabric of the traditional family system and moral standards of the community. Finally, it has been argued that the failure rate associated with condom use (about 10 percent) suggests that condoms are not foolproof in preventing HIV transmission.

Despite efforts to eradicate advertising that allegedly promotes sexual activity, teenagers are influenced by the behaviors of adult role models and television and film portrayals of sex (Hechinger, 1987). A 1987 national survey conducted by Louis Harris and Associates indicated that 72 percent of the adult respondents said they would not be offended by condom advertising on television, and 60 percent believed that TV stations should be permitted to advertise them (Belkin, 1987). Similarly, a survey of white, middle– to upper-class adolescents being treated in a private medical practice and their parents revealed that 83 percent of the parents, 89 percent of the adolescent females, and 92 percent of the adolescent males approved of condom advertisements on television (Buchta, 1989). Sex education teachers also report that teaching about homosexuality and birth control methods is their greatest difficulty because of parental resistance and/or pressure from the community or school administration (Forrest & Silverman, 1989). In reckoning with and attempting to balance these liberal and conservative forces, schools face a difficult challenge in providing neutral course content about how to prevent the spread of AIDS.

An AIDS prevention advertising campaign developed by the New York City Department of Health (1987) to reach adolescents urged parents to talk candidly about sex, condoms, and AIDS with their children "before it hits home."

> Tell them if they're having sex, they must always use a condom. And not having sex is still the best protection. Tell them that AIDS is incurable, there's no vaccine, and once you get it you'll likely die. Then tell them it's preventable. Tell them everything you can about AIDS. But make sure you tell them now. Because by the time you think they're old enough to know, it just might be too late.

Studies that examine the efficacy of sex education or family life classes in reducing "undesirable" behaviors have yielded contradictory findings and are thus inconclusive. Some have found that such education did not have an impact on attitudes about premarital sex, knowledge about sexuality, contraceptive behavior, or pregnancy rates (Eisen & Zellman, 1986). Data from the nationwide School Health Education Evaluation project, however, revealed that exposure to health education curricula can lead to changes in health knowledge, attitudes, and practices, particularly in relation to cigarette smoking, and that such changes increase with increasing instruction (U.S. Centers for Disease Control, 1986). A 1981 national survey of children indicated that among 15- and 16-year-olds, there was an association between classroom sex education and occurrence of sexual activity (Furstenberg et al., 1985). Other programs indicate that an experientially focused curriculum, such as skills training, can bring about behavioral change (Herz et al., 1986). Evaluation of a 50-minute multimedia AIDS instruction program presented to Seattle high school students indicated a significant increase in knowledge one month following the intervention; this increase was retained eight weeks after the intervention as well. There were no significant changes in perception of personal risks at either assessment (Miller & Downer, 1987). Clearly, numerous AIDS surveys among both adolescents and adults indicate that HIV-related knowledge can increase personal awareness of the disease, but it is not sufficient to promote risk reduction.

Though risk-reduction issues are central to AIDS education programs in the schools, schools also need to be responsive to the social and psychological impact of the disease on adolescents. In particular, sensitive treatment of persons with AIDS should be stressed, especially within the context of community and parental stances toward discrimination. In inner-city areas, adolescents may increasingly confront a parent, other relative or family acquaintances who are likely to be HIV-infected. As adolescents are seeking to validate their sexual identity, tolerance of alternative lifestyles should be fostered. Supportive counseling services and/or a teens' AIDS hotline may be required for students who attend school with a person with AIDS to help mitigate fears of contracting AIDS through casual contact. Psychosocial supportive services will also be needed to help adolescents deal with AIDS-related loss of friends and family members.

Preventive Intervention Methods

Cognitive and behavioral methods rooted in social learning theory can guide health behavior risk-reduction interventions with teenagers. AIDS requires that people learn and process new information. Education involves teaching individuals how to change unhealthy behaviors as well as behavioral shaping of low-risk alternatives to high-risk activities (Kelly & St. Lawrence, 1986). In addition, intervention programs must aim to make the threat of AIDS more real to youth. When the threat of disease is perceived to be remote, it will be difficult to convince adolescents to abstain from sex, use condoms or refrain from experimenting with "shooting up" and sharing "works." One innovative approach adopted in San Francisco entails using people with AIDS (PWAs) as promoters of AIDS education in the classroom, followed by group discussion of the students' reactions to the person with AIDS several days later (Bishop, 1988). The agenda for AIDS prevention programs in the schools should provide students with basic information about AIDS and promote responsible health behaviors. The educational focus needs to be directed toward high-risk behaviors rather than high-risk groups, that is, what people do, not who people are. Students need to understand how they can protect themselves from HIV infection, how to recognize symptoms of HIV infection, how to negotiate for safer sex with a partner, and how to say no if a partner won't agree to "play safe." In addition, adolescents need to know that there are other forms of sexual expression than intercourse—that there are other ways of being sexual.

Students' baseline levels of knowledge about AIDS should be assessed prior to and following intervention. Information derived from surveys of adolescents' beliefs and attitudes about AIDS will provide a rich source for program content. In this way, educators can design programs that are appropriate for youth. AIDS may best be prevented within the context of other sexually transmitted diseases as well as drug prevention education because of their association with HIV transmission. AIDS instructional modules can be easily integrated with curriculum on other STDs and aspects of sex education.

AIDS prevention modules should cover the following:

Spectrum of HIV-related disease
Epidemiology of AIDS—who gets AIDS?

Other sexually transmitted diseases
Modes of transmission—what are the behavioral risks?
Symptomatology and clinical manifestations
Prevention of HIV
Risk-reduction guidelines

Quackenbush and Sargent's (1986) guide, which includes teaching plans and materials, is an excellent resource for educating high school students about AIDS. Others have developed programs that focus on pregnancy prevention and sexual decision making (for example, see Middleton, 1989; Barth, 1989).

Imagine the following scenario. A school district has mandated AIDS education for all high school students. Curriculum guides developed by a statewide task force have been distributed to the health science and family life faculty. You are the teacher—today you have planned to begin talking about AIDS prevention with your students. How would you introduce the subject?

Case Study

In previous classes we have talked about drugs and unplanned teenage pregnancy. In today's class, we are going to discuss AIDS—acquired immunodeficiency syndrome—I will focus on the nature of the disease, modes of transmission, and prevention methods. AIDS is a sexually transmitted disease, but unlike gonorrhea and syphilis, it is fatal. HIV infection can be transmitted through sexual intercourse with an infected person without proper use of a condom, by sharing dirty needles or "works" for injecting drugs with an infected person, through transfusion of blood or blood products from an infected donor, or through organ transplantation or artificial insemination from a seropositive donor. Mothers can also pass the virus on to their children during pregnancy, delivery, or shortly after birth. Because there is no known cure for AIDS, it is important for all of you to understand the perilous nature of this disease. Some of you may feel uncomfortable in talking openly about sex and how to use condoms. I'll try to put you at ease.

It is essential that cognitive curricula emphasize AIDS-related risk behaviors, modes of disease transmission, other sexually transmitted diseases, and barriers to behavioral change. A prevention program should also address the clinical and social consequences of unsafe sex and drug practices, including the threat of premature death, interpersonal relationships, feelings about dating and sexual relationships, sexual decision making, communication skills, peer pressure, and birth control. Arming adolescents with this knowledge can help correct misconceptions about the disease, sexuality, reproductive anatomy, and physiology. Moreover, through cognitive coping strategies, adolescents can be taught to reward themselves for accomplishments achieved in decreasing their risk of HIV infection.

The positive effects of behavior-oriented strategies in effecting cognitive, attitudinal, and behavioral changes have been noted (Levine et al., 1979). Didactic presentations about AIDS prevention must be accompanied by behavioral techniques to facilitate information processing and to promote candid discussion of sex, including homosexuality. AIDS prevention educators, however, should be aware that some adolescents may become anxious about frank discussion and the use of sexually explicit teaching materials.

Adolescents need to learn specific skills in modifying their behavior to prevent exposure to HIV. Social skills training has been successfully used as a preventive intervention in lowering tobacco use rates among adolescents (Schinke et al., 1986a, 1986b). A social skills approach to AIDS prevention involves providing adolescents with the requisite skills to resist unsafe drug and sexual behaviors. Psychological and peer social influence barriers to adopting safer sex and drug practices must be broken down. Skills training can bolster adolescents' sense of mastery and enhance control and interpersonal competence, all of which should strengthen perceived self-efficacy about performing safer behaviors. Techniques such as modeling, behavioral rehearsal, performance feedback, reinforcement and shaping procedures, and skill transfer procedures can be employed to promote desired behavioral change. The Adolescent AIDS program at New York City's Montefiore Medical Center has implemented and is evaluating a skills training program, ARREST (AIDS Risk-Reduction Education and Skills Training), for students attending truancy prevention and after-school programs.

Instilling responsibility for personal health behaviors is a primary objective and should encourage active decision making and problem solving. Training will promote effective verbal communication and assertiveness and aims to teach adolescents how to set safe limits with sexual partners and other peers and thus avert adverse outcomes. Exercises can be geared to:

> what it means not to have sex, such as listing the advantages and disadvantages of not having sex, why it's difficult not to have sex;
> uncovering attitudes about birth control, such as listing why you would use or not use specific birth control methods;
> what you would tell your best friend about how to prevent pregnancy;
> how to put off having sex with someone who won't take "no" for an answer;
> developing a plan of action to prevent HIV infection or pregnancy;
> setting personal health and life goals to attain over the next 12 months;
> how to ask sex partners whether they engage in any risk behaviors; and
> how to talk to your best friend(s) about sex

Behavioral rehearsal as described next has been used to enhance social competency skills. Adolescents can be asked to call an AIDS hotline to obtain information about HIV testing, go to a drug store to buy condoms, convince a friend to use condoms, conduct a market research-oriented condom survey with friends about the brand of condoms they use and what they like and dislike about them, or visit a family planning clinic.

The modeling or responsible behaviors in which adolescents are given the opportunity to practice and sharpen decision making and communication skills is an integral part of skills training. In the role-play scenarios that follow, students rehearse problem situations so as to facilitate their abilities to solve specific problems and make sound decisions. Following the role-play, small group discussion should be held so that group members can provide critical performance feedback to the student actors. When possible, the role-plays should be videotaped so that the students can see their "performance."

Role-play 1

SCENE: Two male high school seniors are sitting at a table in the local after-school hamburger hangout.

ROLE A: Tom had experimented with shooting up heroin two years ago. He shared needles with his buddies at weekly Friday night beer parties. Tom no longer lives his life in the fast lane. He is afraid that he might be infected and is considering being tested for HIV but is skeptical.

ROLE B: Greg has been best friends with Tom since the age of 10. He was aware of Tom's drug use but never shot up himself. Greg believes that Tom's knowledge of his antibody status will be beneficial and help him practice safer sex.

After enactment of the role-play, classroom discussion should address the following questions:

1. If you are HIV-seropositive, how would you change your personal behavior?
2. Who would you tell about these results?
3. If you are HIV-seronegative, how would you change your sexual behavior?
4. If you got tested but choose not to learn your test results, how would you handle this situation?

Role-play 2

SCENE: Maria and Antonio are in the tenth grade and began dating each other one month ago. They have had three dates and are in love. They have not yet had sex together, but both feel ready for it.

ROLE A: Maria has learned about AIDS by watching television and is fearful of getting the disease. Maria has had sex with another boy a year ago. She knows that using a condom with a water-based lubricant can help protect her from becoming infected with HIV. Maria is afraid to have unprotected sex with Antonio but is also too shy to ask him to wear a rubber.

ROLE B: Antonio has decided that tonight he will "put the move" on Maria and have sex with her. He is a "macho" young man and perceives that women should be submissive to men. Antonio has never used condoms and believes that they will take the spontaneity and fun out of sex.

After five minutes of role-playing, the teacher should direct students to answer the following questions:

1. How would you feel in this situation?
2. How can you convince a partner to practice safer sex?

3. What do you do if your partner refuses to wear a condom?
4. What are ways other than intercourse of having safer sex?
5. Why is safer sex important?

Role-play 3

SCENE: Brett and Sally have been dating for a month and Brett has been pressur-
         ing Sally to have sex. Brett tells Sally that he really loves her and that
         she could show her love by having sex with him. Sally really likes Brett
         but feels that she is not ready to have sex. She is also afraid of catching
         AIDS and getting pregnant. How can Sally say no to having sex without
         losing Brett?

The following vignette presents a dialogue between a 17-year-old sexually active high school student and a health educator about prevention of AIDS and
other STDs. The vignette illustrates several problem situations: adolescents'
perceived vulnerability to and denial of their risks for contracting AIDS and related
disorders, ignorance about how to prevent STDs, difficulty in talking about condoms and other safer sex practices, and resistance to condom use.

Judy made an appointment to see the public health nurse about a chronic
vaginal discharge. She is worried that she might have gonorrhea. The following
dialogue occurs between Judy and the nurse:

JUDY: For the past two weeks I have had this foul-smelling discharge. Do you
         think that it is gonorrhea?
NURSE: I don't know yet, but we can find out. I'll take a culture and send it to
         the lab for analysis. Have you been having sex with anyone?
JUDY: In the past two months, I have been dating two guys and slept with both.
NURSE: Have you been using birth control?
JUDY: I'm on the pill!
NURSE: You know, oral contraceptives may prevent you from getting pregnant,
         but they don't prevent sexually transmitted diseases like gonorrhea,
         chlamydia, syphilis, or AIDS.
JUDY: I'm not worried about AIDS. AIDS is a disease that gay men get. My
         boyfriends are not gay. I'm not promiscuous. Besides, I only sleep with
         guys I know. These guys are clean; they come from nice families. Also,
         I keep myself clean and wash after having sex.
NURSE: Well, Judy, anyone can get AIDS. Being clean has nothing to do with
         it. You can get AIDS by having sex with an infected person or sharing
         dirty needles and other drug paraphernalia. Washing immediately after
         sex will not prevent AIDS. Use condoms. They do not offer 100 percent
         protection, but they are the best means we have other than not having
         sex.
JUDY: Condoms aren't for me. None of my girlfriends use them. My boyfriends
         don't either. We always have sex without them. How can I ask them to
         use condoms now? They'll think I have something or that I don't trust
         them.

NURSE: But you may have gonorrhea, and condoms can prevent STDs that are spread through vaginal and anal sex. You also put yourself at risk for AIDS if you don't use a condom. Even if you know your partners really well, you can't be sure. Your partners may not tell you about all of their experiences with drugs and sex. Also, they may not know that they've been exposed to the virus.

JUDY: I hear what you're saying, but I don't know how to start talking about condoms with my boyfriends.

NURSE: Tell them that you care about them and if they care about you, they will use a condom.

JUDY: Thanks for rapping with me and telling me the hard facts.

NURSE: Come back in five days and I'll have the results of your culture. In the meantime, be smart. Use a condom. If you do have gonorrhea, you can pass it on to your boyfriends.

Role-play 4

SCENE: You live in the Williamsburgh section of Brooklyn, New York. Every day, you are confronted with drug dealers in your neighborhood. You see them wearing fine clothes, sporting gold chains and watches, and driving nice sports cars. Crack cocaine is the drug of choice because it is relatively cheap. You are invited by one of your neighbors to a crack house. You want to finish school and take auto mechanics classes. If you don't go, you are afraid you won't be perceived as cool. Going to the house and smoking crack or going on a "mission" to obtain drugs will provide you with money and mean that you can dress cool and have a red van decked with brightly polished chrome.

What will you do? What are your various options? What is the consequence of your involvement in the crack tade? What are the consequences of your refusing your neighbor's offer?

Social system influences, which draw on the subjective social norms of peer group, family members, and media communications, also provide an underlying framework for AIDS-preventive interventions. Adolescents typically want to gain acceptance from their peers and act in ways that are consistent with group norms. Peers are a supplemental source of behavioral influence to parental modeling in adolescence, and peer pressure often exerts stronger effects on promoting or deterring detrimental health behaviors than parental pressure (Gottlieb & Baker, 1986). The peer group also provides a source of informational influence through the adolescent's identification with group social images, perceptions of the negative physical and social consequences as a result of engaging in the risky sexual or drug behavior, and opinion formation through conformity with a group's position (Sussman, 1989). Intervention geared to changing social norms would attempt to establish conservative norms about the prevalence and susceptibility of premarital sexual intercourse and drug use and use peer leaders to model acceptable opinions and hence behaviors.

Numerous studies have highlighted the importance of the peer group as a resource in preventive interventions (Davis et al., 1977), especially its influence on teenagers' sexual and contraceptive behaviors (Kar & Talbot, 1981; Zelnik & Kantner, 1979), smoking (Evans et al., 1979; Banks et al., 1981), and alcohol use (Rohrbach et al., 1987). Whether preventive interventions reduce susceptibility to peer pressure has not been empirically tested, however (Dielman et al., 1987). Some data indicate that teen counselors are particularly useful in reaching teenagers from ethnic minority groups, who have higher premarital pregnancy rates than white teens (Broznan, 1987). Informal rap groups led by student counselors could provide a forum for fellow students to discuss their concerns about AIDS. In New Jersey, high school juniors have been trained to teach other high school students as well as elementary students about AIDS using a movie and small group discussion (James, 1989).

Also useful are AIDS speakers' bureaus or hotliine services whereby teens are trained to provide information, education, and referral services to other youth who may feel uncomfortable calling AIDS hotlines manned by adults. In April 1988, the first national toll-free AIDS hotline, Teens Teaching AIDS Prevention (Teens TAP), sponsored by the Good Samaritan Project, was opened in Kansas City (*The New York Times*, 1988b). The hotline is staffed by volunteers six days a week, from 4:00 to 8:00 P.M. Similar to the adult hotlines, callers have asked questions about the signs and symptoms of HIV infection, risks associated with various sexual practices, and proper condom use, The Rhode Island Project/AIDS has initiated an AIDS peer education program in which trained adolescents conduct workshops and outreach to their peers (Foundation for Children with AIDS, 1989).

Teenagers have to realize that they have choices, but they need guidance in establishing a framework of limits. Some will need help in how to set limits for themselves and find an acceptable way of refusing. Others will be unable to maintain behavioral limits steadfastly because of peer pressure, while still others will clearly desire to abstain from sex or drugs. Skills training should enable adolescents to maintain their status quo healthy behavior and resist peer pressures to take drugs and engage in unprotected sex. Resistance to peer pressure can also be achieved by teaching them to withdraw from their group's demands or informational control by avoiding high-risk situations, rejecting behavioral demands, and countering social pressures to engage in high-risk sex or drug use (Sussman, 1989). Practice and skill development in sexual negotiations or in refusing to take drugs—that is, how to say no assertively—and strategies for conflict resolution are other means for countering social influence. Roleplays, such as those described earlier, are ideal for teaching skills training. One school system has begun teaching students "refusal skills." Strategies geared to maximizing positive peer influence in shaping healthy behaviors are integral to AIDS prevention programs. Reinforcing a positive self-image and responsible sexual and contraceptive decision-making practices should thus lower adolescents' risks of HIV exposure and transmission.

Another cognitive and behavioral problem-solving technique entails the use of self-assessment activities. For example, adolescents can keep diaries to monitor their own cognitions, feelings, behavioral intentions, and behaviors related to noncompliance with unsafe AIDS health practices. By identifying behavioral patterns and stimuli that trigger their practice of high-risk AIDS behaviors, adolescents can learn to anticipate barriers and examine their options for safe resolution.

The diary should be maintained on a weekly basis.* Students can initially be asked a series of nonthreatening questions that begin with ratings of physical health and emotional health (for example, "On a scale of 1 to 10, where 1 indicates terrible and 10 indicates wonderful, how did you feel physically today? How did you feel emotionally today?"). The structured questions in the diary might then progress to drug practices ("What kind of prescription and nonprescription drugs, if any, did you take today? What about shooting dope? If you did drugs, what did you do? Where were you before you took drugs? Where did you take drugs? What factors influenced your decision to do drugs?"). The diary would then culminate in a series of questions relating to sexual practices ("Were you treated by a doctor or nurse for any sexually transmitted diseases like gonorrhea, syphilis, chlamydia, or trichomonas? Did you talk with anyone in your family about sex today? With any of your friends? If you had any kind of sex today, what kinds of sexual activities? What influenced your decision to have sex? Where did you have sex? Did you use a condom? If yes, who initiated the discussion, and brought the condom, you or your partner? If you had unsafe sex, what could you have done to make it safer?"). Other questions might focus on adolescents' concerns about getting AIDS.

Sociocultural Considerations

The likelihood of complying with safer sex practices and avoiding drugs is affected by sociocultural prescriptions of behavior. The design and health education messages of AIDS preventive interventions must be culture- and class-sensitive to the traditional values, heritage, religious beliefs, and social customs of targeted ethnic minority groups. Professionals need to build on rather than work against traditional cultural values. A bicultural perspective is essential to culturally sensitive risk-reduction programs. Despite homogeneity of a shared characteristic such as race, within-group differences of an ethnic or racial group must be recognized. For example, there is cultural disparity between black adolescents born to Haitian immigrants and those of American-born parents. Similarly, there are language and cultural differences among groups of Latinos. Thus Haitian blacks and Dominicans who only speak French and Spanish, respectively, may be more misinformed or have a lower level of knowledge about modes of HIV transmission than their counterparts who speak English in addition to the language of their native country.

Language of AIDS prevention messages has to be geared toward the language skills and educational level of the group. When risk-reduction materials are translated into a foreign language, they must not be literal. Moreover, AIDS prevention must be sensitive to the cultural taboos about sexuality in certain

---

*Questions in the proposed diary have been adapted and modified from a diary developed for a risk-reduction intervention for men who have sex with men (Mantell et al., 1986).

minority or ethnic groups. For example, Latino men who have sex with other men may not identify themselves as gay or bisexual and may perceive such behavior as reinforcing their *machismo* (Campagnet, 1987). Sexually explicit language may offend some minority communities (Communication Technologies, 1986). "Rap," black vernacular speech that involves spontaneous rhyming with a structured rhythm, is an ideal means for reaching teens about drugs, AIDS, and other sexually transmitted diseases. The San Francisco City Department of Public Health and the Bayview–Hunter's Point Foundation recently held a rap music contest for teens to develop a 60-second AIDS prevention rap in a culturally relevant manner (Fullilove, 1987).

Improving self-esteem has become a focus of intervention for youth. Self-esteem is thought to transcend all areas of living and affect teens' predisposition to risky behaviors.

Theater, street mime, and other improvisational techniques are being increasingly used as intervention strategies to engage adolescents in HIV prevention education. For example, Teatro Vida/Life in the Bronx, New York, uses professional actors in real-life skits about AIDS, sexuality, drugs, and family life and encourages participation from the dialogue with youth at schools and community centers. Hospital Audiences, Inc. presents theatre workshops to youth attending religious and recreation programs, in housing projects, at counseling centers, group homes, family shelters and youth shelters, as well as in schools and community centers in New York City (*HAI News,* 1990). Youth participate in role-play scenarios. The theatre is an excellent educational tool because it enables the actors to address sensitive issues in a culturally acceptable form. In addition, role-plays can help youth form opinions and clarify their values.

In addition, differences in family and kinship structure, level of acculturation, and traditional sex roles affect behavioral risks and adoption of healthy practices and should be considered in the planning of an AIDS intervention modality. For example, among Latinos, the informal social network can be engaged as a powerful ally in precipitating and reinforcing behavioral change. The support of extended family of Puerto Rican adolescents, such as older siblings, grandparents, and godparents, should be enlisted. The strength and cohesiveness of extended kin and friends as primary supporters in the black family lend credence to their role as resources for health information (Mantell et al., 1984). In addition, preventive interventions directed toward black youth should incorporate the concept of empowerment to bolster perceived self-efficacy to change high-risk behaviors (Solomon, 1976). The primacy of the church and the influence of key indigenous leaders in the black community make it essential to tap these sources of power to spearhead risk-reduction programs for blacks.

Cultural, religious, and moral barriers constrain condom use among some groups. As noted earlier, the Catholic church prohibits the use of condoms as an AIDS prevention device for its members. Traditional sex roles in Hispanic cultures provide highly specific behavioral norms and social expectancies. The pervasive cultural role ideal of male dominance and female submission in Latino cultures renders women especially vulnerable in sexual situations. Women who yield to the sexual wishes of their men are apt to refrain from candid discussions about sex. Advocating that young Latinas carry condoms is culturally dissonant because such premeditated action is perceived as a sign of loose or whorelike behavior (Worth & Rodriguez, 1987). Furthermore, fear of rejection may also make young Latinos unable to negotiate protected sex with a partner. Moreover, male Latino adolescents may equate pregnancy with a sign of their virility, a belief that reinforces the ideal of *machismo*, and thus militates against condom use as an AIDS prophylaxis. Despite differences in cultural values, we must be creative and learn how to use a group's values to convey the importance of AIDS prevention. Also, variations in age, gender, personality, values, and environment among children must be considered in targeting prevention messages. Health educators and media specialists need to understand that a uniform message will not be effective for all adolescents (MacDonald, 1987).

Prevention activities must be targeted to all youth, with emphasis on those living in the inner cities. Numerous studies have documented a consistent association between lower education and unhealthy behaviors (Stevens & Schoenborn, 1988). Prevention services must be linked to school, clinic, and mobile health services (Shulman et al., 1990). Most HIV education efforts have been targeted to youth in school, with minimal attempts to reach unaffiliated or streeth youth. Though some claim that out-of-school youth are difficult to reach, they can be found in the Job Corps, in bus terminals, in railroad stations, at piers, at sports events, at playgrounds and other public social gatherings, at rock concerts, in record stores, in video game centers, in bars, on the streets, and in gangs, especially through nontraditional means such as one-to-one outreach workers, comics or *fotonovelas*, street theater, and rap sessions.

 Special initiatives must be directed toward reaching these youth outside of the school setting. These efforts include the devising of outreach strategies that will be acceptable to out-of-school populations and the development of appropriate educational materials (U. S. General Accounting Office, 1990b). A number of agencies throughout the country have rallied to the needs of this youth population. One model AIDS education program for street youth is the hustler outreach program of the Colorado AIDS Project. Through street outreach, street youth are recruited to serve as peer leaders, distributing condoms, giving AIDS presentations, and making referrals to health and social service agencies (Gonzales, 1988). In New York City, several agencies serving such youth have incorporated AIDS prevention into their menu of services. The Victim Services Agency provides counseling and food coupons to youth in the Times Square area. The New York City Department of Health's outreach workers counsel youth on the streets and distribute educational materials and condoms and make referrals. Covenant House operates a hotline and a short-term residential facility, while the Hetrick-Martin Institute for the Protection of Lesbian and Gay Youth offers drop-in counseling services for lesbian and homosexual youth in a storefront setting. The Los Angeles Youth Network operates Project Homeless Youth, a 20-bed shelter where homeless youth can stay for as long as 60 days, and provides a spectrum of counseling, life skills training, and job development programs.

CONCLUSIONS

In conclusion, the following suggestions are offered:

1. Schools need to reassess their response to sex education and prevention of HIV infection. AIDS prevention education must be institutionalized within school systems so that a framework for ongoing education is established. For example, the New York State Education Department proposed a statewide AIDS education curriculum that is age-appropriate, from kindergarten through high school, which stresses the communicable nature of AIDS, methods of avoidance, information and counseling resources, and the socioeconomic impact of AIDS (Carmody, 1987). The State University of New York at Stony Brook has designed and field-tested a curriculum for young adults that includes sessions on the purpose of studying AIDS, basic facts about AIDS, the human context of AIDS, AIDS and sexuality, AIDS and substance use, the ethics of AIDS, services and resources, and decision making and AIDS (Walton et al., 1987). The school setting affords the opportunity of multisystem exposure to and reinforcement of AIDS education, and the school can play a primary role in AIDS prevention activities.

2. Although we have focused on children as direct targets of preventive interventions, the school is also a vehicle for access to parents and school personnel. Changing the behaviors of parents is key to changing the behaviors of their children. Education of parents can serve to reinforce the teachings of the school health educator. Parental involvement in AIDS education, curriculum review, selection of educational materials, and advisory committee deliberations may break down the resistance of parents who refuse to permit their children to participate in specialized programs as well as those who are against sexual instruction. Although parents generally provide an initial model of sexuality and sexual values for their children, they often fail to discuss sex with them. Thus parental AIDS education and sex education may increase parents' ease with the subject and enable them to begin an open dialogue with their children. Moreover, a school's solicitation of parental participation communicates a respect for and validation of the parental role.

Parent education may also prove helpful in mitigating a community's misperceptions and fears about the disease–education essential to prevent community hysteria and rejection of children and teachers with AIDS, such as happened in the widely publicized cases in New York, Indiana and Florida or as has been proposed by a New Jersey representative's plan to remove seropositive teachers from their jobs and to segregate children who test positive from uninfected children in the classroom* (Nelkin & Hilgartner, 1986; *The New York Times*, 1988a; Kerr, 1989).

*There is no evidence that AIDS presents a risk in the classroom as a result of an infected student's fights or nosebleeds that potentially could expose other students to infected blood. In New York City, children with HIV-related disease are evaluated by a special panel to determine their appropriateness to attend a public school.

3. All staff of youth-serving agencies need to be trained about AIDS as well. As these staff members reach adolescents in their natural social settings and have the experience in working with youth, AIDS services should be integrated into the programs of these agencies. Also, staff should be trained in how to talk to teens about sex and how to work more effectively with them. Training in specific techniques for communicating this information candidly and comfortably is required for service providers to move beyond a superficial level of discussion (Boyer, 1988; Di Clemente, 1989; Rosenfeld et al., 1988). Such training may require not only knowledge enhancement and communication skills building but also sexual and drug behavior values clarification and desensitization techniques and techniques for dealing with discrimination issues.

Organizations that serve youth should incorporate AIDS into a health promotion program that is accompanied by programs in life planning, job training and career counseling, and responsible decision making.

4. An integrated, comprehensive approach to AIDS prevention is required. Unlike adults, AIDS prevention activities directed toward youth have typically taken place within the context of family, school, and church (Rumsey, 1987). Although the schools are a major channel for information dissemination and education, other avenues must be pursued to ensure multiple sources of exposure. In particular, greater outreach to youth in the streets and other natural social settings is essential. Many kids learn about sex education in the streets and from their peers.

Appropriate venues for accessing youth also include the clergy, church youth groups, scouting groups, summer camps, after-school clubs, settlement houses, Ys, music stores, housing projects, shopping malls, drug treatment programs, runaway shelters, community centers, detention centers, and jails. Movie theaters and music and record stores, prime recreational outlets for youth, and libraries can be tapped to provide AIDS prevention education. In addition, youth counselors need to accelerate their outreach to street youth and adolescents who engage in prostitution and drugs (Quackenbush, 1987). Programs that are not school-based can be directed to reach youth who are school dropouts.

5. Environmental and communitywide approaches must also be considered. Television and advertising can exert a powerful influence on health behaviors. For example, a recent survey revealed that television (84 percent) and magazines (79 percent) were the primary sources of AIDS information among a sample of Seattle high school students (Miller & Downer, 1987) and may be more influential message senders than parents or the school system.

The media can create environments that are conducive to AIDS prevention by promoting condoms in appropriate settings (Wallack & Corbett, 1987). Increasing teenagers' access to condoms is another route to AIDS prevention. The strategic placement of machines that sell condoms, such as in school restrooms and locker rooms, food stores and newspaper stores, can facilitate adolescents' purchasing of condoms. Displaying condoms on shelves with personal hygiene products rather than behind counters in pharmacies may increase a teen's comfort and thus enhance the purchase of condoms. Free condoms could also be

distributed at public places known to be hangouts for teen runaways and pros-
titutes. In addition, manufacturers' sensitivity to the design, packaging, and mar-
keting of condoms for women may enhance product appeal to female adolescents
and hence increase consumption levels.

6. Concerted educational efforts must be directed toward black and Latino
youth because of the high incidence of AIDS among adults and the lack of HIV-
related knowledge in these groups. As IV drug use is the primary mode of HIV
transmission in minority communities, this must be stressed in preventive interventions with black and Hispanic adolescents.

7. Careful consideration should be given to the relevant medium for
delivering AIDS prevention messages to teens. Comic books have been developed
by some organizations such as the Health Education Resource Organization
(HERO) (1987) in Baltimore and the Hetrick-Martin Institute for the Protection
of Lesbian and Gay Youth (ILPGY) (1987) in New York. For example, one HERO
comic book deals with the importance of condoms for safer sex and modes of
disease transmission. The comic also stresses that AIDS is not a gay disease and
that even healthy and clean-looking people can be infected with HIV. *Fotonovelas*,
street mime, and theater improvisations may successfully attract Latino youth.

8. Booster AIDS prevention sessions can be implemented after initial interventions to sharpen and reinforce adolescents' knowledge and skills acquisition and thus serve to maintain behavioral and cognitive changes. Emerging studies
of adult men who have sex with men indicate that some are relapsing into unsafe
sexual practices (Stall, 1989). In addition, semiannual booster sessions throughout
the course of high school will provide adolescents with an institutional outlet for
discussing difficulties in adapting to recommended AIDS prevention practices.

9. An agenda for future research of AIDS prevention among youth might
include assessment of the efficacy of gender-specific interventions and of the use
of peer AIDS prevention counselors in lowering risk of infection. Another fruit-
ful area of investigation is to examine whether these prevention programs change
social group norms as well as social skills (Flay, 1985).

10. Finally, the bottom-line question that begs for an answer is whether
prevention programs can make a difference in changing adolescents' high-risk
behaviors. Experience with other health behaviors, such as pregnancy prevention
and contraception, has shown that by and large, success has been limited. Thus
it is essential to evaluate program content and intervention approach and their
effectiveness in changing AIDS-associated knowledge, attitudes, behavioral intentions, and behaviors. In addition to assessment of baseline measures, repeated
test assessments at three- or six-month intervals will determine the longer-term
stability of change. Professionals can convene focus groups with targeted adolescent groups to identify attitudes toward AIDS prevention messages and communication channels currently used. Members of these groups can refine risk-
reduction programs by adding new content and increasing the age and culture
relevance of AIDS prevention activities.

SUMMARY

This chapter provided a practice framework for preventive interventions with adolescents at risk for the spectrum of HIV infection. The interventions outlined in the chapter drew upon social learning theory, gender role, cultural role perspectives, social skills training, and social support network theories. These concepts are relevant for HIV prevention among minority and majority-culture youth and can also be applied profitably to prevention initiatives targeted to people in other age groups and settings.

As we have entered the decade of the 1990s, a new phase of the AIDS epidemic is upon us. As the numbers of people living with the disease are increasing each year because of effective treatment, AIDS is now considered to be a chronic disease. The challenge that lies before us is keeping the uninfected from becoming infected. The intensity of AIDS risk-reduction campaigns must continue. This will require multiple messages delivered through multiple channels multiple times (Tolsma, 1987). Innovative and aggressive prevention approaches targeted toward adolescents are essential to stemming the tide of the epidemic to prevent youth, our future generation of workers, from being infected with HIV. While adolescents are prime targets for education, comprehensive outreach to preadolescents, hopefully before sexual activity has been initiated, should become a priority as well. With a systematic AIDS prevention campaign that promotes low-risk behaviors, adolescents can own up to their risks and take steps to protect themselves from AIDS. Failure to institute such precautionary practices will result in a legacy of infected young adults.

REFERENCES

ALEXANDER-RODRIGUEZ, T., and S. H. VERMUND. (1987). "Gonorrhea and Syphilis in Incarcerated Urban Adolescents: Prevalence and Physical Signs." *Pediatrics, 80,* 561–564.

AMARO, H., B. ZUCKERMAN, and H. CABRAL. (1989). "Drug Use Among Adolescent Mothers: Profile of Risk." *Pediatrics, 84,* 144–151.

ANDERSON, P., K. MCPHERSON, H. BEECHING, J. WEINBERG, and M. VESSEY. (1978). "Sexual Behavior and Contraceptive Practices of Undergraduates at Oxford University." *Journal of Biosocial Science, 10,* 277–286.

AXTHELM, P. (1988). "Somebody Else's Kids." *Newsweek,* pp. 64–68.

BACHMAN, J. G., L. D. JOHNSTON, and P. M. O'MALLEY. (1987). *Monitoring the Future: Questionnaire Responses from the Nation's High School Seniors, 1986,* Ann Arbor, Mich.: Institute for Social Research.

BACON, K. H. (1989). "Nearly 0.2% of College Students in U.S. Who Were Tested Carry the AIDS Virus." *Wall Street Journal,* p. B4.

BANKS, M. H., B. R. BEWLEY, and J. M. BLAND. (1981). "Adolescent Attitudes to Smoking: Their Influence on Behavior." *International Journal of Health Education, 24,* 39.

BARTH, R. P. (1989). *Reducing the Risk. Building Skills to Prevent Pregnancy.* Santa Cruz, California: Network Publications.

BELKIN, L. (1987, March 21). "TV Contraceptive Ads Backed in Poll." *The New York Times,* p. 54.

BENNETT, W. (1986). *Schools without Drugs.* Washington, D.C.: U.S. Department of Education.

BISHOP, K. (1988). "San Francisco Pupils Told about AIDS by Victims." *The New York Times.*

BLYTHE, M. J., B. KATZ, D. P. ORR, V. A. CAINE, and R. B. JONES. (1988). "Historical and Clinical Factors Associated with Chlamydia Trachomatis Genitourinary Infection in Female Adolescents." *Journal of Pediatrics, 112,* 1000–1004.

BOYER, C. B. (1988). "Strategies for Developing School-based AIDS Prevention and Risk Reduction Intervention Programs for Adolescents." Testimony presented to the President's Commission on AIDS, Washington, D.C., March 3.

BROZNAN, N. (1987, March 14). "Success in Preventing Teen-age Pregnancy." *The New York Times.*

BUCHTA, R. M. (1989). "Attitudes of Adolescents and Parents of Adolescents Concerning Condom Advertisements on Television." *Journal of Adolescent Health Care, 10,* 220–223.

BURKE, D. S., J. F. BRUNDAGE, M. GOLDENBAUM, L. I. GARD-NER, M. PETERSON, R. VISINTINE, R. R. REDFIELD, and the Walter Reed Retrovirus Research Group. (1990). "Human Immunodeficiency Virus Infections in Teenagers." *New England Journal of Medicine, 263,* 2074–2077.

CAMPAGNET, A. (1987). "Latino Community Services." *NAN Multicultural Notes on AIDS Education and Services, 1,* 1–2.

CAPLAN, G. (1964). *Principles of Preventive Psychiatry.* New York: Basic Books.

CARMODY, D. (1987, June 20). "State Proposes AIDS Education for All Students." *The New York Times,* p. 32.

COLLINS, G. (1987, March 9). "AIDS and TV: What to Tell a Young Child." *The New York Times.*

Communication Technologies and Research and Decisions Corporation. (1986). *Reaching Ethnic Communities in the Fight against AIDS.* San Francisco: San Francisco AIDS Foundation.

DALEY, S. (1988). "New York City Street Youth: Living in the Shadow of AIDS." *The New York Times,* pp. A1; B4.

DAVIS, A. K., J. M. WEENER, and R. E. SCHUTE. (1977). "Positive Peer Influence: School-based Prevention." *Health Education Monographs, 8,* 20–22.

DAVIS, K., P. FITZGERALD, A. GARRETT, J. LIN, J. NATALE, AND J. WIESMAN. (1986, May). "AIDS Education Study: Assessment of Knowledge and Attitudes among Junior High and High School Students." Department of Epidemiology and Public Health, Yale School of Medicine, New Haven, unpublished manuscript.

DI CLEMENTE, R. J., C. B. BOYER, and E. MORALES. (1988). "Minorities and AIDS: Knowledge, Attitudes, and Misconceptions among Black and Latino Adolescents." *American Journal of Public Health, 1,* 55–57.

DI CLEMENTE, R. J., J. ZORN, and L. TEMOSHOK. (1986). "Adolescents and AIDS: A Survey of Knowledge, Attitudes and Beliefs about AIDS in San Francisco." *American Journal of Public Health, 76,* 1443–1445.

DI CLEMENTE, R. J. (1988). "Policy Perspectives on the Implementation and Development of School-based AIDS Prevention Education Programs in the United States." *AIDS & Public Policy Journal, 3,* 14–16.

DI CLEMENTE, R. J. (1989). "Prevention of Human Immunodeficiency Virus Infection among Adolescents: The Interplay of Health Education and Public Policy in the Development and Implementation of School-Based AIDS Education Programs." *AIDS Education and Prevention, 1,* 70–78.

DIELMAN, T. E., P. C. CAMPANELLI, J. T. SHOPE, and A. T. BUTCHART. (1987). "Susceptibility to Peer Pressure, Self-esteem, and Health Locus of Control as Correlates of Adolescent Substance Abuse." *Health Education Quarterly, 14,* 207–221.

DI VITTIS, A. T., A. HERNANDEZ, J. E. MANTELL, C. L. PACK, S. SHIFLETT, D. K. WHITTIER, M. J. KENNEDY, P. LA-QUEUR, G. WILSON, M. GUZMAN. (1990). "Self-Reported HIV Risk Perceptions and Behaviors among Women Receiving Obstetrical/Gynecological Services in an Inner-City Hospital." Poster Session, American Public Health Association, New York City, October.

DOLCINI, P., N. ADLER, C. IRWIN, S. MILLSTEIN, J. CATANIA, S. KEGELES, and L. D. COHN. (1988). "Adolescents and Sex: Can They Assess their Risk of Contracting HIV and Other Sexually Transmitted Diseases." Fourth International Conference on AIDS, Stockholm, June.

Drug Abuse Warning Network. (1984). National Institute on Drug Abuse, Rockville, Md.

EISEN, M., and G. L. ZELLMAN. (1986). "The Role of Health Belief Attitudes, Sex Education and Demographics in Predicting Adolescents' Sexuality Knowledge." *Health Education Quarterly, 13,* 9–22.

EVANS, R. I., A. HENDERSON, P. HILL, and B. RAINES. (1979). "Smoking in Children and Adolescents: Psychosocial Determinants and Prevention Strategies." In N. A. Krasnegor (Ed.), *The Behavioral Aspects of Smoking,* GPO No. 017-024-00947-4, NIDA Research Monograph No. 26 (pp. 69–96). Washington, D. C.: U.S. Government Printing Office.

FLAY, B. R. (1985). "Psychosocial Approaches to Smoking Prevention: A Preview of Findings." *Health Psychology, 4,* 449–488.

Foundation for Children with AIDS. (1989, May). "Teenagers Helping Each Other: Two Programs That Are Working." *Children with AIDS,* p. 60.

FRIEDLAND, G. H., B. R. SALTZMAN, M. F. ROGERS, P. A. KAHL, M. L. LESSER, M. H. MAYERS, and R. S. KLEIN. (1986). "Lack of Transmission of HTLV-III/LAV Infection to Household Contacts of Patients with AIDS or AIDS-related Complex with Oral Candidiasis." *New England Journal of Medicine, 22,* 915–927.

FORREST, J. D., and J. SILVERMAN. (1989). "What Public School Teachers Teach about Preventing Pregnancy, AIDS and Sexually Transmitted Diseases." *Family Planning Perspectives, 21,* 65–72.

FULLILOVE, M. T. (1987, Spring). "Teens Rap about Drugs, STDs, and AIDS." *Multicultural Inquiry and Research on AIDS,* p. 1.

FULLILOVE, M. T., and R. E. FULLILOVE. (1989). "Intersecting Epidemics: Black Teen Crack Use and Sexually Transmitted Disease." *JAMWA, 44,* 146–153.

FULLILOVE, R. E., M. T. FULLILOVE, B. P. BOWSER, and S. A. GROSS. (1990). "Risk of Sexually Transmitted Disease Among Black Adolescent Crack Users in Oakland and San Francisco, Calif." *Journal of the American Medical Association, 263,* 851–855.

FURSTENBERG, F. F. JR., K. A. MOORE, and J. L. PETERSON. (1985). "Sex Education and Sexual Experience Among Adolescents." *American Journal of Public Health, 75,* 1331–1332.

GALLUP ORGANIZATION (1987). *The 1986 Survey of Public Awareness of AIDS.* Princeton, N. J.

GOLAN, N. (1978). *Treatment in Crisis.* New York: Free Press.

GOLEMAN, D. (1987). "Teen-Age Risk Taking: Rise in

Deaths Prompts New Research Effort." *The New York Times,* p. C1.

GONZALEZ, J. (1988). "The Colorado AIDS Project: The Hustler Outreach Program". Paper presented at the International Lesbian and Gay Health Conference and AIDS Forum, Boston, July.

GOTTLIEB, N. H., and J. A. BAKER. (1986). "The Relative Influence of Health Beliefs, Parental and Peer Behaviors, and Exercise Program Participation on Smoking, Alcohol Use, and Physical Activity." *Social Science and Medicine, 22,* 915–927.

GREEN, L. W., M. W. KREUTER, S. G. DEEDS, and K. B. PARTRIDGE. (1980). *Health Education Planning: A Diagnostic Approach.* Palo Alto, Cal.: Mayfield.

GUTTMACHER INSTITUTE. (1981). *Teenage Pregnancy: The Problem That Hasn't Gone Away.* New York.

HAWKINS, R. O., JR. (1982). "Adolescent Alcohol Abuse: A Review." *Developmental and Behavioral Pediatrics, 3,* 83–87.

Health Education Resource Organization. (1987). *Andrea and Lisa,* Baltimore.

HECHINGER, F. M. (1987, June 23). "Teenagers and Sex." *The New York Times,* p. C11.

HEIN, K. (1987). "AIDS in Adolescents: A Rationale for Concern." *New York State Journal of Medicine, 87,* 290–295.

HEIN, K. (1988). "AIDS in Adolescents." Paper prepared for the National Invitational Conference on Adolescents and AIDS, Washington, D.C., March.

HERZ, E. J., J. S. REIS, and L. BARBARA-STEIN. (1986). "Family Life Education for Young Teens: An Assessment of Three Interventions." *Health Education Quarterly, 13,* 201–221.

HETRICK-MARTIN Institute for the Protection of Lesbian and Gay Youth. (1987). *Tales of the Closet, 1,* 1–24.

HILTS, P. (1989). *"World AIDS Epidemic Draws New Warnings," The New York Times,* p. D19.

Hospital Audiences, Inc. (1990). "AIDS Prevention Program for Adolescents." *HAI News,* (Spring), pp. 3; 6.

HUDSON, R. A., B. A. PETTY, A. C. FREEMAN, C. E. HALEY, and M. A. KREPCHO. (1989). "Adolescent Runaways' Behavioral Risk Factors, Knowledge about AIDS, and Attitudes about Condom Usage." Poster Session, Fifth International Conference on AIDS, Montreal, June.

HUNTER, J., and R. SCHAECHER. (1987). "Stresses on Lesbian and Gay Adolescents in Schools." *Social Work in Education, 9,* 180–190.

Institute of Medicine, National Academy of Sciences. (1986). *Confronting AIDS: Directions for Public Health, Health Care and Research.* Washington, D. C.: National Academy Press.

JAFFEE, L. R., M. SEEHAUS, C. WAGNER, and B. J. LEADBETTER. (1988). "Anal Intercourse and Knowledge of Acquired Immunodeficiency Syndrome among Minority-Group Female Adolescents." *The Journal of Pediatrics, 112,* 1005–1007.

JAMES, G. (1989). "AIDS Prevention 1A: Use a Student to Teach a Student." *The New York Times,* p. B1.

JESSOR, R., J. E. DONOVAN, and F. COSTA. (1986). "Psychosocial Correlates of Marijuana Use in Adolescence and Young Adulthood: The Past as Prologue." *Alcohol, Drugs, and Driving, 2,* 31–49.

JOHNSTON, L. D., P. M. O'MALLEY, and J. G. BACHMAN. (1986). "Drug Use among American High School Students, College Students, and Other Young Adults: National Trends through 1985." Rockville, Md.: National Institute on Drug Abuse.

KAR, S. B., and J. TALBOT. (1981). "Impact of Peer Counseling on Teen Contraception in Los Angeles." Paper presented at the American Public Health Association's Annual Convention.

KEGELES, S. M., N. E. ADLER, and C. E. IRWIN. (1988). "Sexually Active Adolescents and Condoms: Changes Over the Year in Knowledge, Attitudes, and Use." *American Journal of Public Health, 78,* 460–461.

KELLY, J. A., and J. S. ST. LAWRENCE. (1986). "Behavioral Interventions and AIDS." *Behavioral Therapist, 6,* 121–125.

KERR, P. (1987). "High-school Marijuana Use Still Declining, U.S. Survey Shows." *The New York Times,* p. A21.

KING, W. (1989). "On the Sad Trail of Street Youths, Drugs and AIDS." *The New York Times,* pp. B1; B8.

KOOP, C. E. (1986). *Surgeon's General Report on Acquired Immune Deficiency Syndrome.* Washington, D.C.: U.S. Government Printing Office.

LEMP, G. F., J. L. BARNHART, G. W. RUTHERFORD, and D. WERDEGAR. (1987). "Predictors of Survival for AIDS Cases in San Francisco." Poster session, Third International Conference on AIDS, Washington, D.C., June.

LEVINE, D. M., L. W. GREEN, S. G. DEEDS, J. CHWALDI, R. PATTERSON, R., and J. FINLAY. (1979). "Health Education for Hyperactive Patients." *JAMA, 241,* 1700–1703.

LINDEMANN, E. (1944). "Symptomatology and Management of Acute Grief." *American Journal of Psychiatry, 101.*

LOPEZ, D. J., and G. S. GETZEL. (1984). "Helping Gay AIDS Patients in Crisis." *Social Casework. The Journal of Contemporary Social Work,* pp. 387–394.

LOUIS HARRIS and Associates. (1987). "Attitudes about Television, Sex, and Contraception." Study Number 874005, (February).

LUMIERE, R., and S. COOK. (1983). *Healthy Sex.* New York: Simon & Schuster.

MACDONALD, I. (1987). "An Approach to the Problem of Teenage Pregnancy." *Public Health Reports, 102,* 377–385.

MAKULOWICH, J. S. (1988). "Adolescents Face Up to AIDS." *AIDS Patient Care,* pp. 38–42.

MANTELL, J., K. ELL, and M. B. HAMOVITCH. (1984). "Ethnic Variations in Social Support Systems." In *Proceedings of the Fourth National Conference on Human Values and Cancer, 1984,* Professional Education Publication No. 4346 (pp. 67–72). New York: American Cancer Society.

MANTELL, J. E., L. M. KOCHEMS, A. T. DI VITTIS, P.

MASTROIANNI, and K. MAHONY. (1986). "Prevention of HIV transmission: AIDS Risk-Reduction Intervention with High-Risk Groups," Cooperative Agreement No. U62/CCU201065-01. Atlanta: Centers for Disease Control.

MARTIN, A. D. (1982). "Learning to Hide: The Socialization of the Gay Adolescent." In S. C. Feinstein, J. G. Looney, A. Z. Schwartzberg, and A. D. Sorosky (Eds.), *Adolescent Psychiatry*, vol 10 (pp. 52–65). Chicago: University of Chicago Press.

MCAULIFFE, K. (1987, January 12). "AIDS: What You Need to Know and What You Should Do." *U.S. News and World Report*, pp. 60–70.

MCCAUL, K. D., and R. GLASGOW. (1985). "Preventing Adolescent Smoking: What Have We Learned about Treatment Construct Validity?" *Health Psychology*, 4, 361–387.

METRO-HELP, INC. (1984). "Runaways: The Status of Life on the Road." Chicago.

MIDDLETON, K. (1989). *The Sexuality Decision-Making Book for Teens*. Santa Cruz: Network Publications.

MILLER, L., and A. DOWNER. (1987). "Knowledge and Attitude Changes in Adolescents Following One Hour of AIDS Instruction." Paper presented at the Third International Conference on AIDS, Washington, D.C., June.

MORRISON, D. M. (1985). "Adolescent Contraceptive Behavior: A Review." *Psychology Bulletin*, 98, 538–568.

NADELSON, C., M. T. NOTMAN, and J. W. GILLON. (1980). "Sexual Knowledge and Attitudes of Adolescents: Relationships to Contraceptive Use." *Obstetrics and Gynecology*, 55, 340–345.

National Center for Health Statistics. (1987). *National Adolescent Student Health Survey*. Rockville, Md.

NELKIN, D., and S. HILGARTNER. (1986). "Disputed Dimensions of Risk: A Public School Controversy over AIDS." *Milbank Memorial Fund Quarterly*, 64 (Supp. 1), 118–142.

NEWCOMB, M. D., and P. M. BENTLER. (1986). "Cocaine Use among Adolescents: Longitudinal Associations with Social Context, Psychopathology, and Use of Other Substances." *Addictive Behaviors*, 11, 263–273.

New York City Department of Health. (1987, July 24). "Talk about AIDS Before it Hits Home." *The New York Times*, p. A11.

New York Daily News. (1989, July 20). "Teen AIDS Help from New York Youth Shelter."

New York State Senate Majority Task Force on AIDS. (1987). *The AIDS Crisis in New York*. Albany.

PAHWA, S., M. KAPLAN, S. FIKRIG, R. PAHWA, M. G. SARNGADHARAN, M. POPOVIC, and R. C. GALLO. (1986). "Spectrum of Human T-Cell Lymphotropic Virus Type III Infection in Children." *JAMA*, 255, 2299–2305.

PARAD, H. J. (Ed.). (1965). *Crisis Intervention: Selected Readings*. New York: Families Service Association of America.

QUACKENBUSH, M. (1987). "Educating Youth and AIDS." *Focus*, 2, 1–3.

QUACKENBUSH, M., and P. SARGENT. (1986). *Teaching*

AIDS: A Resource Guide on Acquired Immune Deficiency Syndrome. Santa Cruz, Calif.: Network Publications.

RAPOPORT, L. (1962). "Working with Families in Crisis: An Exploration in Preventive Intervention." *Social Work*, 7, 48–56.

RAVEIS, V. H., and D. B. KANDEL. (1987). "Changes in Drug Behavior from the Middle to the Late Twenties: Initiation, Persistence, and Cessation of Use." *American Journal of Public Health*, 77, 607–611.

REMAFEDI, G. (1987). "Adolescent Homosexuality: Psychosocial and Medical Implications." *Pediatrics*, 79, 331–337.

RICKERT V. I., M. S. JAY, A. GOTTLIEB, and C. BRIDGES. (1989). "Adolescents and AIDS. Female's Attitudes and Behaviors Toward Condom Purchase and Use." *Journal of Adolescent Health Care*, 10, 313–316.

ROGEL, M. J., M. E. ZUEHLKE, A. C. PETERSON, M. TOBIN-RICHARDS, and M. SHELTON. (1980). "Contraceptive Behavior in Adolescence: A Decision-making Perspective." *Journal of Youth and Adolescence*, 9, 491–506.

ROSENFELD, S., J. M. BATH, J. DAY, M. GROSS, L. SIMMONS, and C. HAUG-SIMMONS. (1988). "Reaching Adolescents through Team Training of Educators." Paper presented at the Fourth International Conference on AIDS. Stockholm, June.

ROTHENBERG, R., M. WOELFEL, R. STONEBURNER, J. MILBERG, R. PARKER, and B. TRUMAN. "Survival with the Acquired Immunodeficiency Syndrome." *New England Journal of Medicine*, 317, 1297–1302.

RUMSEY, S. (1987, July 24). "Teens and AIDS." WNYC-TV Town Meeting.

SAVIN-WILLIAMS, R. C., and R. E. LENHART (in press). "AIDS Prevention among Lesbian and Gay Youth: Psychosocial Stress and Health Care Intervention Guidelines." In D. G. Ostrow (Ed.), *Behavioral Aspects of AIDS and Other Sexually Transmitted Diseases*, New York: Plenum.

SCHINKE, S. P., L. D. GILCHRIST, R. F. SCHILLING, W. H. SNOW, J. K. BOBO. (1986a). "Skill Methods to Prevent Smoking." *Health Education Quarterly*, 13, 23–27.

SCHINKE, S. P., L. D. GILCHRIST, R. F. SCHILLING, and V. A. SENECHAL. (1986b). "Smoking and Smokeless Tobacco Use among Adolescents: Trends and Intervention Results." *Public Health Reports*, 101, 373–378.

SHULMAN, L., J. E. MANTELL, C. EATON, and S. SORRELL. (1990). "HIV-Related Disorders, Needle Users, and the Social Services." In C. G. Leukefeld, R. J. Battjes, and Z. Amsel (Eds.), *AIDS and Intravenous Drug Use: Future Directions for Community-Based Prevention Research*, NIDA Research Monograph 93 (pp. 254–276), Rockville: National Institute on Drug Abuse.

SMITH, E. A., and J. R. UDRY. (1985). "Coital and Non-coital Sexual Behavior of White and Black Adolescents." *American Journal of Public Health*, 75, 1200–1203.

SOLOMON, B. B. (1976). *Black Empowerment*. New York: Columbia University Press.

SPITZ, A. M., L. T. STRAUSS, B. J. MACIAK, and L. MORRIS. (1987). "Teenage Pregnancy and Fertility in the United States, 1970, 1974, and 1980." *Morbidity and Mortality Weekly Report, 36*, 1SS-10SS.

STALL, R. (1989), Personal communication, May 26.

STEINFELS, P. (1989). "Bishops Shift Earlier Stance on AIDS." *The New York Times*, p. A14.

STEPHENS, T., and C. A. SCHOENBORN. (1988). *Health Habits in the United States and Canada*. National Center for Health Statistics, DHHS Publication No. (PHS) 988-1429. Vital and Health Statistics, Series 5, No. 3, Washington, D. C.: Government Printing Office.

STRUNIN, L., and R. HINGSON. (1987). "Acquired Immunodeficiency Syndrome and Adolescents: Knowledge, Beliefs, Attitudes and Behaviors." *Pediatrics, 79*, 825–828.

SUSSMAN, S. (1989). "Two Social Influence Perspectives on Tobacco Use Development and Prevention." *Health Education Research, 4*, 213–223.

The New York Times. (1987). "U. S. Plan Issued on AIDS Education."

The New York Times. (1988a). "6 Connecticut Bishops Urge Better Education on AIDS," p. 30.

The New York Times. (1988b). "Classroom Booth Asked For Girl, 6 with AIDS," p. A12.

The New York Times. (1988c). "Hot Line on AIDS is Aimed at the Teenager," p. 25.

THOMAS, S. B., A. G. GILLIAM, and C. G. IWREY. (1989). "Knowledge about AIDS and Reported Risk Behaviors among Black College Students." *Journal of American College Health, 38*.

TOLSMA, D. (1987). "Effective School Health Education about AIDS." Paper presented at the National Conference on Sexually Transmitted Diseases, Atlanta, August.

TORRES, A., and S. SINGH. (1986). "Contraceptive Practice among Hispanic Adolescents." *Family Planning Perspectives, 18*, 193–194.

U.S. Centers for Disease Control. (1986). "The Effectiveness of School Health Education." *Morbidity and Mortality Weekly Report, 35*, 593–595.

U.S. Centers for Disease Control. (1989). "Update: Heterosexual Transmission of AIDS and HIV Infection-U.S." *Morbidity and Mortality Weekly Report, 38*, 423–434.

U.S. Centers for Disease Control. (1990a). *HIV/AIDS Surveillance Report*. (May), pp. 1–18.

U.S. Centers for Disease Control. (1990b). "HIV Prevalence, Projected AIDS Cases Estimates: Workshop, October 31–November 1, 1989." *Morbidity and Mortality Weekly Report, 39*, 110–119.

U.S. Centers for Disease Control. (1990c). "Update: Acquired Immunodeficiency Syndrome-United States." *Morbidity and Mortality Weekly Report, 39*, 81–86.

U.S. Centers for Disease Control. (1990d). "Survey Shows Support for AIDS Education in Schools." *CDC AIDS Weekly*. (February 19), p. 10.

U.S. General Accounting Office. (1990a). *AIDS Education: Public School Programs Require More Student Information and Teacher Training*. (GAO/HRD-90-103, May). Washington, D.C.

U.S. General Accounting Office. (1990b). *AIDS Education: Programs for Out-of-School Youth Slowly Evolving*. (GAO/HRD-90-111, May). Washington, D.C.

U.S. Conference of Mayors. (1987). "Local School Districts Active in AIDS Education." *AIDS Information Exchange, 4*, 1–10.

U.S. Department of Health and Human Services. (1983). *Runaway and Homeless Youth: National Program Inspection*. Washington, D.C.: U.S. Government Printing Office.

U.S. Department of Health and Human Services. (1986). *Fiscal Year 1985 Study of Runaways and Youth*. Washington, D.C.

VAN BIEMA, D. (1987, April 13). "What's Gone Wrong with Teen Sex." *People*, pp. 110ff.

WALLACK, L., and K. CORBETT. (1987). "Alcohol, Tobacco and Marijuana Use among Youth: An Overview of Epidemiological, Program and Policy Trends." *Health Education Quarterly, 14*, 223–249.

WALTON, R., R. C. JOHNSTON, and B. COPPOLA. (1987). "Medical, Psychological, and Social Implications of AIDS: A Curriculum for Young Adults." Stony Brook: State University of New York, School of Allied Health Professionals (mimeographed).

WILLIAMS, T., C. E. STERK, S. R. FRIEDMAN, C. E. DOZIER, J. L. SOTHERAN, and D. C. DES JARLAIS. (1988). "Crack Use Puts Women at Risk For Heterosexual Transmission of HIV." Poster Session, International Conference on AIDS, Stockholm, June.

WOLF, S. M. (1990). "The Health Care Needs of Homeless and Runaway Youth." Letter to the Editor. *JAMA, 263*, 811–812.

World Health Organization. (1989). "Health of Adolescents: Results from the National Adolescent Student Health Survey." *Weekly Epidemiological Record, 64*, 233–235.

World Health Organization. (1990). "Statistics from the World Health Organization and the Centers for Disease Control." *AIDS, 4*, 375–379.

WORTH, D., and R. RODRIGUEZ. (1987, January-February). "Latina Women and AIDS." *SIECUS Report*, pp. 5–7.

WORTHINGTON, G. M. (1986). "Adolescence and Youth: Some Educational and Epidemiological Aspects of the AIDS Crisis." Testimony presented to the Standing Committee on Health, State of New York Assembly, December 19.

YATES, G. L., R. MACKENZIE, J. PENNBRIDGE, and E. COHEN. (1988). "A Risk Profile Comparison of Runaway and Non-Runaway Youth." *American Journal of Public Health, 78*, 820–821.

ZABIN, L. S., and S. D. CLARK, JR. (1981). "Why They Delay: A Study of Teenage Family Planning Patients." *Family Planning Perspectives, 13*, 205–217.

ZELNIK, M., and J. KANTNER. (1979). "Reasons for Nonuse of Contraception by Sexually Active

Women Aged 15–19." *Family Planning Perspectives,* *11,* 289–296.

ZIEGLER, J. B., D. A. COOPER, R. O. JOHNSON, and J. GOLD. (1985). "Postnatal Transmission of AIDS-associated Retrovirus from Mother to Infant." *Lancet,* *1,* 896–898.

Suicide Intervention in the Schools

John Kalafat

INTRODUCTION

Case Study

A high school senior arrives at a meeting with his academic adviser with a loaded handgun and threatens to kill himself. The adviser calls the principal in, and the two school officials talk to the distraught youngster while the assistant principal calls the police and initiates the policy for responding to on-premises suicide threats.

The other students, who have heard something about the event, are kept in their classes while designated school personnel inform them of the facts and quash incorrect rumors about a hostage situation. The student is persuaded to go with the police, who take him to the local psychiatric emergency service.

The media are informed by the assistant principal and, by prior agreement, run no photographs or other identifying information with their articles. Consultants from the local crisis service are called in to assist in standard postvention (intervention after a suicide) procedures, including debriefing with faculty, arranging drop-in discussion groups for students, contacting students potentially at risk, and scheduling a parents' meeting.

Case Study

That same fall, a guidance counselor from another local school, concerned about the number of attempts among students during the past year, calls the crisis consultants for their recommendations and assistance. The principal agrees to review the school procedures with the consultants, particularly because the school has been unsuccessful in obtaining any information about attempters returning to school from the local hospital. He defers, however, any decision on a faculty in-service or classroom education program for the students.

These two scenarios, representing, respectively, effective and insufficient responses to the increased incidence of adolescent suicide behavior, are being repeated many times a year in schools throughout the country.

This chapter will review the incidence and prevalence of adolescent suicidal behavior and our current understanding of this phenomenon. The basic premise of this chapter is that both the nature of adolescent suicide and our current state of knowledge in regard to it clearly point to classic crisis intervention procedures as our most appropriate and effective response at this time.

SUICIDE RATES

Between 1960 and 1980, the suicide rate for youths between 15 and 19 years of age increased from 5.6 to 13.8 per 100,000 for males and from 1.6 to 3.0 for females. In 1983, there were signs that the increase might be leveling off, but in 1984, suicide rates for white males reached a record high of more than 21 per 100,000 (National Center for Health Statistics, 1986).

Most observers consider these figures underestimates because many suicides may go unreported and because many suicides may masquerade as accidents, the leading cause of death among adolescents. Although these increases are alarming, the present rates indicate that the likelihood that a given school system will experience a completed suicide is still relatively low. However, these data do not tell the entire story.

Various data indicate that the ratio of suicide attempts to completions among adolescents may be over 100 to 1 (Smith & Crawford, 1986). Surveys of adolescents reveal that between 10 and 15 percent report having made a suicide attempt (Boggs, 1986; Shaffer et al., 1988; Smith & Crawford, 1986) and between 40 and 60 percent have thought about killing themselves (Curran, 1987; Smith & Crawford, 1986).

Also, Smith and Crawford's (1986) survey indicated that almost 90 percent of the students who indicated that they made an attempt did not receive medical attention for their attempt. Other studies also indicate that most teens who report having made suicide attempts will not have received treatment (Garfinkel et al., 1982; Shaffer & Caton, 1984). While this may indicate that many of these attempts were not seriously injurious, it also shows that most attempters cannot be identified through medical contacts.

It is important to note, however, that attempts often do result in serious injury, including paralysis and brain damage (Kleiner, 1981). Such effects receive less media attention, and therefore adults and, more important, adolescents tend to think of suicide as an either-or act: either one dies or one survives and is OK. Clearly, this is not necessarily true.

Moreover, the risk of completed suicides among adolescents who have made attempts is significantly higher than the general adolescent population rates.

Approximately figures reported from a variety of sources by Shaffer, Garland, and Bacon (1987) indicate the following:

1. Boys who have made an attempt serious enough to be admitted to a psychiatric inpatient facility: 10,000/100,000
2. Girls who have made an attempt serious enough to be admitted to a psychiatric inpatient facility: 1,000/100,000
3. Boys who have made an attempt but are not admitted to a psychiatric inpatient facility: 600/100,000
4. Girls who have made an attempt but are not admitted to a psychiatric inpatient facility: 37.5/100,000

Shaffer, Bacon, Fisher, and Garland (1987) reviewed research that indicates that attempters and completers are not distinguishable in terms of demographics (aside from sex, in that females attempt suicide about nine times more than males and males complete suicide five times more often than females, probably because males use more lethal means), diagnostic profiles, previous attempts, or familial history. Thus we cannot predict which attempters will go on to kill themselves. The authors concluded that a conservative approach seems justified in that any suicidal behavior should be seen as presaging completion.

These attempt data mean that the probability of a given school system's experiencing suicidal behavior among its students is in fact quite high, and such behavior is too dangerous to be ignored.

CURRENT KNOWLEDGE

There are a variety of theories as to the causes of the rise in suicide rates, including family disorganization, substance abuse, social alienation, pressures related to the population dynamics of the "baby boom" generation, unemployment among youth, declining communication opportunities and skills, and high expectations and achievement demands (Maris, 1985). At present, the complex relationship among these general factors and between them and suicide are poorly understood and not yet established.

Research on the specific characteristics of known attempters and completers has yielded information that may have more practical relevance for intervention efforts. Studies of clinical populations, though plagued with methodological flaws and carried out for the most part with adults, have generally yielded psychiatric diagnoses of conduct disorders (aggression and/or impulsivity) and depression and personality factors of hopelessness or cognitive rigidity associated with suicidality (Blumenthal & Kupfer, 1988). These authors also reviewed research on biological and genetic factors as well as family history of suicide, all of which appear to be associated with suicide.

The methodologically superior psychological autopsy approach yields similar clinical results as well as information about other characteristics that are more prevalent among suidical youths. In the largest controlled psychological autopsy study carried out to date, Shaffer and a variety of associates at Columbia University (reported in Shaffer, Garland, & Bacon, 1987, and in Spano, 1988) are currently studying a sample of 175 consecutive teen suicide completers, attempters matched by age, race, and sex who had been hospitalized, and a matched sample of nonsuicidal controls. The study is ongoing, and the findings are subject to revision, but so far the following characteristics were found to be more prevalent among the suicidal youths:

> Previous attempts
> Substance abuse
> Learning disorders
> Impulsive and aggressive behavior
> Family history of suicide
> Depression without aggressive behavior (less common and found mainly in girls)
> Perfectionistic character traits (feelings that one must do things "just right"; excessive anxiety before tests, anticipated moves, and other major events)

Shaffer's research has found no evidence for the often cited characteristics of early losses, "broken homes," or early family aggression. It has been found that an unusually high number of the suicidal youths know other youths who have committed or attempted suicide. Shaffer's research has also identified some common precipitants, or events that are not causes but seem to have triggered suicide in vulnerable youths. These are some of them:

> Getting into trouble and being afraid or uncertain about the consequences
> Recent disappointment or rejection (spat with girlfriend or boyfriend, examination failure, failure to get a job or a place in the armed services)
> Closeness in time to one's own birthday or the anniversary of the death of a friend or relative
> Anxiety over an impending change

Other research has also identified such characteristics and events as a recent humiliating experience, "loner" status or increasing isolation, and recent sexual abuse or assault (Blumenthal & Kupfer, 1988; Smith & Crawford, 1986; Shafii et al., 1984). Much of the research indicates that a disproportionate number of suicide completers had seen a therapist or a physician for somatic concerns related to stress or depression. This in itself is not surprising, but it also indicates that the suicidality may not have been detected by the professionals.

Finally, drawing on research and the experiences from applied settings, lists of "warning signs" have become generally available (Kalafat & Underwood, 1989). These are not considered as direct indicators of suicidality (except for the threats) but are signs that a youth is troubled, and given the current context, clusters of them may indicate a suicidal risk.

PREVENTION: GENERAL IMPLICATIONS

What implications for interventions does the current knowledge base on adolescent suicide have? First, neither the causes nor the specific dynamics of the increase in incidence of adolescent suicidal behavior have been established. Thus a long-range primary prevention strategy of reducing or eliminating the known causes or stressors associated with self-destructive behavior is not yet possible. There is general agreement that such behavior is the result of complex interactions among biological factors, psychological events and conditions, and personal traits and vulnerabilities. Models for prediction, identification, and intervention that are based on the relative contribution of each of these variables must be developed (Blumenthal & Kupfer, 1988).

Suicide can best be thought of as an inappropriate response to the internal and external conditions created by these variables, and thus programs starting in the early school years that address such areas as problem solving, self-esteem, and communication skills may ultimately prove to be important components of school-based prevention efforts (Peck et al., 1985; Durlak, 1983).

Second, while evidence is accumulating concerning characteristics, precipitants, and warning signs associated with suicidal behavior, these are, as Shaffer Garland, and Bacon (1987) describe them, "sensitive, but not specific" (p. 1) in that they may accurately describe suicidal individuals but would also include very large numbers of those who are not suicidal. Although current research does not permit identification of youths who will commit suicide (Pokorny, 1983), it has been suggested that such information may still serve as a useful guide for intervention (Murphy, 1972). Specifically, the identified trends and patterns may be thought of as risk factors that may increase the probability of suicide, even though they do not predict the event (Ford et al., 1984).

To the extent that suicide prevention can involve early identification of and interventions with at-risk students, professionals consulting and working with school systems may take the conservative approach of tolerating false positives more than false negatives (Grob et al., 1982).

It is important to note that current research has identified a number of variables, particularly the stressors that serve as precipitants, that appear to be characteristic of *many* teens. Thus we cannot say why, in similar circumstances, one teen will be suicidal and another won't. As Albee (1982) pointed out, any attempt to account for dysfunctional behavior must include what have been called buffers, protective or supportive factors. Many researchers in this field have identified social supports, such as family and friends, as a factor that may attenuate suicidality (Blumenthal & Kupfer, 1988; Sudak et al., 1984; Shafii et al., 1984), as have adolescents themselves (Nelson et al., 1988). Thus an important preventive intervention must include identifying, enhancing, and mobilizing these social supports.

This leads to a consideration of the role of peers in suicidal behavior, and evidence so far indicates that they can have positive as well as negative effects. First, the experience of practitioners, research on attempters and completers, and surveys of unselected teens all indicate that a suicidal youth may communicate intent to someone else, and peers are by far the most likely to be told (Boggs, 1986; Bowers & Gilbert, 1987; Shaffer et al., 1988). Often peers are sworn to secrecy or fail to take action for a number of reasons. The surveys reveal that a disturbing minority (up to 25 percent) of youths would tell *no one* of a suicidal friend (or of their own suicidal plans). Because of the possible influence of socially desirable response set (i.e., students may be reluctant to report that they would fail to take action) or the vicissitudes of the actual situation, an even greater percentage may actually fail to take action.

In any case, as Shafii and his colleagues (1984) conclude the report on their psychological autopsies, "The role of friends and peers in early recognition of suicidal behavior and prevention of suicide cannot be overemphasized" (p. 293).

On the negative side, the fact that knowing someone who has attempted or completed suicide has been identified as a risk factor, plus the evidence for suicide clusters or contagion (Coleman, 1987), indicates that suicidal youth can have a negative impact on their vulnerable peers.

The issue of contagion has also been investigated in reports on increases in adolescent suicide as they relate to television news stories on suicide (Phillips & Carstensen, 1986) and television programs depecting fictional suicides (Gould & Shaffer, 1986). Studies by Phillips and Paight (1987) and Berman (1988) failed to replicate Gould and Shaffer's findings, although Bereman found evidence for an imitation effect specific to the method used in one TV film.

Recently Gould reported that there is growing evidence for imitative suicides following media coverage of actual suicides, including a relationship between the amount of publicity a suicide receives and the magnitude of associated increases in suicide (Spano, 1988). She also summarized specific aspects of media coverage that may encourage imitative suicide:

> Detailed depiction of method (e.g., "how-to")
>
> Minimal or no presentation of physical consequences of an attempt (e.g., paralysis or brain damage)
>
> Minimal or no presentation of mental health problems in the victim (e.g., "all-American" suicide)
>
> Trivial precipitant or trigger to suicide (e.g., low grade on SAT)
>
> Victims possessing engaging qualities, attractiveness, or high status (characteristics that encourage modeling)
>
> Rewards associated with suicide (e.g., "getting even")
>
> No depiction of models of effective treatment; rather, simplistic and inappropriate strategies are endorsed, such as "reaching out and touching"

Sowers (1988) indicated two additional conditions under which contagion may occur: high emotional arousal or an emotionally charged environment and a perceived similarity between the victim and the vulnerable youth. The implications of these media findings will be discussed later in relation to specific suicide programs.

Finally, it should be noted that while some problems may be long-standing, most adolescent suicides appear to be impulsive acts carried out by a person in a state of crisis. The crisis state is characterized by "tunnel thinking" in which the problem is viewed in a black-or-white, all-or-none fashion, the person becomes increasingly blind to other options besides suicide, and the person feels increasingly isolated from other people (Mitchell & Resnik, 1981; Golan, 1978). Smith (1988) thus indicated that suicide interventions must include the provision of mental "slowdowns" or buffers for suicidal youth in that tunnel. This would seem to involve clear, immediate options or alternatives, including responsive, continuously available supports and a consistent message to use them.

To summarize what has been said so far, researchers and practitioners agree that available information about adolescent suicide suggests a number of strategies to be included in any suicide response effort.

> Although the causes of adolescent suicide are still unclear, everyone endorses the continuation or development of early education programs in cognitive, affective, and interpersonal domains that may have primary preventive effects.

> While research on the characteristics of suicidal youth and the circumstances of attempts and completions is accumulating slowly and still lacks precision, the clustering of certain variables may indicate a higher risk of suicide. Caregivers in schools and communities should be kept apprised of these "risk markers," and caregivers as well as peers should be made aware of warning signs, precipitants, and available supports or resources.

> Vulnerable youths must be provided with clear, immediate options or alternatives.

> Responsive supports must be provided to suicide attempters as well as survivors in the community after a completion.

THE ROLE OF THE SCHOOL

Suicide is a problem that must be addressed by schools. Some guidelines for the type of programmatic response required can be deduced from our present knowledge base. However, although responsible school officials acknowledge the need for action, they are concerned about the limitations of overburdened school systems. Hence the appropriate role of the school in handling the issue of adolescent suicide must be defined.

Some school officials question any responsibilities beyond basic education, and others raise concerns about possible liability involved in suicide response programs. Though the legal issues are not yet settled, and each case has its individual merits, a 1985 federal court decision (*Kelson* v. *City of Springfield, Oregon*, 767 F. 2d 651, Ninth Circuit Court of Appeals) held that parents of youth suicide may sue a school if the death allegedly resulted from inadequate training in suicide prevention.

In California, the parents of a 12-year-old boy who committed suicide have filed suit against a teacher for failing to inform them that the student had expressed that intention (California State Department of Education, 1987a).

In New Jersey, a legal opinion provided by the State Bureau of Controversies and Disputes (Weiss, 1986) in regard to possible staff liability involved in the provision of suicide educational programs to students indicated that teachers would be protected under "save harmless" statutes.

In New York, the State Senate Committee on Mental Hygiene published a thorough report reviewing the issues in providing school-based suicide response programs and concluded: "In the Committee's view no convincing evidence warrants any further hesitation in establishing statewide school-based suicide prevention programs addressed to students" (Spano, 1988, p. 46). Senator Spano introduced a comprehensive legislative package to address adolescent suicide on a wide variety of fronts.

David Shaffer, a leading researcher in adolescent suicide who has been most cautious in his views concerning prevention programs, concluded a recent review (Shaffer, Garland, & Bacon, 1987) by stating, "There's very little research to go on, which is very different than saying that there is an abundance of research which tells us not to go on" (p. 37).

Moreover, with increasing frequency, schools serve as liaison and meeting ground for youth, families, and outside human service agencies. This role has been formalized in a federal statute (PL94-142) and many similar state statutes that mandate a role for the school in a broad range of problems, including the impact of emotional difficulties on academic performance (Grob et al., 1982). Also, most states have something similar to California's Code of Ethics of the Teaching Profession (Section 80130 of the California Administrative Code, Title 5, "Education"), Principle 1 of which refers to protecting the health and safety of students (California Department of Education, 1987a).

A broad range of school personnel have acknowledged their role in responding to adolescent suicide and have expressed a need for additional training and resources to carry out their responsibilities in this area. Eighty respondents to a Boston area survey that included administrators, teachers, nurses, guidance counselors, and mental health staff delineated specific responsibilities that included assessment of risk, referrals within and outside the school system, and the maintenance of contact and support (Grob et al., 1982). They expressed the need for trained professionals within the school, greater access to external professionals, peer supports and curricula for students, and the need for open communication and efficient referrals among the staff and between them and external resources.

A similar survey of 107 school districts in southern New Jersey (Comer, 1987) yielded equivalent results, and a national survey of school psychologists identified a strong involvement and the need for more training in crisis intervention with students (Wise et al., 1987).

Professional school consultants have identified general prevention methods that can be carried out in the school in an effort to avert crises. These include educational workshops (for faculty and staff), anticipatory guidance (classroom lessons), screening, consultation to enhance school staff efficacy, and research (Sandoval, 1986; Davis, 1985).

Finally, consultants have identified a number of barriers to effective intervention in schools, including an emphasis on competition and academic excellence, which translates into basics to the exclusion of mental health topics; poor communication between schools and parents or community agencies; and departmentalized instruction, which precludes obtaining a whole picture of a student (Perlin, 1988; Perrone, 1987).

The role of the school system, then, is crucial and consists of three basic areas:

1. *Identification.* As the sole compulsory institution serving youngsters in this country, school staff members see students in a relatively structured environment for more of their waking hours than parents or other adults. Within this context, changes in students that may indicate that they are experiencing some difficulty may be more easily detected. Examples include drops in performance, excessive misbehavior (for that student), fatigue, ceasing to care about appearance, or negative themes in written materials.

2. *Support and response.* Because of their broader developmental and protective mandates, schools may have a variety of medical, counseling, and consultative resources in place. Also, teachers and staffers may have contacts with students, particularly outside of classes, that may allow the adults to notice troubles more readily and respond to them or to be approached by students for help. As noted before, peers are usually the first to learn about a possibly suicidal youth, and they must therefore be included in any response program.

   Teachers, staff, and students need not provide counseling—a supportive initial response and help and encouragement for obtaining additional help is all that is called for.

   Administrators and special support staff, such as counselors or nurses, require additional training in identification, assessment, and crisis intervention. They must also form a coordinated response hierarchy in the school with prearranged, coordinated support services (consultation, crisis intervention, and treatment) from the local mental health system.

3. *Education.* This is, of course, the basic role of the school. Students, faculty, and staff must learn how to identify and respond to troubled students as well as become familiar with local resources and the ways to access them. Troubled students must learn about available resources and preferable options for coping with their distress.

To carry out these functions, there is general consensus (Perlin, 1988; Spano, 1988; Barrett, 1980; Kalafat & Underwood, 1989) that schools must have the following program elements in place:

1. *Administrative policies and procedures.* These include specific written guidelines for dealing with at-risk students, attempts, and completions. Those procedures should detail exactly what school personnel are to do and whom to turn to in a given situation.

2. *Informed faculty and staff.* All school personnel, including such support staff as bus drivers and clerical, custodial, and cafeteria workers, should be given an overview of practical and relevant facts about adolescent suicide, the rationale for and details of the school's response program, the adults' specific roles and responsibilities, basic guidelines for responding to troubled students, and the appropriate in-school and community resources. Specialized counseling and support staff members should receive added training in assessment, crisis intervention, and referral procedures.

3. *Informed parents.* Parents should be apprised of relevant information about adolescent suicide, the rationale for and elements of the school's program, their responsibilities, and school and community resources.

4. *Informed students.* Students should be provided with specific lessons presented in the health or family life curriculum. These lessons should address basic information relevant to suicide, appropriate resources, and the extreme importance of taking appropriate action (telling an adult) in the event of suicidal feelings in themselves or their peers.

5. *Community liaison.* Schools are not expected to deal with adolescent suicide on their own. The implementation of all the elements of a response program should be carried out along with consultants from local health, mental health, or crisis services. Also, solid working relationships need to be established with such local providers, who will be assisting the school in the initial response to suicidal behavior, receiving referrals from the school, and working closely with school personnel in managing the return of a suicide attempter to school.

From here on, the term *comprehensive program* will refer only to programs that feature all five elements.

The goal, then, of comprehensive suicide response programs is to establish school-based expertise, backed by local providers, for responding to adolescent suicidal behavior. The objectives of such programs are to increase two probabilities:

1. That persons who may come into contact with potentially suicidal adolescents can more readily identify them, know how to respond to them initially, know how to obtain help for them rapidly, and are consistently inclined to take such action

2. That troubled adolescents are aware of and have immediate access to helping resources and may be more inclined to seek such help as an alternative to suicidal behavior

CONCEPTUAL BASES

Such a suicide response program clearly involves the application of classic crisis intervention tenets. The basic thrust of crisis intervention involves the provision of structure and support to an individual who is confused or overwhelmed by the crisis situation. It is an ecological approach that requires the assessment and mobilization of both internal and external resources (Golan, 1978; McGee, 1974). Effective crisis intervention usually engages a network of supports and services and is characterized by well-planned, prearranged coordination among the players in that network (Lynch et al., 1985). Support and structure cannot be provided by persons who are not clearly aware of their specific roles and functions and thoroughly familiar with the roles, functions, and means of accessing other caregivers. Crisis intervention is a practical, action-oriented service that must be immediately and continuously available, since crises do not occur on a schedule. It cannot be practiced by helpers who prefer to "wait and see" or who have the luxury of long-term contact with their clients.

For those who understand the nature of school systems, adolescents, and the impact of suicidal crisis, it is difficult to imagine any other approach that would work for this setting.

Knowledgeable consultants and school officials agree that the role of the school should be to provide readily available initial contact and supports and to refer troubled adolescents for any treatment beyond this crisis-oriented care.

Adolescents themselves have indicated that they are more likely to use hotlines than other mental health services (Boggs, 1986; Bowers & Gilbert, 1987; Shaffer et al., 1988), do not comply well with traditional psychotherapy regimens (Shaffer, Bacon, Fisher, & Garland, 1987), and may best benefit from crisis-oriented community-based care in which brief inpatient crisis stabilization represents but one component of a continuum of care (Landers, 1988).

And as the case studies at the start of this chapter demonstrated, suicide situations call for a planned, coordinated, rapid response in order to prevent the crisis from escalating for the individual and the system.

Suicide intervention in the schools must be carried out on primary, secondary, and tertiary levels of prevention. Primary prevention involves the reduction of the incidence of a disorder by reducing known stressors or causes and by enhancing the capacity of individuals to cope and increasing the efficacy of supports or buffers. Again, known causes or stressors have not been clearly established, so the efficacy of anticipatory guidance efforts aimed at unselected groups cannot yet be assessed. However, originally Lindemann (1944) and more recently Bloom (1979) proposed a model of primary prevention that consists of crisis intervention during stressful events in an effort to promote effective and prevent maladaptive responses. Thus, interventions with students and faculty after an attempt or completion are aimed at preventing contagion and other maladaptive responses. Also, training students and staff to identify and respond appropriately to troubled youths may prevent attempts.

Many activities are carried out at the secondary prevention level, including ensuring that schools have established clear procedures and linkages with community services and ensuring that mental health and health professionals both in the school and the community are prepared to identify, respond to, and work with suicidal youths and their families. Although a variety of comprehensive programs have emphasized consultation and training for school personnel, this is turning out to be insufficient. In many cases, such trained school personnel are making referrals to community providers, including mental health services, that are ill prepared to deal with suicidal youths (Kalafat, 1984). Thus training and consultation in this area must include a full range of community providers, including health and mental health, clergy, police, and other emergency service personnel (Ryerson, 1988).

Given the high-risk nature of suicide attempters, tertiary prevention is a very important component of suicide intervention in schools. Here again, a coordinated system is called for—and often lacking. That is, once a student who has made an attempt returns to school, close communication among mental health providers, parents, and school personnel is important for ensuring the supportive environment that is necessary for continued recovery. Releases must be obtained so that relevant information (management issues, not personal information) can be shared with school personnel on a "need to know" basis (that is, teachers or staff who interact with the student must know such basic information as recommended workloads for the student).

SUICIDE PROGRAMS

While researchers carefully develop descriptive and predictive models and some professionals debate the utility of various approaches, the rising tide of adolescent suicide has prompted the development of response programs throughout the country. As was the case with the development of the first crisis intervention procedures (Butcher & Maudal, 1976), these have been grass-roots efforts carried out by front-line workers, usually consisting of local crisis or mental health staff called in by concerned school officials. Pioneering efforts to develop school-based programs in California were reported by Ross (1985), and one of the first comprehensive programs in the country was developed in the Cherry Creek schools in Denver. A guide to that program was made available in 1980 (Barrett, 1980).

The California State Legislature passed a bill (Senate Bill 947) in 1983 authorizing the statewide Youth Suicide Prevention School Program. The program was begun in 1984, and a detailed manual was published in 1987 (California State Department of Education, 1987a).

In New Jersey, legislation was passed (Cody, 1984) in 1985 that established a three-year demonstration youth prevention program to serve as a basis for future statewide programs. Included in that project were early versions of two comprehensive school programs that were begun in 1980 and have been subsequently revised and expanded, based on experience in that project (Ryerson, 1986; Kalafat & Underwood, 1989).

One state, Wisconsin, in 1985 mandated a suicide prevention program in every school district (Intergovernmental Health Policy Project, 1987).

At the federal level, various bills have been introduced since 1986 that provide for youth suicide prevention programs, but none has been passed.

A recent national survey by the American Association of Suicidology Committee on School Programs (Smith et al., 1987) found 114 programs, 94 of which had classroom components for students.

A survey by the Columbia Department of Child Psychiatry has also obtained basic information on a comparable number of programs throughout the country (Garland, Shaffer & Whittle, 1989). These programs have been in existence for up to 20 years and range from one-hour presentations to faculty or students to comprehensive programs involving several hours of student classroom instruction, consultations with school personnel, and linkages with mental health services. Shaffer and his colleagues estimated that over 200 programs were in existence.

The existence of these programs is clear evidence of a significant need experienced by schools and communities in the face of the increased incidence of youth suicidal behavior. There is also a significant felt need for models and guidelines for effective programming. Evidence for this need was provided by the attendance of over 200 professionals from mental health and educational settings at a symposium on school programs given on a Sunday morning on the last day of the 1988 annual conference of the American Association of Suicidology (Perlin, 1988).

Though few of these grass-roots programs have been accompanied by research, there is some consensus as to the generic components of effective school-based programs. These programs fall roughly into four separate but related areas: comprehensive programs, special crisis training for key school personnel, peer counseling programs, and community mobilization efforts.

The comprehensive programs contain the five elements noted earlier and can be illustrated by two examples: the Suicide Prevention Program for California Public Schools (California State Department of Education, 1987a) and Lifelines, a school-based adolescent suicide response program (Kalafat & Underwood, 1989). Each has been implemented in a variety of school systems and provides a detailed manual that includes lesson guides for material appropriate for grades 8–12. A wide variety of caveats apply to the adaptation of these programs, including the fact that they are meant to be implemented by experienced professionals in mental health and educational settings working in close collaboration.

The first step in the implementation of these programs is to ensure that the school system has clear, written policies and procedures for responding to at-risk students, attempts, and completions. Such policies and procedures can be adapted to the needs of a particular setting as long as they conform to basic crisis intervention principles. A more standard approach is recommended for postvention (Kalafat & Underwood, 1989; Dunne et al., 1987). At this time, liaisons between the school and other community providers such as mental health, health, crisis, and clergy, is reviewed and enhanced, if necessary.

Next, presentations, usually lasting an hour or two, are made to all faculty and staff. The presentations include practical information about suicide, an overview of the student program, the role of the school, attendees' specific roles in responding to suicidal behavior, and a review of procedures and resources. Again, this presentation is meant to reinforce identification of, initial contact with, and referral of suicidal students. Practical guidelines are emphasized, since theoretical or clinical presentations tend not to be well received.

At about the same time as the faculty presentations are scheduled, a parents' presentation is also scheduled. This covers similar material to the faculty and staff presentation, with added material on the role of parents. It is usually difficult to obtain turnouts of more than 25 to 30 parents, so this presentation is often repeated up to three times to reach more parents. Low parent participation generally plagues school programs at the secondary level, and more parents can generally be reached through churches.

Finally, faculty are chosen who will be teaching the classrom lessons to the students. Explicit lesson plans are provided for three or four classes, usually as part of the health or family life curriculum. Special sessions for students outside of regularly scheduled classes may be popular but are impractical and unlikely to be retained in busy school schedules.

Over half the programs in Smith and colleagues' (1987) survey have external consultants, usually local mental health professionals, teach these lessons. However, I feel that this defeats the purpose of enhancing continuously available school supports. That is, exposing students to external experts whom they never see again is not as useful as providing added expertise and visibility for classroom teachers.

Teachers of these lessons should be doing so on a voluntary basis and should receive special training to do so. A one-day workshop, followed by a booster practice session or classroom observation and feedback, covers background rationale, attitudes toward suicide, special issues, and the lesson materials.

The lessons address knowledge about suicide and resources; attitudes toward suicide, help seeking, and giving up a secret; and practice in talking to possibly suicidal peers, breaking a secret, and obtaining help. Additional exercises on problem solving and assessing one's supports are also included. The lessons employ established instructional principles (Knowles, 1973):

> They are problem-centered rather than content centered; material is organized around issues that students are currently dealing with rather than abstract developmental or clinical concepts.
>
> Lessons include exercises and media that promote participatory learning and acknowledge students' experience.
>
> Each lesson covers about three basic points, which is the most that students (or adults) can absorb in a 45-minute period.
>
> General manuals are eschewed in favor of detailed, sequential lesson plans that include specific times for each component.

The lessons are also developmentally grounded. This concept is being used in two ways. First, it is important to teach the material at a level that is appropriate for the age and sophistication of the students. The same points must, of course, be presented differently to eighth graders and to twelfth graders. Furthermore, different issues must be addressed to, say, seventh-grade students, who may not yet grasp the permanence of death, and high school seniors, who may need to learn how to find help on a college campus. Second, it is important for educational material to address adolescent developmental issues, including the struggle toward autonomy from adults, which makes it difficult for teens to turn to adults for help, and the importance of developing and maintaining peer relationships, which makes it difficult to betray a confidence from a peer who may be considering suicide.

Finally, Lifelines (Kalafat & Underwood, 1989) and other programs include wallet cards printed on sturdy stock that contain basic points about suicide, helping, and local crisis and emergency numbers. These cards are based on an understanding of students, in whose hands page-sized handouts rarely survive, and on crisis intervention principles that hold that a person in crisis needs a readily available, uncomplicated alternative.

It should be noted that the greatest resistance to school-based programs is in the area of classroom lessons for students. This can be blamed on the old myth that talking about suicide may plant the idea in a student's head. But given the evidence for the effects of media on suicide, this concern has to be addressed.

First, it can be noted that students have been consistently exposed to media dealing with suicide such that no classroom lesson will be their introduction to the topic (Spano, 1988). Many consultants have noted that students' knowledge about suicide has been steadily increasing (Boggs, 1986; Ross, 1988; Kalafal & Underwood, 1989). I have also found that about 75 percent of students report knowing someone from the school or community who has made an attempt or actually committed suicide.

Second, a number of programs have been in operation since about 1980 (Barrett, 1980; Ryerson, 1986; Ross, 1987; Kalafat & Underwood, 1989) and have found no increase in attempts or any completions in the many schools in which their programs are implemented. This is probably so because carefully developed, grounded programs do not fit the criteria for contagion noted earlier. Nevertheless, extreme care must be used in choosing media, and no media that depict attempts or completions should be used. Such media miss the point, in any case, which is to emphasize the consequences of suicide and the impact on survivors.

Although Smith and colleagues' (1987) survey identified 40 programs in the United States and Canada as having carried out some type of evaluation of classroom curricula, data comparing trained and untrained students are available on only a few programs. Project Lifesaver (Boggs, 1986) was a one-session classroom presentation provided by the Suicide Prevention Center of Dayton, Ohio, in two school systems. Before and after questionnaires addressing knowledge and attitudes about suicide were obtained from students in seventh, eighth, and ninth grades who attended the program, as well as from students who did not attend. An early version of the questionnaire yielded significant increases in the ability to recognize warning signs and willingness to confide in a teacher on the part of students who attended the program. On the 1986 questionnaire, significantly more program attendees, as compared to nonattendees, indicated that they would tell a friend's parents, another friend, or a teacher if a friend were in crisis, and a lower percentage of attendees would tell no one if a friend were in crisis. Program attendance appeared to have less effect on students' actions if they themselves, rather than a friend, were in crisis.

There was a ceiling effect on most of the questions about suicide facts, and for items that did not have high accuracy on the pretest, program attendees showed substantial gains in accurate responses (pretest and posttest correct responses on these three items were 27 versus 70 percent, 50 versus 67 percent, 75 versus 91 percent).

About 8 percent of the seventh graders and 13 percent of the eighth graders reported having made a suicide attempt, and a smaller percentage of these students indicated that they would tell an adult of their own or a friend's crisis (13 versus 33 percent would tell a parent; 20 versus 30 percent would tell a counselor). A greater percentage of attempters (34 versus 23 percent) would tell no one. Both attempters and nonattempters who attended the program showed increases in willingness to call a crisis service.

Bowers and Gilbert (1987) reported a study of the impact of the Richmond, Virginia, crisis center suicide education program for grades 8, 10, and 12 in a local school system. Grades 8 and 12 showed significant increases in the percentage of correct responses to a true-or-false questionnaire and in knowledge of the crisis center and comfort in using it. Mixed results were obtained among sexes and grades as to program effects on actions taken if a friend or oneself were in crisis.

Between 7 and 11 percent reported having made a suicide attempt, with the exception of twelfth-grade females, 23 percent of whom reported having made an attempt.

An evaluation report on the California comprehensive program, comparing program schools against matched control schools, included the following results (California State Department of Education, 1987b):

> Ninety percent of the students thought it is a good idea to talk about suicide in school.
>
> The program markedly increased students' confidence in knowing how to talk to someone who is suicidal (from 31 to 75 percent). Significantly more program students came to feel that asking someone if he or she were thinking about suicide would not "put a bad idea in that person's head." Students were also less inclined to feel that they had to solve their friends' problems for them and more inclined to listen, share feelings, and get help.
>
> After the program, students were significantly more aware of local crisis resources. However, the percentage who listed "get help" for a friend on the questionnaire did not markedly increase (from 16 to 21 percent). And the program did not change the minds of approximately 25 percent of the students, who felt it helpful to keep a friend's sucidal intentions a secret.
>
> The number of students who listed "get help, counseling" for their own depression rose only from 3 percent to 4 percent.
>
> Students in all the schools had a good foundation of information about suicide to begin with. They knew, for example, the relationship between substance abuse and suicide risk, and 75 percent recognized the danger of keeping a friend's suicidal confidence a secret.

Shaffer, and colleagues (1988) evaluated the impact of three suicide education programs carried out in six New Jersey high schools. Before and after questionnaires assessing knowledge and attitudes about suicide, help seeking, and suicidality were administered to 1,140 ninth- and tenth-grade students in the treatment schools and 1,043 students in five control schools (the two treatment schools from one program refused to include the questions on sucidality, and these questions were therefore also omitted from the matched control schools for this program). The results were instructive:

> Approximately 90 percent of the students felt that the programs should be delivered in other schools. Fewer than 10 percent were distressed by the program or knew someone who was. A main reason for this was regret over a missed opportunity to help a suicidal friend. A large number of students felt that the program made it easier to deal with their own problems and those of their friends.
>
> There was no evidence that the programs had induced suicidal behavior in any of the students.
>
> On seeking help for one's own problems, only 5 percent of the students said that they usually talk over their problems with a teacher or counselor, and only 13 percent would definitely take their troubles to a mental health professional. These proportions were unchanged by exposure to a program. There was, however, an increase in the number of program students who would make use of a hotline (24 to 34 percent) and who would recommend a hotline to a suicidal friend.

Sixty-five percent of the students would share another student's suicidal disclosure with an adult, about 10 percent would keep it a secret, and about one-third would share it with another friend. These proportions were unchanged by exposure to a program. This pattern of responses whereby a majority of students would behave responsibly and a minority unfavorably, with neither group being influenced by the programs, recurred in several areas.

Students' knowledge of suicide warning signs increased after exposure to a program, but the number who knew of community mental health resources (40 percent) remain unchanged.

As with the Dayton study, students who reported having made an attempt (11 percent) differed from the nonattempters in that they were half as likely to give up a secret if a friend were suicidal or to tell anyone if they felt suicidal. They also held more negative views about help from professionals and, not surprisingly, were more likely to endorse suicide as a solution to problems. With the exception of calling a hotline, none of these attitudes was affected by the programs. Attempters also were more likely to rate the programs as boring (38 versus 23 percent), providing little new information (39 versus 21 percent), and distressing (12 versus 6 percent), largely because they now have regrets over missed opportunities to take constructive action for themselves or a troubled peer.

Educators responded in a generally favorable fashion to the programs. A majority indicated that although they knew that school policies for the management of emotional disturbances in students existed, they were generally ignorant about how these were implemented. Knowledge about this increased dramatically as a result of exposure to the program. Knowledge about treatment resources and suicide warning signs also increased after exposure to the programs.

In summary, these evaluations have found a similar pattern of results, including generally positive responses to the programs, some knowledge gains, and little change in attitudes about help seeking, except with respect to the use of hotlines.

All of these results must be tempered by methodological issues associated with each study and the general caveat that applies to self-report data. Behavioral measures of program effects are still being obtained for many programs. Ross (1987) reported that in California the number of students referring themselves or friends to the suicide prevention center grew from 166 to 437 the year after the program began. This increase in referrals matches anecdotal reports from other programs.

The possible impact of these programs on suicidal behavior has yet to be rigorously assessed, although one article (Barrett, 1985) reports no incidence of suicide in the Colorado schools where the pioneering Cherry Creek prevention program was developed in 1980.

Another important approach to enhancing the supports available in the schools involves specialized training in assessment and crisis intervention for selected school personnel. The Suicide Prevention Project, a program developed by the Office of Prevention Services of the University of Medicine and Dentistry of New Jersey, consists of 16 hours of experiential and didactic training that was piloted in a variety of schools for two years (Heiman et al., 1987). The program addresses both cognitive and affective aspects of suicide intervention and includes an overview of adolescent suicide, assessment of suicidal risk, crisis intervention, enlisting family support, mobilizing the peer system, postvention, and organizational strategies for suicide prevention, including development of school procedures and liaison with community services. The program is offered only on a voluntary basis, using an eight-week, on-site format that appears to include the skill specification, demonstration, and practice recommended for learning concrete skills (Kalafat, 1983). Participants reported that they felt more comfortable about the subject of suicide, were better able to recognize the warning signs, and had improved their ability to talk with suicidal students and intervene in the various systems involved.

Even before concerns about suicide arose, many schools had mobilized students into peer support or peer counseling groups. The original rationales for the use of paraprofessional helpers were that indigenous helpers selected from the target population would form a "bridge" between professionals and clients and that helping others would enhance the growth of the helper as well (Reiff & Riesman, 1965). These tenets appear to apply particularly well in the school setting, where students consistently indicate a preference for discussing concerns with peers and "growth through helping" is consonant with the schools' educational and socialization mandates.

Peer counseling programs have received attention in the national media (Leslie et al., 1988), and they have become involved in the schools' efforts to deal with suicide. While the efficacy of selected, trained paraprofessional helpers has been clearly established (Durlak, 1971), particularly in the area of crisis intervention (Dublin, 1969), there is no research with helpers below the college level.

Although I have been a strong proponent of paraprofessionals (Kalafat & Boroto, 1977; Kalafat & Schulman, 1982), extreme care is recommended in the selection, training, and supervision of student helpers who may be dealing with the volatile phenomenon of suicide. Such helpers particularly feel the dilemma posed by the requirement that they break confidence and tell an adult when they learn or suspect that a student is suicidal.

Finally, there is consensus that schools cannot address youth suicide on their own. Effective crisis intervention invariably involves a coordinated network of services. A model program of community mobilization is being developed in Bergen County in northern New Jersey (Ryerson, 1988). The multidisciplinary County Task Force on Youth Suicide Prevention was established in 1987 by the County Board of Chosen Freeholders. The task force has developed action plans and budget proposals for the implementation of the following programs:

> Public information and Gatekeeper Education: ongoing information and training through printed materials, interactive videos, and trainer training
>
> The Workplace Group: partnership between business and human service providers for education, referral information, and a service directory
>
> Media Relations: standard press packet including a media protocol for use during a mental health crisis
>
> Police Training: prosecutor's mandatory in-service training programs
>
> Clergy Outreach: information and crisis training

Municipal Crisis Response Teams: postvention teams composed of educators, clergy, police, government, and mental health professionals

School Programs: building on comprehensive school programs through investigation and incorporation of other model program elements

Advertising and Public Relations Campaign: public awareness about suicide and resources

Although this project represents an ambitious undertaking by a county noted for its resources, other communities can lay the foundation for effective crisis intervention for youth suicide by developing agreed-on procedures and, more important, familiarity among caregivers from schools and the community (Kalafat & Underwood, 1989; Lynch et al., 1985).

SUMMARY

The rise in the incidence of adolescent suicidal behavior since the 1970s has created the need for some type of intervention at the primary, secondary, and tertiary levels of prevention. Because of their extended contact with youth and their educational and development roles, schools have become the focal point of efforts to deal with this phenomenon.

Rigorous research on youth suicide has been accumulating slowly, partly because of the relatively low incidence of completed suicides. Information as to the etiology and dynamics of youth suicide is still rather sparse, and we must await further results from such critical studies such as Shaffer's to inform intervention efforts systematically.

In the meantime, some response is called for, and available data provide some guidelines for systemic, crisis-oriented programs. This represents the best available approach and is also most suited to the school setting and to the target population: young people and the professionals who work with them.

A variety of interrelated approaches have been developed to address suicide in the schools, including comprehensive educational and consultative programs for all school personnel from administrators to students and their parents; specialized training for school staff and peer helpers; and community mobilization and education programs.

The goal of such programs is to enhance the quality, amount, and availability of school and community supports for troubled youth and their families and peers. Early identification and supportive initial response, followed by coordinated secondary and tertiary interventions, are aimed at ultimately reducing the incidence of completed suicides as well as the prevalence of suicidal youths in the school community.

Descriptions of some model programs were provided, along with some initial evaluative data.* Continued systematic program development informed by built-in, ongoing evaluation is clearly needed.

---

*The description of programs was meant to be illustrative rather than exhaustive. A variety of exemplary programs exists that could not be reviewed.

At present, continued effort is needed in research on youth suicide, outreach to schools lacking programs, increased coordination between schools and community services, and the development of services that are competent and appropriately organized to meet the special needs of troubled youth.

REFERENCES

ALBEE, G. W. (1982). "Preventing Psychopathology and Promoting Human Potential." *American Psychologist, 37,* 1043–1050.

BARRETT, T. C. (1980. *The Self-destructive Behavior of Adolescents: Seeking solutions: Inservice and Resource Guide.* Denver: Cherry Creek Schools.

BARRETT, T. C. (1985). "Does Suicide Prevention in the Schools Have to Be a Terrifying Concept?" *Newslink, 11,* 3.

BERMAN, A. L. (1988). Fictional Depiction of Suicide in Television Films and Imitation Effects." *American Journal of Psychiatry, 145,* 982–986.

BLOOM, B. L. (1979). "Prevention of Mental Disorders: Recent Advances in Theory and Practice." *Community Mental Health Journal, 3,* 179–191.

BLUMENTHAL, S. J., AND D. J. KUPFER. (1988). "Overview of Early Detection and Treatment Strategies for Suicidal Behavior in Young People." *Journal of Youth and Adolescence, 17,* 1–23.

BOGGS, C. (1986). *Project Lifesaver: Child and Adolescent Suicide Prevention in Two School Systems,* Dayton, Ohio: Suicide Prevention Center, Inc.

BOWERS, C., AND J. GILBERT. (1987). *Survey of Effectiveness of Suicide Education Program in Richmond Schools,* Richmond, Va.: Crisis Center.

BUTCHER, J. N., AND G. R. MAUDEL. (1976). "Crisis Intervention." In I. Weiner (Ed.), *Clinical Methods in Psychology.* New York: Wiley.

California State Department of Education. (1987a). *Suicide Prevention Program for California Public Schools.* Sacramento.

California State Department of Education. (1987b). *Youth Suicide Prevention School Program: Final Report of Evaluation.* Sacramento.

CODY, R. (1984). New Jersey Senate No. 2005, establishing a youth suicide prevention program.

COLEMAN, L. (1987). *Suicide Clusters.* Boston: Faber & Faber.

COMER, R. C. (1987). *Adolescent Suicide Prevention/Intervention: A Report on Findings of the RCSU-South Survey of Needs in New Jersey Southern Region Public Schools.* Trenton: New Jersey Department of Education Regional Curriculum Services Unit-South.

CURRAN, D. K. (1987). *Adolescent Suicide Behavior.* Washington, D.C.: Hemisphere.

DAVIS, J. M. (1985). "Suicide Crises in Schools." *School Psychology Review, 14,* 313–324.

DUBLIN, L. I. (1969). "Suicide Prevention." In E. S. Shneidman (Ed.), *On the Nature of Suicide.* San Francisco: Jossey-Bass.

DUNNE, E. J., J. L. MCINTOSH AND K. DUNNE-MAXIM (Eds.). (1987). *Suicide and Its Aftermath: Understanding and Counseling the Survivors.* New York: Norton.

DURLAK, J. A. (1971). "The use of Nonprofessionals as Therapeutic Agents: Research, Issues, and implications." *Dissertation Abstracts International, 32,* 2999B–3000B (University Microfilms No. 71-29,298).

DURLAK, J. A. (1983). "Social Problem Solving as a Primary Prevention Strategy." In R. D. Felner, L. A. Jason, J. N. Moritsugu, and S. S. Farber (Eds.), *Preventive Psychology: Theory, Research, and Practice,* Elmsford, N.Y.: Pergamon Press.

FORD, A. B., N. B. RUSHFORTH, AND H. S. SUDAK. (1984). "The Causes of Suicide: Review and Comment." In H. S. Sudak, A. B. Ford, and N. B. Rushforth (Eds.), *Suicide in the Young.* Boston: Wright-PSG.

FULERO, S. M. (1988). "Tarasoff: 10 Years Later." *Professional Psychology: Research and Practice, 19,* 184–190.

GARFINKEL, H., A. FROESE, AND J. HOOD. (1982). "Suicide Attempts in Children and Adolescents." *American Journal of Psychiatry, 139,* 1257–1261.

GARLAND, A., D. SHAFFER, AND B. WHITTLE. (1989). "A National Survey of School-based, Adolescent Suicide Prevention Programs." *Journal of the American Academy of Child and Adolescent Psychiatry, 28,* pp. 931–934.

GOLAN, N. (1978). *Treatment in Crisis Situations.* New York: Free Press.

GOULD, M. S., AND D. SHAFFER. (1986). "The Impact of Suicide in Television Movies: Evidence of Imitation." *New England Journal of Medicine, 315,* 690–694.

GROB, M. C., A. A. KLEIN, AND S. V. EISEN. (1982). "The Role of the High School Professional in Identifying and Managing Adolescent Suicide Behavior." *Journal of Youth and Adolescence, 12,* 163–173.

HEIMAN, M., F. JONES, F. LAMB, K. DUNNE-MAXIM, AND C. SUTTON. (1987). *Beyond Suicide Awareness: School Strategies,* Piscataway, N.J.: University of Medicine and Dentistry, Office of Prevention Services.

Intergovernmental Health Policy Project. (1987). *State Health Reports on Mental Health, Alcoholism, and Drug Abuse.* Washington, D.C.: George Washington University.

KALAFAT, J. (1983). "Training for Crisis Intervention." In L. Cohen, W. Claiborn, and G. Specter (Eds.), *Crisis Intervention.* New York: Human Sciences Press.

KALAFAT, J. (1984). "Training Community Psychologists for Crisis Intervention." *American Journal of Community Psychology, 12,* 241–242.

KALAFAT, J., AND D. R. BOROTO. (1977). "The

Paraprofessional Movement as a Paradigm Community Psychology Endeavor." *Journal of Community Psychology, 5,* 3–12.

KALAFAT, J., AND A. SCHULMAN. (1982). "Telephone Crisis Counseling Service." In N. S. Giddan and M. J. Austin (Eds.), *Peer Counseling and Self-help Groups on Campus.* Springfield, Ill.: Thomas.

KALAFAT, J., AND M. UNDERWOOD. (1989). *Lifelines: A School-based Adolescent Suicide Response Program.* Dubuque, Iowa: Kendall/Hunt.

KLEINER, A. (1981, Summer). "How Not to Commit Suicide." *CoEvolution Quarterly,* pp. 89–111.

KNOWLES, M. (1973). *The Adult Learner: A Neglected Species.* Houston, Texas: Gulf Publishing.

LANDERS, S. (1988). "Misleading Ads May Lead Parents to Commit Teens Unnecessarily." *APA Monitor, 19,* 51.

LESLIE, D., D. L. GONZALEZ, N. ABBOTT, S. HUTCHINSON, AND T. NAMUTH. (1988, October), 31. "Listening, Feeling, Helping: In a Dozen States Peer Counseling Comes of Age. *Newsweek,* pp. 79.

LINDEMANN, E. (1944). "Symptomatology and Management of Acute Grief." *American Journal of Psychiatry, 101,* 141–148.

LYNCH, B., J. KALAFAT, AND J. MECHLIN. (1985). "Expanding Emergency Services." Round-table presentation at the annual meeting of the National Council of Community Mental Health Centers, Washington, D.C., April.

MARIS, R. W. (1985). "The Adolescent Suicide Problem." *Suicide and Life Threatening Behavior, 15,* 91–109.

MCGEE, R. K. (1974). *Crisis Intervention in the Community.* Baltimore: University Park Press.

MITCHELL, J. T., AND H. L. P. RESNIK. (1981). *Emergency Response to Crisis.* Bowie, Md.: Robert J. Brady Co.

MURPHY, G. E. (1972). "Clinical Identification of Suicidal Risk." *Archives of General Psychiatry, 27,* 356–359.

National Center for Health Statistics (1986). Mortality Statistics Branch, Division of Vital Statistics.

NELSON, F. L., N. L. FARBEROW, AND R. E. LITMAN. (1988). "Youth Suicide in California: A Comparative Study of Perceived Causes and Interventions." *Community Mental Health Journal, 24,* 31–42.

PECK, M. L., N. L. FARBEROW, AND R. E. LITMAN. (1985). *Youth Suicide,* New York: Springer.

PERLIN, S. (Chair). (1988). "Tackling the Tough Issues in School-based Suicide Awareness Programs." Symposium conducted at the annual conference of the American Association of Suicidology, Washington, D.C., April.

PERRONE, P. A. (1987, September). "Counselor Response to Adolescent Crisis." *School Counselor,* 51–57.

PHILLIPS, D. P., AND L. L. CARSTENSEN. (1986). "Clustering of Teenage Suicides After Television News Stories About Suicide." *New England Journal of Medicine, 315,* 685–689.

PHILLIPS, D. P., AND D. J. PAIGHT. (1987). "The Impact of Televised Movies about Suicide: A Replicative Study." *New England Journal of Medicine, 317,* 809–811.

POKORNY, A. D. (1983). "Prediction of Suicide in Psychiatric Patients." *Archives of General Psychiatry, 40,* 249–257.

REIFF, R., AND F. RIESMAN. (1965). "The Indigenous Non-professional." *Community Mental Health Journal Monograph Series,* No. 1.

ROSS, C. P. (1985). "Teaching Children the Facts of Life and Death: Suicide Prevention in the Schools." In M. L. Peck, N. L. Farberow and R. E. Litman (Eds.), *Youth Suicide.* New York: Springer.

ROSS, C. (1987). "School and Suicide: Education for Life and Death." In R. F. W. Diekstra and R. Hawton (Eds.), *Suicide in Adolescence.* Amsterdam: Martinus Nijhoff.

ROSS, C. P. (1988). "The California Model for a Curriculum on Suicide." Paper presented at the annual conference of the American Association of Suicidology, Washington, D.C., April.

RYERSON, D. M. (1986). *Adolescent Suicide Awareness Program (ASAP): A Comprehensive Education and Prevention Program for School Communities.* Hackensack, N.J.: South Bergen Mental Health Center.

RYERSON, D. M. (1988). *A Cry for Help That's Dying to Be Heard,* Hackensack, N.J.: Bergen County Task Force on Youth Suicide Prevention.

SANDOVAL, J. (1985). "Crisis Counseling: Conceptualizations and General Principles." *School Psychology Review, 14,* 257–265.

SHAFFER, D., K. BACON, P. FISHER, AND A. GARLAND. (1987). *Review of Youth Suicide Prevention Programs.* New York: New York State Psychiatric Institute.

SHAFFER, D., AND C. L. M. CATON. (1984). "Runaway and Homeless Youth in New York City." Report to the I. Helson Foundation, New York City, January.

SHAFFER, D., A. GARLAND, AND K. BACON. (1987). "Prevention Issues in Youth Suicide." Paper prepared for Project Prevention, American Academy of Child and Adolescent Psychiatry, New York, July.

SHAFFER, D., A. GARLAND, AND B. WHITTLE. (1988). "An Evaluation of Youth Suicide Prevention Programs." In *New Jersey Adolescent Suicide Prevention Project: Final Project Report.* Trenton: New Jersey Division of Mental Health and Hospitals.

SHAFII, M., J. R. WHITTINGHILL, D. C. DOLEN, V. D. PEARSON, A. DERRICK, AND S. CARRINGTON. (1984). "Psychological Reconstruction of Completed Suicide in Childhood and Adolescence." In H. S. Sudak, A. B. Ford, and N. B. Rushforth (Eds.), *Suicide in the Youth.* Boston: Wright-PSG.

SMITH, K. (1988). "How Do We Know What We've Done? Controversy in Evaluation." Panel presentation as part of "Tackling the Tough Issues in School-based Suicide Awareness Programs," symposium conducted at the annual conference of the

American Association of Suicidology, Washington, D.C., April.

SMITH, K., AND S. CRAWFORD. (1986). "Suicidal Behavior among "Normal" High School Students." *Suicide and Life Threatening Behavior, 3*, 313–325.

SMITH, K., J. EYMAN, R. DYCK, AND D. M. RYERSON. (1987). *Report of the School Suicide Programs Questionnaire*. Albuquerque, N.M.: Menninger Clinic.

SOWERS, J. (1988). "Who, What, and How: Curriculum Development and Program Content." Panel presentation as part of "Tackling the Tough Issues in School-based Awareness Programs," symposium conducted at the annual conference at the American Association of Suicidology, Washington, D.C., April.

SPANO, N. A. (1988). *Adolescent Suicide: A Statewide Action Plan*. Albany: New York State Senate Committee on Mental Hygiene.

SUDAK, H. S., A. B. FORD, AND N. B. RUSHFORTH (Eds.). (1984). *Suicide in the Young*. Boston: Wright-PSG.

WEISS, S. (1986). *Liability/Suicide Prevention Program*. Trenton: New Jersey Department of Education.

WISE, P. S., V. S. SMEAD, AND E. S. HUEBNER. (1987). "Crisis Intervention: Involvement and Training Needs of School Psychology Personnel." *Journal of School Psychology, 25*, 185–187.

The Crisis of Teen Pregnancy and an Empirically Tested Model for Pregnancy Prevention

Laurie Schwab Zabin and Rosalie Streett | 13

INTRODUCTION

At times, the crisis in which one is called upon to intervene is not a personal but a social crisis; the intervention, in that case, focuses on prevention. The occurrence of adolescent premature sexual activity, the initiation of coitus at or shortly after puberty, and unwanted conception during the years immediately thereafter have been defined as epidemic in the United States. But epidemics, by their nature, begin quickly and often end equally quickly because solutions are found or because of the nature of the epidemic itself. This is not so with the crisis of teenage pregnancy. It cannot be defined as an epidemic because it shares with other fertility trends the characteristics of most demographic transitions: its roots go deeply into the past, and its ramifications will extend for generations into the future. It is a problem with dimensions ranging from the individual to the family to the community, and even to the nation, and it touches disciplines as diverse as medicine and ethics, science and economics, education and, unfortunately, politics. There will be no simple answers to problems as complex as these.

The United States has always been an early-childbearing society, but only in recent years has so large a proportion of that childbearing been out of wedlock. This has occurred as the age of sexual onset became younger, the age of marriage became older, and menarche leveled out at much earlier ages than in the past—a leveling that occurred several decades ago but may have manifested its social effects only as the sexual revolution gained force. The proportion of females of under 20 years of age who are still single reached 93 percent in 1984, leaving a prolonged period of exposure to premarital pregnancy (Hayes, 1987). However much an in-wedlock pregnancy may hamper the future prospects of a young adolescent, it does not raise the societal concerns that are focused on the sexually active young teen who is neither married at sexual onset nor prepared to consider marriage when conception occurs. In fact, the proportion of births legitimated during pregnancy has dropped, and among younger teens that solution is increasingly rare (Hayes, 1987).

The proportions of teens sexually active and virgin are roughly 50–50, so it is no wonder that we sense an ambivalence that permeates our society and makes the design of appropriate initiatives a senstive and challenging task. But ambivalent or not, large numbers of young people of every social class and ethnic group face problems that demand our serious attention. The 1970s showed a rapid increase in the proportion of sexually active teens, which, despite an apparent small decline between 1979 and 1982, has resulted in 70 percent of unmarried young women and 80 percent of unmarried young men having experienced coitus by age 20.

Despite an increase in the use of effective contraception, sexual activity rates like these result in high conception rates, higher than those in any country in the Western world despite the fact that other developed countries often report ages of sexual onset not very different from those experienced here. It is not among young people alone that contraceptive practice is deficient; adult American women are imperfect contraceptors as well. But perfect or not, had the availability of contraception not increased and had sexually active young men and women not availed themselves of these services, the proportions of sexually active young women ever pregnant would have been even higher than those reported today, when approximately 43.5 percent of all young women will become pregnant before they turn 20 (Hayes, 1987).

Of the over 1 million pregnancies occurring each year in the United States, more than 80 percent of them unintended, about 40 percent result in induced abortion, 47 percent in births, and an estimated 13 percent in miscarriage. Whatever disagreement there is over solutions to the problem, there appears to be little disagreement that each of these outcomes presents problems that demand a societal response. The sequelae of unintended childbearing include educational, social, marital, economic, and even physical consequences, all well documented, and although sometimes the direction of causality is not well understood, it seems clear that childbearing in early teens has an independent effect. Whether or not the young woman presenting with a positive pregnancy test recognizes the crisis she is facing (and we will see that many do not), she may indeed be at a turning point in her life. Some action needs to be taken, and the fact that there are no simple answers should not prevent the design of effective interventions, so sorely needed now.

The range of initiatives necessary to meet this challenge is as large as might be suggested by the complexity of its etiology. Preventive strategies include programs that *directly* address the needs of young people for education, counseling, and medical services in the area of reproductive health and programs that *indirectly* affect their motivation and hence their use of such services. In the second category are programs that influence their self-image, their economic well-being, their educational achievement and aspirations, their ability to communicate with partners, parents, and professionals, their general health status, or their associated risk behaviors. So comprehensive, indeed, and so unproven is the field of prevention that the task would seem too formidable to begin were it not for an important feature of all these service areas, a positive characteristic they share: they are clearly of value in themselves, worthy of a societal investment whether or not they should succeed in reducing the rate of unwanted conception. It is time to test a wide range of interventions.

In addition to these preventive services, an equally impressive list of interventions after conception can be cataloged, including abortion services; prenatal, obstetric, and neonatal services based on the premise that the younger adolescent group should be assumed to be in a higher than average risk category; nutritional services; parenting education and well-baby care; and counseling for the young mother. The attempt is to prevent a recurrence of her nonprotective behavior and whenever possible to return her to the school setting—hence day care services must be incorporated as well. The catalog is a long one!

This article cannot address the entire range of services but will focus on prevention. Clearly, true crisis intervention, on an individual basis, might be better defined as the care provided to a young woman at the time of conception. However, since ultimately the national focus must be on preventing the pregnancy itself, we will discuss a means of intervention in the social crisis through prevention of the first unwanted pregnancy. Some of the points raised in this connection, however, will have relevance to the treatment of the adolescent who conceives, as well as the adolescent who is successfully reached with education and medical services in time to prevent the need for crisis care.

One such intervention, interesting not only because it was successful but also because a strong evaluation component was built into it from its outset, will be described in this chapter. An attempt will be made to understand the derivation of the model, which grew out of the joint experience of the service and research team that designed it. A discussion of the concepts on which its design was based will be followed by a discussion of the process of establishing the model in a local setting. The roles of key staff members will be described, as will the design of the intervention itself. Finally, we will review the methods that were used to assess the effects of this particular intervention and will propose a model for program evaluation that could help to propel the field of adolescent pregnancy prevention into a new generation: the dissemination of proven, successful service models.

THE JOHNS HOPKINS ADOLESCENT PREGNANCY PREVENTION PROGRAM

In 1981, a combined service and research team was assembled by Dr. Janet B. Hardy, a pediatrician at the Johns Hopkins University School of Medicine, to design a three-year, privately funded pregnancy prevention model for the adjacent community (Zabin et al., 1984, 1986a, 1986b). The service team had been involved with the adolescent age group for many years, in the area of reproductive health, both in the treatment of adolescent women during their pregnancies and in services to teen mothers and their babies in the two or three years immediately following childbirth. They had had marked success in helping young mothers, traditionally a group at very high risk of repeated conception, to avoid further pregnancies, to return to school, and to learn improved techniques for parenting their babies. It was time to turn the skills the staff had gained to preventing the first conception. From the research staff, several specific findings suggested directions a prevention program might take.

1. It had been established that the risk of pregnancy to sexually active teens peaks in the first month of coital activity; 50 percent of all first premarital conceptions among teens occur in the first six months of intercourse, 20 percent in the very first month (Zabin et al., 1979).
2. The proportion of risk experienced in the early months is highest for those who initiate sex at the earliest ages (Zabin et al. 1979).
3. The delay between first intercourse and first clinic attendance has a median, in this age group, of at least one year. Only 14 to 15 percent of teenage women attend contraceptive facilities before the onset of intercourse to obtain preventive contraception. The majority wait many months postcoitus, and 36 percent attend professional facilities only when they already believe themselves to be pregnant (Zabin & Clark, 1981).
4. One of the prime reasons for delay, as reported by the teenagers themselves, is fear that their parents will find out. Confidentiality is therefore an important ingredient of successful service (Zabin & Clark, 1981). Cost is a factor of extreme importance because of their inability to deal with parents on this issue.
5. Teenagers, especially young teenagers, require services in close proximity to their usual haunts; they have difficulty negotiating health systems that are unfamiliar, and distance compounds the problem. They require a highly supportive, caring atmosphere.

From the service staff came several specifics learned during their years of rendering services to adolescents:

1. Medical and educational services for adolescents should be available at the same site; teenagers frequently do not value the educational component enough to return at a separate time or to a separate place once their immediate needs have been met.
2. Nonetheless, a separate staff is required to deliver these services. The medical staff, no matter how supportive and caring, may not relate to teens in the way that is required for optimal education and counseling. Even if they do, the costs of rendering this kind of service, which requires a great deal of time, may be too high if the medical staff is expected to handle the entire process.
3. Adolescents require continuity of care. It takes time to build trust, and a great deal more can be accomplished if it is not necessary for them to reestablish a relationship and rebuild confidence in the counselor each time they return.

Out of these several concepts grew a model that became the Self Center. Because the risk of conception looms so early in a young woman's sexual career, it was clear that an intervention could best be undertaken in cooperation with an institution that was in contact with young women before the onset of their sexual behavior. To await first intercourse to establish a connection with young people at risk would probably mean that it would be too late to prevent at least half of the adolescent conceptions one was seeking to avoid. Therefore, close collaboration with one or more schools was clearly indicated. In view of the high risk to young teens, it was highly advisable that a junior high school be involved. By senior high school, in a relatively permissive setting with early coital onset, a great deal of the highest risk is already past. A small professional staff, linked with the schools but also linked with the source of clinical services, was an important component of the model, in order to meet the adolescents' need for continuity of care and to provide a bridge from the school to the clinic. The clinic was established in close proximity to both schools and became a source of the free medical services to male and female students, a site for continuing education and counseling, and the administrative center for the program as well.

The model included two teams, each consisting of a social worker and a nurse practitioner (or nurse midwife) and each assigned to one of two schools, a junior high and a senior high. The teams spent a large part of each morning in their respective schools, delivering classroom lectures or leading discussions, or in the health suite running rap sessions, doing individual counseling and, at times, making appointments for the clinics, which they manned in the afternoon.

At the beginning of each semester, a schedule was established for the social worker and sometimes the nurse to give a presentation to every class in the school. The choice of a school setting is predicated on the principle that young people can be reached even when they do not seek out services themselves. Therefore, the classroom contacts are of great importance; there will be some students who have no other contact with the program, no matter how successful its outreach may be. The typical presentation lasted for the full 45-minute class period and was more formal and informational than many of the other group sessions. The first class presentation had three main objectives:

1. To introduce the Self Center services to the students
2. To begin to raise the consciousness of the students about the consequences of unprotected sexual activity
3. To support students who were not sexually active

During this first session, students viewed *A Matter of Respect*, a film featuring Jesse Jackson. It focuses on adolescent pregnancy as a problem for boys and girls alike, and all ages could relate to it. It was extremely well received by the students and was the catalyst for many philosophical discussions, which served to create a bond of understanding between the staff and the students. This bond, in fact, was the main purpose of the session: to communicate to the students that it was all right to raise any questions, discuss any subject, even when they had never done so with adults before. They left knowing that they could talk, in the school or across the street, and their response was often immediate. Also during this session, all of the components of the Self Center were described to the youngsters, and they were informed about how to access the services in both locations.

The second session usually dealt with contraception, sexually transmitted diseases, and the decision-making process. By this time, the students knew the Self Center staff, or at least knew of them. Many of the teens were already using the program, and even those who were not actually enrolled were aware that services were offered. By this time, a small group of students had been recruited to serve as a peer resource team, receiving a great deal of special education and orientation into the goals and methods of the program. Their roles as a resource to students and staff alike did not qualify them as peer "counselors" as some programs have attempted. Counseling, in this context, was not seen as a venture that these untrained young students should essay. Rather they were representatives and spokesmen for the program and handled some specific tasks with visual aids as well. They were identified by T-shirts or large red buttons saying, "Ask me about the Self Center," and although their orientation was, in itself, a time-consuming task, they were a useful resource. They contributed, too, to the sense of ownership in the program that was encouraged in all the students, ownership and participation that was an important part of the schools' relationship with the program.

Although there were only two class presentations mandated by the program, many students received more than two. The Self Center staff actively sought out opportunities to make these presentations, offering their services to teachers whenever possible. Many teachers availed themselves of this resource and called on the nurses or social workers when a relevant unit was being taught.

In addition to giving semiannual classroom presentations, the staff was able to meet with the students in groups in other settings in the school. The two major occasions for group sessions were (1) in the Self Center health suite in the school, when small groups of students showed up informally, and (2) when a teacher identified a particular group of students among whom a specific issue needed to be addressed—suspected teen prostitution, physically immature youngsters who were being teased, and so on. The group sessions held at the Self Center in the school usually occurred spontaneously when several young people happened in at the same time. During these informal sessions, the social worker might begin conversations about any one of several topics, such as working toward the future, making good decisions, peer pressure, drugs and alcohol, the consequences of being a teen parent, or boy-girl relationships. Sometimes when the students came to the "SC" in the school, they would sit down to a game of Transformer, an educational game that attempts to simulate a day in the life of a teen parent, or Humanopoly, a game that teaches anatomy and raises values issues. After playing Transformer or Humanopoly, they would discuss some of the issues that got the biggest response from the players. Thus these small group discussions coalesced around a need, expressed by the students or perceived by the leader, and became the most important educational experience the program could offer. The staff was not merely equipped to answer the questions raised in the course of these rap sessions but was also trained in group process and skilled enough to allow the sessions to go wherever they might lead. Didactic education would not go far in identifying the emotional needs and concerns that were picked up in these discussions, needs that might be openly expressed or only indirectly suggested by the youngsters. These concerns might be addressed in the context of the small group, or in some cases, needs might lead the staff person to propose individual sessions for one or another participant.

Many opportunities existed for individual contact in the schools. Since each social worker had a well-publicized, easy-to-get-to office in the school, the students felt that she was available to them for private consultations. The social worker used the peer resource students to show movies or lead informal rap sessions in the outer office so that she might be free to consult with the student in an individual session. The students sought out the social worker to discuss relationship problems with boyfriends, problems at home, possible pregnancies, and a host of other personal matters requiring resolution. Because of the time limitations that the school setting imposed on these sessions, the importance of this meeting was often the fact of contact, the fact that the student sought out the professional and began to build a relationship of trust. In such a setting, with the counselor responsible for the health suite, with one ear open for the outside office even if a peer resource helper was there, it was not feasible to seek resolution of the individual problem. Therefore, the counselor would often encourage the youngster to come to the clinic; in other cases, the worker would arrange for weekly visits, either in school or in the clinic, but for issues of any serious nature, the clinic session was more conducive to confidence and relaxed interchange. It should be recalled by those who must build this kind of relationship in a school setting that a great deal of time and privacy are required to make students as free with their communication inside the school environment as they can be in a more neutral setting.

Almost all youngsters who came into the clinic, with or without an appointment or even without the intention of setting up an appointment, received some form of educational intervention. Groups were held either in a planned group session in the "Rap Room," right in the waiting room in an informal, seemingly unplanned session, or in the social worker's or administrator's offices. These small group sessions were similar to those described earlier, but without the strict time limitations the school schedule imposed. Once again, the neutral environment and the students' sense of ownership of the clinic itself led to a relaxed and freer spirit of communication, with the students speaking more openly and the staff better able to give them the time their problems required.

Other forms of educational intervention occurred in the waiting room around the automatic filmstrip-audiocassette machine, strategically placed in the corner. It should be recalled that an after-school clinic delivers most of the patients to the waiting room at the same time. There is no opportunity for scheduling their arrival to avoid a waiting period, and every effort was made to use the inevitable delays to provide a learning experience. The staff changed the filmstrips according to the types of patients who were expected on a particular day. For example, on a day when there were to be several follow-up appointments for patients who had been treated for a sexually transmitted disease, the audiovisual aids that were displayed related to this topic. If several middle school patients were expected, the material might be about body changes or how to talk to one's parents about sex. Of course, it was not always possible to anticipate who would come in that day, but a variety of filmstrips was available, and the selection changed regularly. The equipment in the waiting room, the interaction of the visitors, patients or not, with the staff and peer resource students, and the informality of the setting were not incidental but critical to the planned intervention: the very sense of responsibility for the clinic that was created in the students was a part of the message of responsible personal behavior that was at the core of all the program's offerings.

In addition to the groups and the filmstrip-cassette machine, the games of Humanopoly and Transformer were always out on a large table in the middle of the waiting room so that a teen or a staff person could organize a game, which would in turn provide an excellent vehicle for starting conversations about the responsibilities of parenting, how the reproductive system works, and any number of topics relevant to reproductive health care. These discussions might or might not include adult participation, and good things could happen in either case. Once again, it was the stress on *their* ownership of the facility and the program that contributed to the students' perception of themselves as worthy of and capable of responsible behavior.

Registered patients received individual social work services in the clinic. In fact, often it was through the need to speak with a social worker that a student became an enrollee. All new patients who enrolled in the Self Center received an intake interview, in which relevant personal information was asked. This private session, which lasted from 20 minutes to an hour, depending on the issues raised, sometimes led to several more individual counseling sessions. The issues raised ranged from the student's wish to discuss a family fight to the need to work through a prior abortion, a current pregnancy, or a current relationship or to the discussion of school problems. The enrollees knew that the social workers were always available and frequently would ask to see them although they had not made an appointment in advance. The differences, then, between individual sessions in the clinic and in the school related, as suggested above, to the atmosphere of the clinic setting but even more specifically to the time that could be invested in each session in the afternoon.

The social workers were available to the students for counseling and also provided much of the education of the patients. An individual who had repeated bouts with sexually transmitted diseases, for example, would receive, in addition to counseling, a session on the causes, spread, and treatment of STDs. Frequently, the nurses and the social workers discussed ahead of time how the patient would be taught about a particular topic. Roles were very fluid.

Only students who were enrolled in the clinic were permitted to use the services of the medical providers. The teens who did use the medical services were given thorough, comprehensive examinations by the nurse practitioner, certified nurse-midwife, or gynecologist who saw them. The initial visit was usually the longest, since the health care provider wanted to form the foundation on which a relationship would be built. The provider, in addition to caring for the patients' physical needs, was able to address the emotional issues that often influence adolescents' compliance with health care. The staff was aware of the issues that got in the way of complying with appointment keeping, contraceptive use, early pregnancy testing, and follow-up on medical problems. To the extent possible, during their private times together, the provider tried to raise problems as well as teach the patient about her body and its functions and rights.

As has been discussed, the clinicians' roles were frequently blurred, and work was achieved through a transdisciplinary rather than an interdisciplinary or multidisciplinary method of service delivery. The transdisciplinary model allows the staff person who may not be the traditional provider of that particular service to provide it nonetheless, with the use of extensive consultation from the more usual service provider. There are many reasons why one might use this approach with teens.

There are times that a young person presents in the clinic with such fear or resistance to the program that her very return to the clinic is doubtful. Yet she may be desperately in need of the intervention. Frequently, this patient establishes trust, after some hesitancy, with one staff person. To attempt to transfer or extend this tenuous relationship to another adult may not be possible; the teen may not return or may stop disclosing important information. Except in circumstances that call for immediate crisis intervention that can only be delivered by a highly trained professional (gynecological examinations, suspected abuse), there is no need to jeopardize trust. Both social worker and nurse can discuss pregnancy options, the results of a pregnancy test, or the repeated contraction of STDs.

The primary service goal is to address the needs and concerns of the patient effectively. Clearly, a secondary goal is to assist the adolescent to make appropriate use of the available services. To facilitate this, it is sometimes necessary to do a "good enough" job, not the best job. As the relationship develops, it becomes easier to bring in other staffers.

Referral

The same is true of referrals. It may be extremely difficult to ensure that a teen patient follows through on a referral. In the best of circumstances, this situation provides a teaching and counseling opportunity for the clinician. However, it can also provide a clinical dilemma: How much should the clinician do for the patient in terms of the referral? What fosters dependence, and what is necessary to bring the teen to the point at which she is mature enough to follow through on her own?

There are times, if the crisis is not severe and the consequences of going through the process would be more instructive and ultimately helpful to the adolescent patient, when it is wiser not to take over. Other situations require immediate action, and they too are easy to assess. The difficulty for the clinician seems to arise over whether or not making the phone call or taking the patient to the referral is appropriate in nonemergency situations. These, the staff of the Self Center believed, were decisions that could best be made on a case-by-case basis. Very few hard-and-fast clinic policies governed this situation. Instead, the relationship between patient and provider determined how involved the adult would become in the referral.

Clearly, the kinds of services rendered in this program demanded considerable investment of time in each presenting student. Some required an inordinate amount of staff time, returning for countless individual sessions over the years that the program was available to them. Other programs will have to make decisions with regard to the distribution of staff time; it may be that such clients become too much of a drain on the resources of a school-linked project and require referral for the kind of supportive work that this staff was able to provide. In any case, it is crucial that the on-site staff be equipped to make responsible judgments as to what problems must be handled by the familiar and available staff and which can safely be referred to outside providers.

Program Goals

It should be clear that the program embraced a number of objectives, some related very specifically to the prevention of premature conception and others addressing more general developmental needs. Thus preventing pregnancy was seen in the context of the whole person's physical, cognitive, and emotional stage of development. Intervening goals in pregnancy prevention among the currently or soon-to-become sexually active included increasing clinic attendance, increasing the use of effective contraception, ensuring continuation on a contraceptive method, and increasing the ability of young people to discuss problems of pregnancy prevention with their partners and their parents. A parallel objective among those not yet involved in coital relationships was empowering the young people to resist peer pressure, to say no. In each case, the ability to communicate with a professional was an important first step.

The fact that we are addressing adolescent pregnancy in the context of so-called crisis care should not imply that the young people who presented for services necessarily perceived themselves to be in crisis situations. Often, even major problems such as the diagnosis of serious sexually transmitted disease or unintended pregnancy were handled with complete equanimity. Adolescents often wear a mask of maturity or of noncommitment or unconcern that may suggest that they are hiding their vulnerability or may reflect the fact that they are truly not concerned. Since it would be unusual in the kind of clinic situation we describe to have the time or the resources to provide deep therapy, it may be beyond the capacity of the program to deal in any depth with their artful masquerades. There will probably not be an opportunity for the probing and exploration that would be indicated in a therapeutic rather than a clinical setting. What is necessary here is to deal with the immediate demands of the situation and to be certain that the patient understands the seriousness of the decisions and/or the treatments she must face.

This awareness of the seriousness of her situation extends beyond the young woman (or in the case of sexually transmitted disease, perhaps the young man) to others who may be involved. Thus in the case of a gonorrhea diagnosis, for example, the patient has to be aware of the need to track and treat the partner. In the case of a positive pregnancy test, the patient needs to face the ramifications of her conception for her partner as well as for herself and must face her parents' involvement as well. In fact, fear of parents' reactions is one of the emotions that compound the confusion many young women feel because that fear can obscure the range of her emotions for both the youngster and her counselor. Even in a situation in which the professional is aware of her limited opportunity to act as therapist, she must still help the patient work through those emotions sufficiently to be able to deal with the demands of the situation for quick and comprehensive action.

In summary, then, the young woman may react to a pregnancy diagnosis with emotions running the gamut from intense despair through disappointment and ambivalence to joy. Whatever her initial reaction, she needs to be brought to a level of realism that is not the accustomed posture of adolescence, and helped to deal not only with her own predicament but the needs and reactions of others who will necessarily be involved.

Vignettes

So many and varied were the young people's needs, and so well were they sometimes masked, that it would be difficult to give any sense of a "typical" presentation. Three very different cases may illustrate this variety.

Case Study: Anthony, Age 13

Many seventh- and eighth-grade boys presented at the Self Center. Most memorable was Anthony, a 13-year-old seventh grader who had not yet begun his growth spurt. Like many other prepubertal youngsters, he strutted through the front door of the clinic requesting condoms. After a fairly lengthy private interview, Anthony was able to admit that he had only experimented with intercourse once, did not foresee that he would be needing condoms in the very near future, and was terribly concerned that he was not as tall as the other boys in the school.

To respond to his very real concern about his growth and to assure him that both his growth and his lack of interest in girls were normal, he was invited to join a group of other boys with similar concerns. The group's purpose was to teach the boys about development and to explore thoughts and feelings about growing up. In addition to becoming a member of the group, Anthony was seen individually whenever he felt the need to talk and was weighed and measured every month.

Unsurprisingly, Anthony grew several inches and gained several pounds over the course of the year. He also learned a lot about human sexuality, relationships, birth control, and sexually transmitted diseases. Anthony made at least 30 voluntary clinic visits over the course of the next 12 months. Although many of these visits were unscheduled, he was received warmly each time and encouraged to drop in whenever he desired.

Case Study: Sharita, Age 16

Sharita had visited the clinic many times as a "visitor." Since almost all guests were lured into the group education sessions, Sharita had participated in many groups. However, she claimed that she was not sexually active and therefore had no need of medical services.

After several months of insisting that she didn't need an appointment, Sharita requested a pregnancy test. The test proved positive. Self Center policy mandated that the youngster be seen by a social worker. In the interview, pregnancy options were discussed. In addition, Sharita's obvious ambivalence about becoming pregnant was explored. The teenager was unable to make a decision about how she would handle the pregnancy and was encouraged to go home and talk to her mother, with whom she had a good relationship. The worker discussed with Sharita the kinds of feelings her mother might have about her pregnancy and helped the youngster to anticipate some of the anger and disappointment that her mother might express. The worker made an appointment for Sharita to return the next afternoon to continue the counseling. She also told Sharita that she and her mother could come in together to talk if they so desired.

Sharita returned the next day after having spoken to her mother, who was horrified by the news of her daughter's pregnancy. It was obvious to Sharita that her mother had a lot of the feelings that she and the worker had discussed the day before. Sharita said she was glad they had talked ahead of time. Both the young woman and her mother had agreed that Sharita would terminate the pregnancy. In their discussion, they had talked for the first time about the fact that Sharita's mother had been a teenager when she gave birth to Sharita. Her mother did not want Sharita to struggle as she had and strongly encouraged the abortion.

Sharita's pregnancy was terminated, and she became a family planning patient at the Self Center. She graduated from high school without having a repeat pregnancy.

Case Study: Carol, Age 17

Carol was a senior in high school and had been a patient in the Self Center for six months. During that time, she had been treated twice for sexually transmitted diseases. Policy at the clinic mandated that any teen who repeatedly contracted STDs would be referred to the social worker. Carol fell into this category.

After much denial, Carol admitted that contracting gonorrhea twice within six months could possibly be indicative of a troubled relationship between her and her boyfriend. However, she did not want any intervention from a social worker. She felt she could handle the situation.

Two weeks later, Carol returned to the clinic and asked to see the nurse. Her boyfriend told her that she needed to be checked because he thought that he may have given her gonorrhea again. The nurse talked with Carol about long-term health risks of repeated STDs as well as implications for a happy future with this young man. This time, Carol was receptive to the suggestion that she and the social worker talk about Carol's relationship with her boyfriend. She accepted the referral and was able to do some exploration. However, the relationship continued through two more bouts of STDs before Carol was able to break if off permanently.

As these three cases illustrate, the young person's purported presenting reason was often far from the true reason for the visit. The time that the staff could invest in each youngster allowed the true reason to emerge. Similarly, the location of the clinic so close to the school and the activities available in the waiting areas brought many students in long before their actual registration. With all the support around them, it could still be too late by the time the young person opened up—but perhaps not too late to bring about a resolution that was consonant with the patient's aspirations for the future. When the family could be included in that resolution, prospects for the future were, perhaps, even better. Unfortunately, that was not always the case.

Confidentiality

When students registered at the program clinic, they were asked whether the visit was to remain confidential. The laws of the state permit confidential treatment for minors in the services the clinic rendered, and the staff was aware of the importance of confidentiality for many of the students. In our prior research, we had seen that many young people risk pregnancy rather than risking parental notification; in fact, the fear of discovery was their prime reason for delay in attending a professional facility. The policy of confidentiality was therefore a necessary part of the protocol. However, in their discussions with the young clients, the staff emphasized communication within the family and urged the patients who had not already done so to discuss their sexual behaviors with their parents. It was an explicit objective of the staff to respect the primacy of the parent-child relationship, an objective that was verbalized in counseling sessions, discussed in group sessions, encouraged in written materials, and even rehearsed with the youngsters in role-playing exercises. In many cases, that is exactly what was accomplished. When the patients requested confidentially, a large red CONFIDENTIAL stamp was placed on the file in full view of the patient; time after time, patients returned to say that the stamp could be removed.

This point is stressed because of the perception on the part of a vocal minority that the privacy of the clinic interposes itself between parent and child. In fact, the clinic professional may be the first person to urge communication and, indeed, to facilitate communication at home. Many young people, probably the majority, have already communicated with their mothers before they make clinic visits. Others do so once they feel comfortable with subjects they have never before talked about in the presence of adults. For the few who remain adamant about their need for confidentiality, it is no doubt an important ingredient of the program and must be respected if the young person's problems are to be addressed. The consequences of violating confidentiality might well have been correctly perceived as disastrous by the patient. Even if the results are not as traumatic as the patient had believed, the consequences to the program once the word is out that it cannot be trusted would be difficult to overcome.

Another aspect of confidentiality that presents real problems to the professional operating in a school is dealing with the teacher or even the patient herself outside the private setting. Preserving the all-important right of the patient to privacy implies that others within that environment should not be made aware of the relationship that has been established between the patient and the staff. How, then, to respond to the caring teacher's inquiries, to locate a student who has not returned on schedule for important treatment, or indeed to relate to the student herself without giving away her patient status is a challenge that the professional will need to meet.

Evaluation

When one intervenes in a social crisis with a creative idea and a dynamic program, the payoff can extend well beyond the benefits it brings to those who are served. Even a limited, local intervention can make a big difference if its results can be documented. Only then can its model be understood and its outcomes be worthy of replication.

Evaluation in the field of adolescent pregnancy has many purposes. First, data collection can serve as a means to assess community needs, to document that need, and to focus the planning process. Second, it can serve as an educational device, providing the data that bring the community to some understanding of the problems it must learn to address. Third, it can serve as a tool for administering programs, feeding information back to the administrator that can upgrade, streamline, and improve program services. Fourth, it can provide the information to mobilize the powers that be—the legislators, school boards, health departments, and social agencies that can make a difference. Fifth, it can prove the effectiveness of an intervention in such a way that financial support continues to flow, no small factor in tight-money times. Finally, it can describe a program so that it can be replicated, so that the model becomes accessible to others who understand its impact and seek similar results.

These are some of the reasons a strong evaluation component was built into the Self Center project from the start. By building it in before the clinic opened, even before the first classroom presentation, the researchers were able to collect baseline data before the program began. The methodology used in this assessment is thoroughly described in a book that includes the survey instruments as well (Zabin & Hirsch, 1987); it can only be outlined here.

A survey was administered to all boys and girls in both program schools in the fall of the first year and repeated at the end of each program year. The same survey was administered in two control schools at the beginning and end of the program period. Parents were notified of the forthcoming survey, of its intimate subject matter, and of its voluntary and anonymous nature and were given an opportunity to withdraw their children from the exercise should they wish. Hardly any did. With approximately 98 percent participation of the students in attendance on the days of administration, these questionnaires not only provided a needs assessment and baseline information for the evaluation, but they also served an educational function, allowing the students to become aware of the kinds of intimate areas of discussion that would be legitimate in the ensuing program.

These surveys became the basis for a detailed study of the changes that occurred in the course of the program, and the control schools served to establish that changes were indeed brought about by the program and were not typical of general changes in the schools at large. The follow-up rounds included extra questions on use of the program components so that the relationship between changes and program use could also be addressed and so that findings from the first two years could be fed back into the program to adapt it to the students' needs. Finally, the surveys provided a great deal of material for basic research, including demographic and background information, as well as data on the sexual knowledge, attitudes, and behaviors of a large number of boys and girls, most of them ranging in age from 12 to 19.

Other sources of data came from extensive logs maintained by the professional staff and from clinic records and school rolls as well. Many of these sources were used only because of the extensive basic research; they might well be omitted from studies that merely wish to measure the impact of a new intervention. In this case, they added immeasurably to the richness of the information and provided the basis for a thorough analysis of service components and the use made of them by a highly responsive student population.

What, then, did the findings suggest?

1. The level of use of the program's facilities and offerings was extremely high. Approximately 85 percent of the students from the schools had at least some contact with the program, and more than 60 percent had contacts with the staff that they themselves sought out.
2. The proportion of sexually active young people to use professional contraceptive services soared, males and females alike.
3. Use of effective contraception increased dramatically; for students exposed for the full duration of the program, even the youngest girls were protected at last intercourse in percentages rare for adult females. Since this is the group that is traditionally at highest risk of early, unwanted conception, that is an important achievement.
4. As a result, the pregnancy rate among ninth to twelfth graders in the program schools came down by over 30 percent among those exposed for the full 28 clinic months. During the same period, the rate soared 58 percent in the nonprogram schools.
5. The initiation of sexual activity among those who had not experienced coitus prior to program exposure was delayed a mean of seven months in the course of the brief 28 months the clinic was open. Although there was not time to follow the young women longer, and although that may not sound like a long delay, the difference between a girl of 15 years 7 months and the girl of 16 years 2 months is an important one. Furthermore, this finding proves once and for all that programs of this kind need not encourage sexual onset, as some critics contend. Pregnancy rates can be reduced among the sexually active *and* sexual activity can be delayed by the same program offerings.

SUMMARY

Adolescent pregnancy, seen so often as a crisis in and of itself, is really a symptom of a national condition. The future does not appear to our young men and women to offer them a potential towards which it is worth directing their present options. That is where we need to intervene, not with platitudes to convince them that they are wrong in their perceptions, which may in fact be sadly accurate, but with meaningful programs that provide them with the tools necessary to examine options, learn decision-making and assertiveness skills, strengthen their relationships, increase their knowledge of reproductive health care, and ensure their capacity to utilize program services. Services, in turn, must be affordable, accessible, and appropriate to their age and developmental status. The real crisis may be much greater than even the consequences for individual teenagers of premature or irresponsible sexual behavior—consequences that can include infertility following serious or repeated bouts with sexually transmitted disease, unintended parenthood, abortion, and in the new era of AIDS, even death. The real crisis may be one of national priorities, which will have to begin to focus on our young people's futures if the problem of adolescent childbearing is to be brought under control.

REFERENCES

HAYES, C. D. (1987). "Risking the Future: Adolescent Sexuality, Pregnancy, and Childbearing." Washington, D.C.: National Academy Press.

ZABIN, L. S., AND S. D. CLARK. (1981). "Why They Delay: A Study of Teenage Family Planning Clinic Patients." *Family Planning Perspectives, 13*, 205–217.

ZABIN, L. S., J. B. HARDY, R. STREETT, AND T. M. KING. (1984). "A School-Hospital-, and University-based Adolescent Pregnancy Prevention Program: A Cooperative Design for Service and Research." *Journal of Reproductive Medicine, 29*, 421–426.

ZABIN, L. S., AND M. B. HIRSCH. (1987). *Evaluation of Pregnancy Prevention Programs in the School Context.* Lexington, Mass.: Lexington Books.

ZABIN, L. S., M. B. HIRSCH, E. A. SMITH, R. STREETT, AND J. B. HARDY. (1986a). "Adolescent Pregnancy-Prevention Program." *Journal of Adolescent Health Care, 7*(2), 77–87.

ZABIN, L. S., M. B. HIRSCH, E. A. SMITH, R. STREETT, AND J. B. HARDY. (1986b). "Evaluation of a Pregnancy Prevention Program for Urban Teenagers." *Family Planning Perspectives, 18*,119–126.

ZABIN, L. S., J. F. KANTNER, AND M. ZELNIK. (1979). "The Risk of Adolescent Pregnancy in the First Months of Intercourse." *Family Planning Perspectives, 11*, 215–222.

A Stress Management, Crisis Prevention, and Crisis Intervention Program for Commercial Airline Pilots

Linda F. Little, Irene C. Gaffney, and Judith Grissmer

14

Pilots go through their whole career, no matter where they start it or how they start it, they go through a weeding out process continually. The purpose is to be a survivor all the way through until you get to the point where you are doing a job that hopefully you like, that has some future for you, and after a while you develop a feeling that you are the company and pat yourself on the back because you have had a very satisfying career. What we're seeing now with our company, not only am I ashamed to tell people where I work, I don't feel like the company cares about anything except a piece of paper that I have in my pocket issued by the government. And with that attitude, I don't see any future for me or this company to survive. I don't get support from the other employees on the airline because they are suffering the same way I am, and they don't care anymore to do the job. It just makes it difficult for me to perceive my job as something that I want to do anymore.... Like I say, most of us are operating strictly on professional pride right now, and I'm not sure how much longer we can do that. (Transcript of pilot; Little, 1987).

INTRODUCTION

The Pilot Information, Education, Resources, and Referral Services Program (PIERRS) is a slightly different employee assistance program (EAP) specifically designed to meet the needs of commercial airline pilots and their families. PIERRS became operational in May 1987. During its first ten months of operation, it was conducted as a pilot project under the auspices of the Center for Family Services, Department of Family and Child Development, Virginia Polytechnic Institute and State University's Northern Virginia Graduate Center. It was, and continues to be sponsored by the Airline Pilots Association, International, which is affiliated with labor rather than management. Since March 1988, PIERRS has operated as a private enterprise and continues to provide a unique stress management program whose services range from educational materials to 24-hour-a-day telephone crisis line backed by an established national network of mental health professionals. All services are specifically oriented toward the aviation community.

PIERRS was established because of the belief that subsequent to the 1978 Airline Deregulation Act, much stress had been experienced by large groups of airline pilots as they faced the corporate instability that ensued within the industry. Research was conducted to evaluate whether stress levels of a group of pilots from a financially unstable carrier differed from their peers employed by carriers not experiencing similar instability. The findings from that study, which will be reported later in more detail, provided the justification for immediate attention being directed toward the management of stress of commercial airline pilots and thus the establishment of the PIERRS program.

The Larger Context

Since deregulation of the airline industry, pilots have witnessed or experienced not only major carrier bankruptcies but also numerous mergers and acquisitions, hostile takeovers, threats of job loss, loss of seniority and benefits, pay freezes, forced geographic moves, prolonged labor management strife, extended strikes, and airline failures.

Consumer perceptions of pilots, the individuals responsible for all major decisions regarding the trip from the time the passengers begin boarding the plane until they disembark, are that they are part of the machinery: they have routine tasks and responsibilities to perform, and they are alert to do what they have *all* been *equally trained to do* in that rare case of an emergency, avert a disaster. It is as if the public assumes that the employees live in a vacuum and have no more pressing responsibilities than to perform their tasks and, above all, ensure customer satisfaction. Airline accidents, however, are attributable to pilot error in an estimated 60 to 70 percent of all air disasters, according to statistics kept by the Boeing Company and the Air Line Pilots Association (Lautman & Gallimore, 1987; Thomas, 1987). An alert, well-trained, and well-compensated pilot who is not potentially affected by work-related stressors is becoming more of an ideal than a reality.

According to an airline economics study, 54 mergers and acquisitions took place between 1984 and 1987, compared with only nine in the preceding five years (*Aviation Daily*, 1987). With each merger, employees experienced threats to job security and what has been labeled an emotional roller coaster of hope, fear, anger, bargaining, and depression as many of the newly merged or acquired carriers experienced increasing financial troubles, cutbacks, negative press, or financial disaster (Hurst & Shephard, 1986; Little & Gaffney, 1987a).

The Research on Pilot Stress

Based on these observations, in February 1986, a team of psychologists and family therapists from Virginia Tech University approached the Air Line Pilots Association (ALPA) with a proposal to investigate airline pilots' stress in the context of corporate instability. The purposes of the study were fourfold. The first purpose was to investigate the differences in stress between the pilots in both unstable and stable corporate environments. The second purpose was to see whether differences in stress, if found, would also be found in spouses and carry over into family functioning. A third goal was to develop an index of pilot stress to serve as an indicator, and possibly a predictor, of problematic stress reactions or critical stress symptoms. The fourth purpose was to establish whether significant evidence existed to justify a stress management, crisis prevention, and crisis intervention program for airline pilots and their families.

It was predicted that airline pilots would respond in a similar fashion to other employees who had been observed as experiencing a "roller-coaster ride of emotions" when threatened with job instability and potential job loss (Hurst & Shephard, 1986). It was also predicted that stress symptoms would emerge in the pilots' total context.

Since such a high proportion of all aviation mishaps are attributable to pilot error, it was not surprising that much research had been done in the human factors area in the course of aircraft safety investigations. Yet most of that research focused on human factors from a biotechnical perspective. The investigation of psychosocial factors that affect pilot performance was just emerging. Even at this early stage, however, stress was a factor that was found to coexist with impaired pilot performance. In fact, several studies had linked contextual stress factors such as pilot career strain, financial setbacks, and interpersonal problems directly with aircraft mishaps (Alkov & Borowsky, 1980; Alkov et al., 1982, 1985). Unanswered was the question of how excessive stress levels affect pilot performance. Largely ignored up until this point was the adaptation of airline pilots to the work demands that accompanied changes in the airline industry.

A Systemic Model of Stress

A systemic model of stress investigation (Figure 14-1) purports that actual stressors do not necessarily have a linear relationship to expressed symptoms. Rather, the stress reaction is seen as an interactive, cumulative process that is affected by actual sources of stress (job insecurity, financial strain), perceptions of the stress events (important versus not important, controllable versus not controllable), buffers that either mitigate or exacerbate the stress response (self-esteem, career satisfaction, family adaptability), and the coping strategies used (functional versus dysfunctional). If, for example, a stressor is seen as important and beyond the person's control, if the existence and perception of the stressor lower self-esteem and trigger family conflict, and if dysfunctional coping strategies (increased use of alcohol, aggressive behavior with colleagues) are applied to the problem, symptoms develop that become additive sources of stress and must then be dealt with by the system (Gaffney, Little, & Scheirer, 1987).

The Instrument

To unravel some of the complexities of stress components and their interrelationships, pilots and their spouses were asked to complete questionnaires con-

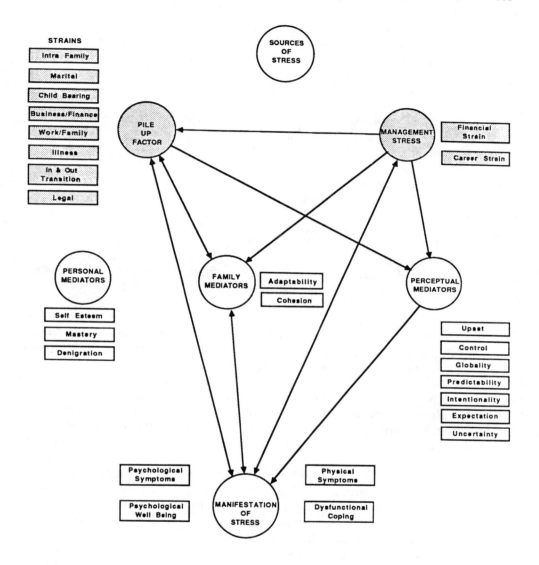

1. Circles denote latent variables or constructs.
2. Rectangles denote measured variables.
3. Arrows denote several proposed directional relationships.

Figure 14-1 Pilot Stress in the Total Context: An Interactive Model

taining a broad spectrum of measures. Twelve measures of stress were used: eight well-established measures, used with permission of their originators, and four additional measures, developed or adapted for the purposes of this survey. Areas investigated were these:

1. Piling up of life events (McCubbins et al., 1981)
2. Economic pressures (Caplovitz, 1979)
3. Psychological well-being (Caplovitz, 1979)
4. Dyadic adjustment (Spanier, 1976)
5. Self-esteem (Pearlin & Schooler, 1978)
6. Mastery (Pearlin & Schooler, 1978)
7. Self-worth/self-denigration (Pearlin & Schooler, 1978)
8. Cohesion and adaptability (Olson et al., 1985)
9. Career satisfaction
10. Stress symptoms
11. Depression symptoms
12. Dysfunctional coping strategies

The complete data collection plan for this study, described in more detail by Gaffney, Little, and Scheirer (1987), included a mail survey designed to investigate stress reported by airline pilots and their spouses. Questionnaires were distributed to a random sample of 839 pilots from the list of members of ALPA. Survey recipients included 401 pilots from an airline considered to be unstable and 215 and 223 pilots, respectively, from two smaller, more stable airlines. The two smaller airlines were selected based on their geographic similarity to the unstable airline and because when combined, the two accounted for a similar number of pilots as those of the larger carrier. Criteria used to differentiate the stable from unstable carriers included the sale, merger, or takeover of the airline during the 12 months prior to the survey, net gain or loss reported for the previous two earning periods, and employee wage and work rule concessions in the past contract negotiations with managements. More specifically, the pilots from the unstable carrier had just experienced the sale of their airline following an extended period of financial losses, corporate unheaval, and labor-management conflict.

Of the 839 pilots surveyed, 432 returned usable questionnaires—212 from the unstable airline and 220 from the stable airlines combined, representing an overall response rate of 51 percent. Questionnaires were returned by 391 spouses from both the unstable and the stable carriers. Preliminary analyses indicated no statistically significant differences between the two stable airlines on any of the 12 stress measures; subsequent analyses were completed with pilots from the two stable carriers combined into one group and defined as the control group.

Despite some demographic effects (age, years at rank) and airline-demographic interactions (education with stress symptoms with carrier affiliation), in no instance could differences on stress measures be attributed to demographic factors rather than to airline affiliation (Little et al., 1988). Pilots from the unstable carrier indicated significantly higher stress on every stress measure when their scores were compared with those of pilots from the stable carriers (see Table 14–1). In fact, scores on the stress instruments were so easily distinguishable by airline affiliation that high-stressed pilots could correctly be classified as belonging to the unstable carrier 85 to 90 percent of the time (Little et al., 1988). Stress was not confined to individual stress symptoms; rather it manifested itself in all realms of the lives of the pilots from the unstable carrier and was also evident in the responses of the pilots' spouses.

Implications

The study was a necessary first step in describing and quantifying pilots' responses to severe work stress. On the basis of data brought together in this report, ALPA felt the need to secure a stress management and crisis intervention program for the pilots and their families at the unstable carrier.

THE DEVELOPMENT OF PIERRS

Learning the Culture

In pilots' and spouses' self-reports of areas and levels of stress symptoms on the stress survey, intervention needs could be identified (see Table 14-1). Methods of intervention had to be developed. In line with a typical pilot's orientation, the PIERRS program was designed to deliver coping strategies that could lead to desired change. While available and prepared to handle crises should they occur, PIERRS wanted pilots to use our services before a crisis and not to conceive of us only as a last alternative. Services were specifically designed to provide education, information, resources, and referrals.

The PIERRS program was tailored around known characteristics of airline pilots, their families, and their professional culture. More than 99 percent of commercial airline pilots are male. Pilots and their families are often private. Pilots are typically highly educated, independent learners who use written materials

Table 14-1 Pilot Stress Response

VARIABLE	UNSTABLE CARRIER (%) (n = 212)	STABLE CARRIERS (%) (n = 220)
Stress or depression symptoms (frequently/almost always)		
4 or more symptoms	25.0	10.5
6 or more symptoms	16.5	3.6
Economic pressures	75.0	25.0
Severe Pressures	36.8	10.9
Low psychological well-being	48.6	20.0
Family strains	33.0	11.4
Work and family changes	44.9	21.8
High career satisfaction	3.9	82.7
Career optimism	1.5	48.6
Perception of mental health as "fair" or "poor"	21.0	7.7
Two or more physical illnesses in the past six months	28.3	10.6
Dysfunctional coping	12.8	4.6
Very high mastery	24.5	45.5

(rather than human resources) as training tools. Pilots are trained to be in control and to solve problems instantaneously. On the job, they are in positions of power and great responsibility. They give orders and make decisions that affect their own lives as well as the lives of crew members and passengers. In their professional roles, they cannot be ambivalent, indecisive, dependent, or overly emotional. As Nance (1986) observed:

> Pilots and operations people were hired to do their jobs without making mistakes. They were required, and ordered, not to let stress, fatigue, boredom, physical incapacity, or psychological aberration affect their performance. . . . If one couldn't perform he should be fired. (p. 86)

This perfectionistic orientation has not been limited to the pilot's professional role but is often carried over to other areas, manifested as an "in-charge" stance that hinders acknowledging problems and seeking help in their resolution (Fry & Reinhardt, 1969; Novello & Youssef, 1974).

Airline pilots are leery of psychologists, psychiatrists, and mental health diagnoses, as well they should be. Airline pilots are rigorously screened for health prior to hiring and on a continuing basis throughout their careers. Captains are required to have complete physical checkups by approved aeromedical physicians twice annually, junior officers once a year. Any threat to physical functioning is a threat to the pilot's continued employment. Pharmaceuticals (such as cold remedies or mild tranquilizers) that pose no threat to the average person's at-work functioning, the use of which is mostly considered a private matter, are either not allowed for airline pilots or must be reported. Use of such products that are not on an approved list will lead to temporary banishment from flying.

Although the Federal Aviation Administration allows "counseling and mental health services," pilots believe that the traditional model of psychiatric diagnosis and treatment threatens their careers, so they avoid it whenever possible. Certain DSM-III-R diagnoses lead to temporary loss of license, and in such cases, pilots have to appear before an FAA review board composed of M.D.'s and FAA psychiatrists to have their licenses reinstated. The emphasis on health, the consequences for acknowledging a perceived need for treatment, and the pilot's independent nature lead in many cases to denial and suppression of problems and skepticism toward traditional mental health services.

Because of observed skepticism of the helping professions among this population, terms such as *psychological, psychiatric,* or *pathological* were not used in the description of services. The licensed (mental health) professionals used as referral sources were described as experts in stress management and brief intervention approaches. Problem resolution, rather than insight, treatment, or therapy, was emphasized.

SERVICE COMPONENTS OF THE PIERRS PROGRAM

PIERRS comprises the following service components for airline pilots and their families:

1. A highly specialized educational program
2. Seven-day-a-week, eight-hour-a-day professional telephone counseling and crisis intervention services
3. A 24-hour toll-free telephone hotline
4. A nationwide referral network of licensed mental health professionals
5. Program evaluation
6. Crisis intervention for pilots and families from airlines that experience an air disaster

Each component will be described in more detail.

PIERRS's Educational Program

There are two components to PIERRS's educational program. First, pilots from a particular carrier are provided with educational material en masse on a regularly scheduled basis. Second, pilots are mailed written materials on particular stress topics on a request basis.

Pilots are responsible for assimilating written materials designed for highly technical training and translating these materials into action. Based on this known characteristic, a vital part of the PIERRS program was designed around self-help literature, to be distributed to the pilots' homes on a regular basis. Reviews from current literature on such topics as stages of professional burnout are synthesized by the PIERRS staff to fit the culture and the current context of the airline pilot and his family. Such materials are compiled into small, readable manuals that contain information, checklists for symptoms, space for problem solving, activities to do with one's spouse, and various other devices designed to encourage personalization of the material.

Manuals are prepared to enable the pilot to see his current situation (financial difficulty, marital tension, physical or behavioral symptoms of pilot or family members) in a larger context. For example, individual responses to corporate instability are normalized as pilots comprehend that other employees under similar working conditions manifest similar symptoms and that such symptoms are predictable (see Figure 14-2). Frustration, anger, apathy, and depression, which because of the pilot's independent orientation could be off limits to discussion, are placed in the larger realm of professional burnout. They are defined as an employee's *normal* response when expectations about career are initially high and all is believed to be within the employee's personal control but performance is never quite satisfactory (see Figure 14-3).

Written materials also address the need for boundaries between work and personal roles. These materials are prepared to strengthen stress buffers off the job. Checklists are provided for spouses' participation, and dialogue between spouses is encouraged. Educational and remedial letters are prepared for spouses (see Figure 14-4). Symptoms that could be related to work stress are clarified, systemic interpretations of symptoms are presented, and coping strategies are suggested.

Materials are designed to educate, to identify strengths (independence, problem-solving orientation, verbal abilities) that are important in the profes-

Research has been conducted on employees' reactions to acquisitions, corporate instability, company failure, and unsuccessful mergers that threaten employees' long-term job security. Employees have predictable responses to this threatening process that have been well documented. These responses also occur in distinct stages that can be directly tied to the actions of the company, the stage of adjustment that the company is in, and the ability of management to weather the predictable stresses of acquisition.

STAGES OF CORPORATE INSTABILITY/EMPLOYEE RESPONSES

Stage 1:

Management	**Employees**
Announces the acquisition or merger	Are often shocked by the news
Gives employees little information	Are uncertain and fearful
Insulates top executives	Are hopeful
Maintains secrecy of corporate goals and plans	Are unable to concentrate
	Are liable to develop physical symptoms
May or may not begin negotiations with employees	May experience shock accompanied by disbelief, passivity

Figure 14-2 Excerpts from: Employees' Response to Stages of Corporate Instability (Manual 3). Adapted from Little and Gaffney (1987a), pp. 4–5.

sion, and to suggest application of these identified strengths to problem resolutions.

The second component of the educational program involves the distribution of self-help materials on specific stress-related topics on a request basis. Educational materials are developed for specific stress concerns identified by callers and are sent to their homes. It is not uncommon for callers to request information on as many as ten stress-related issues (e.g., anxiety, depression, stress symptoms, marital conflict). Counselors develop, update, and coordinate the stress management resource library. Their participation in this process keeps them informed and up to date on various stress-related issues and provides an ever-expanding library that is available to other counselors and to callers. The PIERRS program has developed a resource library of more than 750 articles on over 75 stress-related issues; these can be put together as "stress packets" that specifically address the needs of callers. This service provides a private and individualized means of problem resolution, in many cases enabling pilots to solve their problems without the further assistance of mental health professionals.

PIERRS Counseling and Crisis Intervention Services

The PIERRS counseling and crisis intervention component provides four major services. Counselors are trained to assess level of stress, severity of presenting problem, selection of appropriate educational materials, and selection of referral sources of licensed mental health professionals in the pilots' locality. Calls range

DEFINITION OF PROFESSIONAL BURNOUT

What is burnout? Does it really exist? How can we describe it? Here are some common definitions:

> A syndrome of emotional exhaustion, depersonalization, and reduced personal accomplishment
>
> A state marked by physical depletion, chronic fatigue, feelings of helplessness and hopelessness, negative self-concepts, and negative attitudes toward work, life, and family
>
> A process in which a professional's attitudes and behaviors change in negative ways as a result of work-related frustrations and job strain, which then result in lower employee productivity and morale

By reading this manual and increasing your knowledge of burnout and your ability to recognize warning signs, you have already taken the first step toward change. You are at the gate; we are helping to determine your flight plan, the best way to get to your destination. Before you take off, you need fuel—energy. Use our E-N-E-R-G-Y formula, designed for easy recall to ask yourself daily if you have the energy to change:

> **E**xercise
> **N**utrition
> **E**goism
> **R**elaxation and recreation
> **G**ood times
> **Y**ou and others

Figure 14-3 Excerpts from: Coping with Pilot Burn-out (Manual 2). Adapted from Gaffney, Little, and Stannard (1987), pp. 2, 4.

from information seeking to crisis in process and are treated accordingly. A modified version of the Brief Therapy Center of the Mental Research Institute's problem assessment model is used (Watzlawick et al., 1974). Counselors seek to establish the magnitude of the problem, the timeliness of the problem (chronic or acute), what precipitated the problem, how the problem is perceived (important, not important; solvable, unsolvable; painful, not painful), and what past solutions have been applied but are considered to have failed.

If a symptom is identified and the pilot or pilot's family member expresses casual concern, educational materials may be suggested as a means of establishing whether the caller wishes to take further action. If a symptom is painful, disruptive, or escalating and perceived to be beyond the control of the caller, queries will be made about the caller's attitude toward seeking professional help. Myths about the therapy process might be challenged at this stage. A description of the types of therapists PIERRS has screened to be providers would be given, and optimally (if the caller is not located in an isolated rural area), three therapists are

Many wives of pilots have talked about the difficulties they are having remembering to take care of themselves in the middle of their many responsibilities and concerns with their spouses and others in their families. Here is a list of suggestions for you to help review some areas of self-care. Directions: Set aside 30 minutes, and pick a quiet place with no distractions. Close your eyes and rest quietly for five minutes. Then proceed.

1. Take time every day for yourself. Spend time doing something that you enjoy and that you don't feel pressured to accomplish or succeed at. List three things that you could do during the next week for yourself if you were to follow through with this suggestion.
2. Identify your own feelings and emotional needs. Take seriously your own small stirrings—the need to spend time with someone you love or feel close to, the need to be outdoors, the need for a time or place of peacefulness and reflection, the need for an uplifting or stimulating book, the need for music. Sit still and again close your eyes for two minutes. List two tiny needs that you have had in the past 24 hours that you have brushed aside. What could you do to take these needs seriously in the next 24 hours?

Figure 14-4 Excerpts from Educational Letter Prepared for Pilots' Spouses. Adapted from Grissmer (1987).

given as referrals. Callers are informed of consumers' rights in the selection and maintenance of therapeutic relationships. They are encouraged to be selective and to seek further advice from PIERRS should the referrals not seem appropriate to meet their needs. Referral sources are contacted via phone and alerted that an unnamed referral has been made from PIERRS and that written material describing current working conditions at the carrier and research findings describing pilots' stress reactions will be mailed to their offices.

If a crisis is in process, identifying information is elicited, an immediate referral source is secured (by a backup PIERRS counselor), and an appointment is arranged while the caller remains on the phone. When warranted, permission is sought to contact a family member, friend, or fellow employee to be with the caller until the local mental health professional is available.

Because of the potentially high-risk nature of this population of clients, specific policies and procedures were established by the PIERRS program to ensure confidentiality of clients and to establish the parameters of our EAP responsibility. Because of legal and ethical ramifications, the PIERRS realm of responsibility as an EAP program could not extend to advising pilots on their ability to fly. The FAA has set standards that define when a pilot is or is not capable of performing his duties, and these standards were adopted as a reference for pilots should they question their ability to perform their duties. ALPA pilot members are supported by the Aeromedical team of physicians and psychiatrists who are experts in pilot health concerns. These physicians know FAA regulations and work closely with the FAA in establishing guidelines for individual pilot functioning abilities. ALPA Aeromedical also provides a highly developed program for pilots with substance abuse problems. All calls that dealt with flying proficiency or substance abuse were coordinated with the Aeromedical team. In addition, it was felt that should the pilot question whether his current level of functioning was sufficient to perform, a more in-depth, face-to-face professional appraisal would be indicated. In these cases, referrals to local mental health professionals were coordinated with ALPA Aeromedical.

24-hour Counseling and Crisis Line

Trained professional counselors who are systemically oriented are available to airline pilots and members of their families on a regular eight-hour-a-day, seven-day-a-week basis. The program is supported by a 24-hour professional answering service (specializing in mental health and physician clients) that screens all calls during nonoffice hours. Should an emergency call be received during this period, a trained counselor is on call 24 hours daily. Emergency calls are handled immediately; nonemergency calls are returned on the next working day.

The PIERRS counseling line is staffed by seven mental health counselors and three substitute counselors, all of whom are fully trained in current airline issues. Three initial training sessions and continuing bimonthly training focus on current airline issues, stress management issues, and topics that have surfaced in individual calls. Community experts, university faculty, airline industry experts, and pilots participate in these training sessions.

Line counselors bring individual expertise in many areas to their roles at PIERRS and serve as resources to one another as well as contributing to specialized written materials in their areas of expertise. Specialty training of the clinic staff includes knowledge and experience in areas of stress management, communication, marriage and family therapy, parenting, youth, children, crisis intervention, domestic violence, assessment and research, and substance abuse.

Each caller receives the individual attention of the specific counselor who receives the call. This counselor then goes on to prepare educational material for mailing and locates a therapist in the caller's community who specializes in treatment of the identified problem. Callers who are in crisis or are seriously stressed request and receive calls from counselors on a regular basis until the crisis is past and adequate local support has been put in place.

National Referral Network

Since the PIERRS staff conceptualizes symptomatic behavior as an interactive process occurring between person and environment, we wished to establish a national network of systems-oriented therapists to serve as a referral base. We wanted clinicians with expertise in couples, family, individual, and organizational interventions. We wanted clincians who believed in brief intervention approaches and minimal treatment to effect maximum change.

Letters of introduction with research findings on airline pilot stress were sent to mental health professionals who held clinical membership in the American Association for Marriage and Family Therapy (AAMFT). AAMFT requires specialized academic and clinical training in the areas of systems theory and family therapy practice. Referral networks were established first in regions where the majority of pilot families reside, then nationally, since a large percentage of pilots commute long distances to their base airport. To serve as a referral source, clinicians needed to be licensed mental health professionals (psychiatrists, psychologists, social workers, marriage and family therapists) in their respective states. Credentials of all clinicians who expressed interest in acting as a referral source were scanned, and 2,600 became sources for referrals during the first year of operation.

Evaluation of Services and Statistical Reports

Postcards designed to evaluate services are included in each educational packet mailed to callers. In addition, pilots are periodically requested (twice in the first year) by their ALPA representatives to evaluate the needs and quality of services provided.

Evaluations were also made on the basis of use rate by pilots and their family members. Typical EAP programs with an established history can expect a 5 to 7 percent use rate within a year's period (Spicer, 1987; Spicer et al., 1983). More than 20 percent of pilots and their family members from the unstable carrier used the PIERRS counseling line services at least once during the first 10½ months of operation. One of every five pilot families had used the PIERRS counseling services at least once during the first year, and 50 percent of those who made initial contact with PIERRS during this period used the services more than once. More than 60 percent of callers were pilots rather than family members. Educational packages were mailed to the homes of approximately 75 percent of callers; referrals to local mental health professionals were made for approximately 50 percent of contact families. Presenting problems on the PIERRS toll-free number reflected the stress symptoms (work stress, financial strain, marital discord, physical symptoms) that had been identified in the research survey. Most calls were of a noncrisis nature. However, approximately 11 percent of them were crisis calls (presenting problems such as threats of suicide, homicide, family violence in process, and extreme anxiety that was perceived to interfere with flying), and in all cases the *crises were averted* within this initial 10½ month start-up period.

Crisis Intervention after an Air Disaster

According to official FAA statistics, there were 31 accidents on U.S. airlines flying scheduled flights in 1987. This was the highest recorded number of accidents in 13 years. Four of these accidents alone were responsible for 231 deaths. In the largest accident, the Northwest Airlines crash in Detroit, 156 persons were killed. Not the unstable carrier that had previously been researched, Northwest had recently merged with Republic and was experiencing its own share of corporate instability. The two pilot groups were in the process of negotiating an integrated seniority list. Tensions were high, and the blending of corporate cultures that normally accompanies the merging of companies was at a standstill. In the midst of this cultural merger, a disaster occurred, dramatically affecting not only the two merging groups but also the nation at large. The pilots of the plane that crashed were pilots from the newly acquired Republic, known for surviving a series of mergers, intense employee loyalty, and great company pride. Northwest, a well-established international carrier with a long history of labor-management confrontations, had experienced no prior major air disasters.

The 800 toll-free counseling services of the PIERRS program were extended on a time-limited basis to the pilot groups at Northwest/Republic following the Detroit crash. Contact was made by PIERRS staff with surviving family members of pilots killed in the crash, with the go-team (pilots assigned to work with the various accident investigating teams throughout the aftermath of an air disaster), and with the eyewitness pilots. Other services were developed and executed during this crisis period. For example, a document was written by PIERRS and distributed to the homes of all Northwest/Republic pilots shortly after the crash. The document, titled, *You'd Better Sit Down: There's Been a Crash* (Little & Gaffney, 1987b), addressed the grief response that occurs with intimates and coworkers after the experience of a disaster. It was educational, using specific, current examples of stresses and coping strategies of pilots from the two carriers.

For example, in discussing the disaster with pilots from both carriers, it was determined that the crash was exacerbating the problems between the two merging pilot groups. Republic pilots reported that shortly following the crash, Northwest pilots were silent and distant when in their presence; they interpreted this as blame or hostility. Northwest pilots, for their part, reported being silent out of fear and apprehension; they worried that whatever was said in sympathy would be rejected by their Republic counterparts. The prepared document had three purposes:

1. To educate pilots and family members about the grief reaction
2. To describe and normalize their current situation in the merger process
3. To provide a ritual that pilots and their family members could participate in that would acknowledge the disaster and begin the healing process

What follows are excerpts from that document that demonstrate how these three goals were achieved.

Excerpts from You'd Better Sit Down: There's Been a Crash

With any merger or acquisition, even in the best of circumstances, employees and management of both companies need 6–18 months to adapt. Employees who have a history of crisis management are often skeptical of management's intentions or the intentions of the other pilot group. Employees of the acquired company are concerned about their job security, pay, and seniority, and are sensitive to any suggestion that they are unequal to the employees of the acquiring company. Employees from the acquiring company typically attempt to protect their own status and corporate rules, and are skeptical of change (Marks & Mirvis, 1986).

The quality of the initial adjustment period, and the solutions that emerge from that period, determine, to a large extent, the success of the merger. This is a period of high demands for all. New skills must be learned, old ways of being are challenged, new ways have to be explored that meet the needs of all. And because of these demands the whole system is off balance, in a stage of becoming. When a tragic accident is added to the turmoil that already exists, limits of adaptation are stretched and feelings can become raw.

Experts who deal with grief and loss estimate that 70–90 percent of families experiencing the death of a child eventually separate or divorce (Herz, 1980). Such evidence points to the powerful impact of loss for a family's future. These data have spurred the development of intervention programs to aid families in the healing process, to strengthen families, and to help them find ways to honor their dead while continuing to live—eventually in harmony and acceptance, and optimally with mutual support of family members.

Companies are equally vulnerable to sudden death and disaster that involve group members. They have similar needs to experience a healing process and similar goals for ultimate adaptation.

Airline pilots, unlike military pilots, have no established way to honor their dead. There are no guidelines, no norms, no common message to deliver. For the airline pilot who dies in a crash there are no taps, no formation flights over the grave, no medal, no public acknowledgment by colleagues or professionals. For pilots who commute long distances, live apart in different communites, and fly with different crews, a sense of anonymity develops. The pilot loses ties with other individual pilots and professional group identity.

Pilots are often uncomfortable talking about aircraft accidents, death and dying. Their technical orientation fosters an objectivity that can become a shield against recognizing personal vulnerability, their own mortality, or confronting the eternal human questions of life's meaning.

For all these reasons: personality constraints, a lack of common history at Northwest/Republic, no after-work socializing among pilots due to commuting constraints and merger tensions, and lack of any established guidelines concerning how pilots could respond to a crash and the death of fellow pilots, airline pilots may not know what is proper, acceptable behavior following an aircraft accident.

We at the PIERRS program want to make the following suggestions as a beginning.

1. Nothing is so devastating to your work situation as BLAME. Don't accuse either yourself or your fellow pilots. . . .

2. You can help. There are several simple things you can do now that can be truly helpful. . . . Remember that simple communication is probably the most important thing you can do right now. Speak to each other in the crew lounge. . . . It is not too late to express your concern. . . . Be yourself. Trust your instincts. Use your own words. . . . Accept silence. . . . Listen.

3. The worst possible way for this human tragedy to end would be for the people to be forgotten. We ask that you make a personal commitment to honor the pilots of flight 255. In this way, when you look back on this tragic accident, you can be proud of your performance. And, recognize it as a time when you did your best.

Therapeutic Ritual

PIERRS staff believed that a therapeutic ritual that would facilitate pilots' acknowledgment of the tragedy and provide expression of their grief, honor to their profession, and support to the victims' families was needed to assist the pilot groups in moving beyond the accident. The following ritual was developed to meet these needs.

Four postcards that were addressed to the surviving family members of the pilots killed in the crash were included with *You'd Better Sit Down: There's Been a Crash.* The pilots from Northwest/Republic were asked to write a personal statement to the families if the deceased pilot were known personally. A positive statement about being an airline pilot or just signing one's name were also suggested as ways for individuals to acknowledge the tragedy and express their caring and concern. The postcards were mailed back to the PIERRS offices, compiled in book form, and delivered to the families by pilots who had worked closely with them after the crash.

More than 8,000 postcards were sent from pilots acknowledging the tragedy and providing individual sympathy and caring, both for the pilots who died and for their own profession. Here are a few examples of postcard comments:

> I know the kind of life and work that _____ experienced. Each pilot can almost write the diary of a fellow pilot. I share your loss, you have my personal sympathy.

> We as airline people had good times and bad times and we have stuck together. The great loss you have experienced from _____ 's death is deeply felt by all of us who share a common bond. My prayers are with you and have been since the crash.

> Pilots get to face a dream few others do. That helps to make their life complete.

> To a pilot one of the greatest experiences is to break out on top of a solid overcast into the brilliant sunshine. I like to think that this transition has been a similar one for _____ .

GUIDELINES FOR CLINICIANS WHO WORK WITH AIRLINE PILOTS

The following guidelines have been developed for clinicians working with the airline pilot population.

1. Clinicians who work with airline pilots must be alert to their larger context. This includes awareness of the industry at large (deregulation), awareness of the specific corporate culture (airline) in which the pilot is working, and an understanding of the strict regulatory requirements for pilots regarding seeking professional help. Without this awareness, particularly in the third situation, interventions could escalate rather than diminish stress symptoms. Issues of diagnosis, confidentiality, and medication are primary.

2. Clinicians must be aware of the boundaries that exist between themselves and the agencies that have the legal responsibility to determine if a pilot is capable of flying. Coordination with an approved aeromedical physician regarding these issues is to the benefit of both pilot and therapist.

3. Clinicians who work with airline pilots should have a thorough understanding of what is known regarding the pilot personality (see Gaffney, Little & Miller, 1988). The characteristics that make pilots hesitant to involving others (spouses, friends, family) in their problems are the same characteristics that allow them to be competent in their jobs. They cannot afford to be ambivalent, dependent, indecisive, or overly emotional. Pilots expect much of themselves and can blame themselves when they are unable to solve or work out a problem in their work setting. In

contrast to this, pilots might exacerbate a family problem by bringing their cockpit management style to the family setting. These are key therapeutic issues.

4. Pilots under stress need education regarding the relationship of stress symptoms (physical, psychological, and familial) to the larger corporate structure in which they work. This moderates their tendency to criticize themselves for "weakness" and decreases feelings of isolation. It allows pilots, whether experiencing symptoms from an acute flying crisis or a prolonged crisis of labor-management stress, to see their reactions as normal in the given context and to discuss these symptoms with colleagues, family, or professionals.

5. As described, education in written form that directs the pilot in specific tasks he can undertake to alleviate or ameliorate stress fits in with the pilot's usual approach to problem solving.

6. Brief therapy, focused on stress management and problem solving, is the therapeutic approach most in keeping with the pilot's basic orientation.

7. Referrals of pilots to other professionals may well necessitate education of the professional on many of the issues described.

SUMMARY

The PIERRS program remains in its infancy. The need with carriers is great and the resources few. "In 1987 about 235,000 pilots were qualified to work as airline pilots [in the United States]; of this number 91,287 held airline transport certificates, and 143,645 held commerical pilot certificates" (U.S. Government Accounting Office, 1988). Current efforts at PIERRS include continued research on airline pilot stress and a quest for funding for a national EAP for all commercial airline pilots and other employees in the airline industry (air traffic controllers, flight attendants, machinists) who equally need stress management support services. The concept of stress management is relatively new in the aviation industry, and much education is left to be done. Regional carriers who employ small numbers of commercial pilots and who often serve as a training ground for pilots who will eventually work for larger carriers and fly larger equipment typically have few, if any, mental health support services for their employees. No known organized services are provided for pilots who work for private companies or fly private planes.

Counselors at PIERRS (800-776-8685) would be glad to consult with clinicians working with commercial airline pilots and their families.

REFERENCES

ALKOV, R. A., AND M. S. BOROWSKY. (1980). "A Questionnaire Study of Psychological Background Factors in U.S. Navy Aircraft Accidents." *Aviation, Space, and Environmental Medicine, 31,* 860–863.

ALKOV, R. A., M. S. BOROWSKY, AND J. A. GAYNOR. (1982). "Stress Coping and the U.S. Navy Air Crew Factor Mishap." *Aviation, Space, and Environmental Medicine, 53,* 1112–1115.

ALKOV, R. A., J. A. GAYNOR, AND M. S. BOROWSKY. (1985). "Pilot Error as a Symptom of Inadequate Stress Coping." *Aviation, Space, and Environmental Medicine, 56,* 244–247.

Aviation Daily 290 (7). Intelligence, p. 49.

CAPLOVITZ, D. (1979). *Making Ends Meet: How Families Cope with Inflation and Recession.* New York: Research Foundation, City University of New York.

FRY, G. E., AND R. F. REINHARDT. (1969, May). Personality Characteristics of Jet Pilots as Measured by the Edwards Personal Reference Schedule." *Aerospace Medicine, 40* pp. 484–486.

GAFFNEY, I. C., L. F. LITTLE, AND R. U. MILLER. (1988). *The Pilot Personality.* Fairfax, VA.: Little, Gaffney & Associates, Inc.

GAFFNEY, I. C., L. F. LITTLE, AND J. SCHEIRER. (1987, June). "Deregulation Aftermath." *Air Line Pilot,* pp. 18–23, 32.

GAFFNEY, I. C., L. F. LITTLE, AND C. STANNARD. (1987). *PIERRS Stress Management Series: Coping with Pilot Burn-out.* Fairfax, Va.: Little, Gaffney & Associates, Inc.

GRISSMER, J. (1987). *Letter to Pilots' Spouses: PIERRS Stress Management Series.* Fairfax, Va.: Little, Gaffney & Associates, Inc.

HERZ, F. (1980). "The Impact of Death and Serious Illness on the Family Life Cycle." In E. A. Carter and M. McGoldrick (Eds.), *The Family Life Cycle: A Framework for Family Therapy.* New York: Gardner Press.

HURST, J. B., AND J. W. SHEPARD. (1986). "The Dynamics of Plant Closings: An Extended Emotional Roller Coaster Ride." *Journal of Counseling and Development, 64,* 401–405.

LAUTMAN, L. G., AND P. L. GALLIMORE. (1987, October). "Control of the Crew-caused Accident." *Air Line Pilot,* pp. 10–14.

LITTLE, L. F. (Narrator). (1987). *PIERRS Stress Management Series: Pilot Burnout—Stages and Symptoms* (cassette recording). Fairfax, Va.: Little, Gaffney & Associates, Inc.

LITTLE, L. F., AND I. C. GAFFNEY. (1987a). *PIERRS Stress Management Series: Employee Responses to Stages of Corporate Instability.* Fairfax, Va.: Little, Gaffney & Associates, Inc.

LITTLE, L. F., AND I. C. GAFFNEY. (1987b). *You'd Better Sit Down: There's Been a Crash.* Fairfax, Va.: Little, Gaffney & Associates, Inc.

LITTLE, L. F., I. C. GAFFNEY, M. M. BENDER, F. PROULX, AND C. J. SCHEIRER. (1988). *Pilot Stress Research Project.* Falls Church, Va.: Virginia Polytechnic Institute and State University, Center for Family Services.

MARKS, M. L., AND P. H. MIRVIS. (1986, October). "The Merger Syndrome." *Psychology Today,* pp. 36–42.

McCUBBIN, H. I., J. PATTERSON, AND L. WILSON. (1981). *Family Inventory of Life Events and Changes (FILE), Form C.* St. Paul: Family Social Sciences, University of Minnesota.

NANCE, J. J. (1986) *Blind Trust.* New York, N.Y. W. Morrow.

NOVELLO, J. R., AND Z. I. YOUSSEF. (1974). "Psychosocial Studies in General Aviation: I. Personality Profile of Male Pilots." *Aerospace Medicine, 45,* 185–188.

OLSON, D. H., J. PORTNER, AND Y. LEVEE. (1985). *FACES III.* St. Paul: Family Social Sciences, University of Minnesota.

PEARLIN, L. I., AND C. SCHOOLER. (1978). "The Structure of Coping." *Journal of Health and Social Behavior, 19,* 2–21.

SPANIER, G. B. (1976). "Measuring Dyadic Adjustment: New Scales for Assessing the Quality of Marriage and Similar Dyads." *Journal of Marriage and the Family, 38,* 15–18.

SPICER, J. (Ed.). (1987). *The EAP Solution.* Minneapolis: Hazelton.

SPICER, J., P. OWEN, AND D. LEVINE. (1983). *Evaluating Employee Assistance Programs: Sourcebook for the Administrator and Counselor.* Minneapolis: Hazelton.

THOMAS, P. (1987, April 24). "Bumpy Ride: Pilots Feel the Stress of Turmoil in the Airline Industry." *Wall Street Journal,* p. 37.

U.S. Government Accounting Office. (1988). *An Airline Should Check Pilot Applicants' Safety History* (GAO/RCED-88-154). Gathersburg, Md.

WATZLAWICK, P., J. H. WEAKLAND, AND R. FISCH. (1974). *Change: Principles of Problem Formation and Problem Resolution.* New York: Norton.

Index